SIMMS INTEGRATED MATHEMATICS

A Modeling Approach Using Technology

Level 1, Third Edition

KENDALL/HUNT PUBLISHING COMPANY
4050 Westmark Drive Dubuque, Iowa 52002

CONTRIBUTORS

Masha Albrecht ■ Glenn Allinger ■ Byron Anderson ■ Staci Auck ■ Shirley Bagwell ■ Cliff Bara ■ Gary Bauer ■ Jack Beal ■ Patricia Bean ■ Glenn Blake ■ Kyle Boyce ■ Monty Brekke ■ Ruth Brocklebank ■ Lee Brown ■ Maurice Burke ■ Clay Burkett ■ Randy Carspecken ■ John Carter ■ William Chalgren ■ Terri Dahl ■ Ted Drieth ■ Wendy Driscoll ■ Bonnie Eichenberger ■ Todd Fife ■ Jerry Fisher ■ John Freal ■ John Gebhart ■ Kimberley Girard ■ Janet Higgins ■ James Hirstein ■ Sherry Horyna ■ Jeffrey Hostetter ■ Alexander Johnson ■ Danny Jones ■ Russ Killingsworth ■ John Knudson-Martin ■ Robbie Korin ■ Pam Koterba ■ Janet Kuchenbrod ■ Phillip Lieske ■ Satinee Lightbourne ■ Fred Longhart ■ Karen Longhart ■ Johnny W. Lott ■ Franklin Lund ■ Mike Lundin ■ Joy Lustgraaf ■ Mark Lutz ■ Peggy Lynn ■ Douglas Mack ■ Pat Mauch ■ Patty Mazurek ■ Anne Merrifield ■ Mary Ann Miller ■ Susan Moore ■ Mindy Obert ■ Laurie Paladichuk ■ Roger Patterson ■ Arthur Perleberg ■ Margaret Plouvier ■ Dean Preble ■ Darlene Pugh ■ Peter Rasmussen ■ Howard Reinhardt ■ Kate Riley ■ Todd Robbins ■ Dick Sander ■ Lisa Schlange ■ Verne Schlepp ■ Lisa Scott ■ Dick Seitz ■ Mike Sinclair ■ Ed Sisolak ■ Tim Skinner ■ David Stabio ■ Paul Swenson ■ Thomas Teegarden ■ David Thiel ■ Otis Thompson ■ Michael Trudnowski ■ Deanna Turley ■ Karen Umbaugh ■ Sharon Walen ■ Anne Watkins ■ Marcia Weinhold ■ Daniel West ■ Teri Willard ■ James Williamson ■ Lisa Wood ■ Mike Wood ■ Steve Yockim

SERIES EDITOR

Terry A. Souhrada

TECHNICAL EDITOR

Peter W. Fong

This material is based upon work supported by the National Science Foundation under Cooperative Agreement No. OSR 9150055. Any opinions, findings, conclusions or recommendations expressed in this material are those of the author(s) and do not necessarily reflect the views of the National Science Foundation.

Cover Credits:
© JupiterImages Corporation: top left skier and top right snowflake
© Corbis: bottom left skiers and bottom right snow

ISBN 0-7575-2028-6

Printed in the United States of America.

3 4 5 6 7 8 9 10 10 09 08 07

Contents

1 Reflect on This 1

2 I'm Not So Sure Anymore 31

3 Yesterday's Food Is Walking and Talking Today 53

4 A New Look at Boxing 83

5 What Will We Do When the Well Runs Dry? 101

6 Skeeters Are Overrunning the World 127

7 Oil: Black Gold 151

8 When to Deviate from a Mean Task 173

9 Are You Just a Small Giant? 205

10 Graphing the Distance 237

11 A New Angle on an Old Pyramid 277

12 From Rock Bands to Recursion 311

13 Under the Big Top but Above the Floor 337

14 From Here to There 367

15 Going in Circuits 391

Glossary 413

Selected References 423

Index 427

Preface

In recent years, many voices have called for the reform of mathematics education. The concerns cited include international test scores in mathematics, the retention of students in mathematical and scientific career paths, and the production of mathematically literate adults. Attempts to identify the root causes of these concerns have targeted not only the methods used to instruct and assess students, but also the nature of the mathematics that students learn and the manner in which they are expected to learn.

The Systemic Initiative for Montana Mathematics and Science (SIMMS) began as a five-year, cooperative enterprise of the state of Montana and the National Science Foundation. Funded through the Montana Council of Teachers of Mathematics, and led by mathematics and science teachers from around the state, SIMMS had an ambitious list of objectives, including redesigning the 9–12 mathematics curriculum using an integrated, interdisciplinary approach for *all* students; incorporating the use of technology in all facets and at all levels of mathematics and science; and developing and publishing curriculum and assessment materials for grades 9–16.

With additional funding from the National Science Foundation and the support of teachers, students, and the Kendall/Hunt Publishing Company, these curricular objectives have continued for more than a decade.

What Is Integrated Mathematics?

An integrated mathematics program "consists of topics chosen from a wide variety of mathematical fields . . . . [It] emphasizes the relationships among topics within mathematics as well as between mathematics and other disciplines" (Beal, et al., 1992; Lott and Reeves, 1991).

In its 2000 document, *Principles and Standards for School Mathematics,* the National Council of Teachers of Mathematics addressed curricular reform with these recommendations:

> Mathematics comprises different topical strands, such as algebra and geometry, but the strands are highly interconnected. The interconnection should be displayed prominently in the curriculum and in instructional materials and lessons. A coherent curriculum effectively organizes and integrates important mathematical ideas so that students can see how the ideas build on, or connect with, other ideas, thus enabling them to develop new understandings and skills . . . .
>
> Big ideas encountered in a variety of contexts should be established carefully, with important elements such as terminology, definitions, notation, concepts, and skills emerging in the process . . . .

> In addition, the curriculum should offer experiences that allow students to see that mathematics has powerful uses in modeling and predicting real-world phenomena. (pp. 15–16)

SIMMS *Integrated Mathematics* offers this coherent curriculum, built around big ideas in a variety of contexts, while providing experiences that allow students to model and predict phenomena.

In order to create innovative and accessible materials, a diverse group of more than 80 secondary teachers of mathematics and science, mathematicians, and mathematics educators contributed their skills as writers and reviewers. The SIMMS *Integrated Mathematics* curriculum is expressly designed for use in heterogeneous classrooms, and seeks to encourage the participation of underrepresented groups in mathematics.

Each academic year of SIMMS *Integrated Mathematics* includes algebra, geometry, probability, statistics, and discrete mathematics. Essential mathematical concepts are explored more than once, each time at a slightly higher level—in different settings and in different years—to help students build both vital connections and critical competencies. Students investigate mathematics in the context of crucial social and environmental issues—such as population growth, oil spills, and earthquake damage—along with other real-world topics including mapmaking, business inventory, digital animation, and automobile insurance.

Technology in the Classroom

SIMMS *Integrated Mathematics* focuses on the future needs of mathematically literate adults. Because of this commitment, the use of technology is a fundamental part of curriculum.

In *Principles and Standards for School Mathematics,* the Council noted that "Technology is essential in teaching and learning mathematics; it influences the mathematics that is taught and enhances students' learning" (p. 24). Nearly all current research on the appropriate use of technology in the classroom indicates that students using technology become better problem solvers, without suffering a decline in their more traditional skills.

SIMMS *Integrated Mathematics* works best when students have access to a word processor, spreadsheet, graphing utility, geometry utility, statistics package, and computer algebra system. (Many reasonably priced graphing calculators now include all of these features, with the exception of word processing.)

Student Performance

During the development of SIMMS *Integrated Mathematics,* researchers conducted periodic assessments of student performances in pilot schools. After the publication of the first edition, a four-year longitudinal case study was completed. In these studies, two basic measures—a selection of open-ended mathematical tasks and the PSAT—were administered to experimental and control populations.

On the test of open-ended tasks, technology was made available to both groups. In a comparative analysis, SIMMS *Integrated Mathematics* students were more likely to provide justification for their solutions and made more and better use of graphs, charts, and diagrams. They also demonstrated a greater variety of problem-solving strategies and were more willing to attempt difficult problems.

For the PSAT, technology was not allowed for either group. Student mathematics scores indicated no significant differences in achievement. In other words, although SIMMS *Integrated Mathematics* students were denied access to the technology typically available for classroom work, their performance on the PSAT matched that of their peers.

A summary of the pilot study, as well as a larger National Science Foundation study involving students in selected U.S. cities, is now in print (Senk and Thompson, 2003).

A Look to the Future

Once again in *Principles and Standards for School Mathematics,* the Council argues that:

> When students can connect mathematical ideas, their understanding is deeper and more lasting. They can see mathematical connections in the rich interplay among mathematical topics, in contexts that relate mathematics to other subjects, and in their own interests and experience. Through instruction that emphasizes the interrelatedness of mathematical ideas, students not only learn mathematics, they also learn about the utility of mathematics. (p. 64)

This deep and lasting understanding is what all teachers desire for their students. The third edition of SIMMS *Integrated Mathematics* builds on reform middle-school curricula, and is designed to replace all currently offered secondary mathematics courses, with the possible exception of Advanced Placement Calculus.

—Johnny W. Lott, former co-director of The SIMMS Project and past president of the National Council of Teachers of Mathematics

References

Beal, J., D. Dolan, J. Lott and J. Smith. *Integrated Mathematics: Definitions, Issues, and Implications; Report and Executive Summary.* ERIC Clearinghouse for Science, Mathematics, and Environmental Education. The Ohio State University, Columbus, OH: ED 34701, January 1990, 115 pp.

Lott, J., and A. Reeves. "The Integrated Mathematics Project." *Mathematics Teacher* 84 (April 1991): 334–35.

National Council of Teachers of Mathematics. *Curriculum and Evaluation Standards for School Mathematics.* Reston, VA; NCTM, 1989.

———. *Principles and Standards for School Mathematics.* Reston, VA: NCTM, 2000.

Senk, S., and D. Thompson (eds.). *Standards-Based School Mathematics Curricula: What Are They? What Do Students Learn?* Mahwah, NJ: Lawrence Erlbaum Associates, 2003.

The SIMMS Project. *Monograph I: Philosophies.* Missoula, MT: The Montana Council of Teachers of Mathematics, 1993.

Souhrada, T. "Secondary school mathematics in transition: A comparative study of mathematics curricula and student results." *Dissertation Abstracts International* 62.4 (October 2001): 1355A.

Introduction

When the first edition of SIMMS *Integrated Mathematics: A Modeling Approach Using Technology* was published more than a decade ago, it provided an innovative approach to teaching and learning high school mathematics. The third edition maintains this standard while representing a significant revision of previous versions.

SIMMS *Integrated Mathematics* now includes four levels, offering a comprehensive alternative to traditional secondary mathematics courses. Each year-long level contains 15 modules. All modules are divided into activities, typically including an exploration, a discussion, warm-up problems, a set of homework assignments, and a research project.

Assessment materials—including alternative assessments that emphasize writing and logical argument—are an integral part of the curriculum. Each activity includes one or more suggested assessment items, identified in the Teacher Edition, while each module closes with an open-ended summary assessment. A more traditional assessment, for use at the teacher's discretion, appears in the Teacher Resources, along with short quizzes and review problems, as well as blackline masters for classroom handouts.

Level 1: A First-Year Course

Level 1 concentrates on the knowledge and understanding that students need to become mathematically literate citizens, while providing the necessary foundation for those who wish to pursue careers involving mathematics and science. Each module presents the relevant mathematics in an applied context. These contexts include human nutrition, the properties of reflected light, population growth, structural physiology, and topographic maps, among others. Mathematical content includes data collection, presentation and interpretation; linear, quadratic, and exponential functions; probability; trigonometric ratios; and an introduction to graph theory.

Level 2: A Second-Year Course

Level 2 continues to build on the mathematics that students need to become mathematically literate citizens. While retaining an emphasis on the presentation and interpretation of data, Level 2 also introduces such topics as matrix operations, elementary polynomials, combinatorics, statistics, and fair division. Students investigate traditional geometry, including proof, within the context of home building. They explore transformational geometry through cartoon animation. Other contexts include genetics, business inventory, radioactive decay, and carnival games.

Level 3: A Third-Year Course

This level continues to build mathematical understanding and logical reasoning, based on the first two years of work. Students expand their knowledge of data analysis, algebraic functions, geometric proof, probability, and graph theory. Contexts include map coloring, logarithmic scales, navigation, and quality control, among others. Specific mathematical topics include trigonometric functions, the normal curve, spherical geometry, parametric equations, basic topology, and an introduction to limits.

Level 4: A Fourth-Year Course

For some students, this course represents the end of a high-school mathematical career. For others, this course represents a stepping-stone to advanced placement courses. Because of these different needs, this course is both mathematically and contextually challenging and engaging. Students explore complex numbers, conic sections, hypothesis testing, finite geometry, mathematical induction, and derivatives. Applied contexts include cartography, automobile insurance, and compound interest, among others.

The Student Edition

The third edition of SIMMS *Integrated Mathematics* contains all of the basic elements found in previous editions, along with some new features. For example, each activity now offers an additional problem set, designed to hone mathematical skills before students encounter more complicated assignments. Several individual modules were substantially revised, presenting fresh approaches to geometric proof, hypothesis testing, compositions of functions, and other topics.

Explorations

Nearly all activities contain at least one exploration, giving students a hands-on opportunity to develop their own understandings of mathematical concepts. To facilitate the exchange of ideas and strategies, explorations are designed for work in a variety of instructional formats, including small groups.

Discussions

Discussions give students a structured forum for sharing insights and communicating mathematical ideas, and give teachers a setting for assessing comprehension and reinforcing essential concepts.

Mathematics Notes

Mathematics Notes formally summarize the mathematics students are expected to understand and apply. Each typically includes a definition or explanation, a description of the appropriate notation, and an example or graph.

Warm-Ups

These problem sets—a new feature in the third edition—are designed to review essential mathematical skills and vocabulary before students proceed to the Assignment. Warm-up problems typically do not invoke a real-world context.

Assignments

As in previous editions, most assignment problems present mathematics in applied contexts. Some extend previously learned concepts to other mathematical settings. Students are encouraged to justify their solutions and describe their reasoning.

Research Projects

Many modules contain a Research Project, offering students an opportunity for further study of contemporary or historical mathematics.

Summary Assessment

Summary Assessments typically ask students to demonstrate their problem-solving skills in the same context used in the module. They are often project-oriented and suitable for collaborative work.

Module Summary

At the end of every module, a Module Summary repeats the important mathematics from each activity.

Glossary

The Glossary offers an alphabetical list of definitions for all of the terms and concepts in an entire level (also included in the Teacher Edition).

Selected References

This list provides a helpful compilation of print and other resources for the entire level (also included in the Teacher Edition).

1
module
Reflect on This
AB
(7, 13)
y = ax3
A
B
C

Introduction

Exploration

A kaleidoscope creates fascinating designs that change as it is rotated. You can hinge two mirrors together to model the effects of a kaleidoscope. To make such a model, complete Parts **a–e** below.

a. Place the reflective sides of two mirrors face to face. Tape one set of edges together to make a hinge.

b. Cut small pieces of confetti from colored paper.

c. Overlap a sheet of white paper with a sheet of colored paper. Half of each sheet should remain visible.

d. Position the hinged mirrors across the two sheets of paper as shown in Figure **1-1.** The distance from A to B should be approximately equal to the distance from A to C.

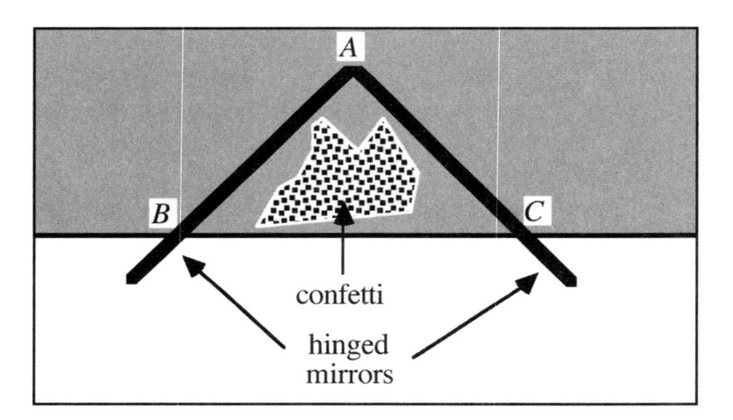

Figure 1-1 Kaleidoscope model.

e. 1. Open and close the mirrors, keeping the distance from A to B approximately equal to the distance from A to C. Observe the patterns formed by the confetti and colored paper.

2. Make a record of the patterns formed by the colored paper.

3. Rearrange the confetti, then open and close the mirrors again. Observe the new patterns that are formed.

Discussion

a. Describe the patterns created by the colored paper in your kaleidoscope.

b. What happened as you opened and closed the hinged mirrors?

c. What is the relationship between the size of the hinge angle and the number of reflections seen?

Opening and closing hinged mirrors causes multiple reflections. These reflections form patterns and shapes similar to those you created with a model kaleidoscope.

mathematics note

A **polygon** is a union of coplanar segments intersecting only at endpoints. At most, two segments intersect at any one endpoint and each segment intersects exactly two other segments. Each segment in a polygon is a **side;** each endpoint is a **vertex** (plural **vertices**).

In Figure **1-2,** for example, points C, G, and O are vertices, while $\overline{AB}$, $\overline{EF}$, and $\overline{MN}$ are sides.

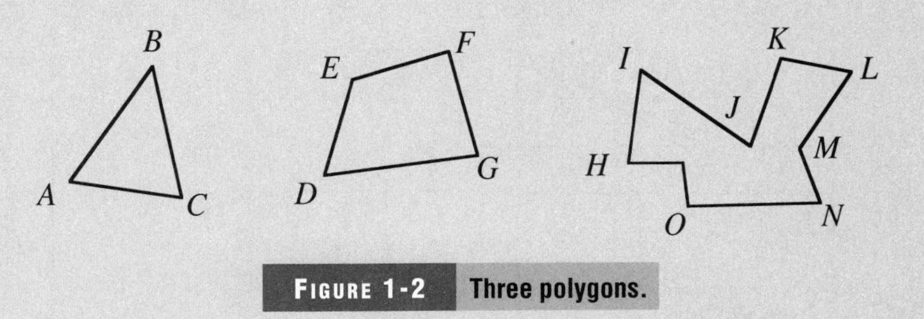

Figure 1-2 Three polygons.

Exploration

In this exploration, you examine the polygons formed by reflections in hinged mirrors and investigate the relationship between these polygons and the hinge angle.

a. Reconstruct the kaleidoscope from the introduction (without the confetti).

b. Begin with the mirrors completely open. Slowly close them until a triangle is formed by the colored paper and its reflections. As shown in Figure **1-3,** the mirrors form a hinge angle at the center of the triangle. Draw this angle and determine its measure.

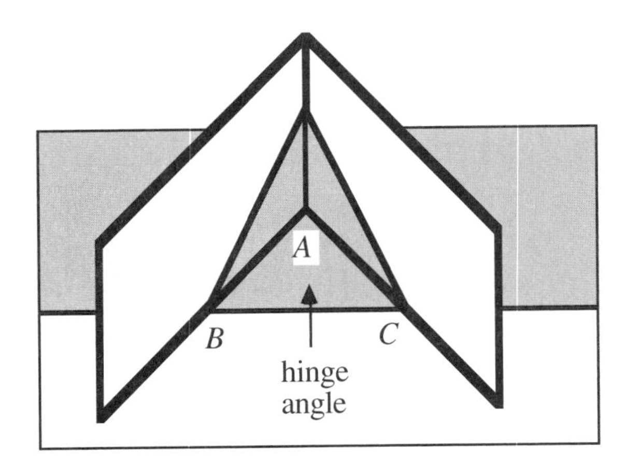

FIGURE 1-3 Triangle with hinge angle.

c. Continue to close the mirrors, keeping the distance from A to B equal to the distance from A to C. Other polygons will appear, such as a quadrilateral, a pentagon, and a hexagon. Record the measure of the hinge angle for each polygon that appears, up to a decagon, in Table **1-1.**

TABLE 1-1 ■ ***Polygon Information***

Polygon	No. of Sides	Measure of Hinge Angle
triangle	3	120°
quadrilateral		
pentagon		
hexagon		
heptagon		$51\frac{3}{7}°$
octagon		
nonagon		
decagon	10	

d. Use the patterns you observe in the table to describe a relationship between the number of sides of a polygon and the measure of the hinge angle.

Discussion

a. What appears to occur as the measure of the hinge angle becomes smaller?

mathematics note

A polygon is **equiangular** if its interior angles are congruent. A polygon is **equilateral** if its sides are congruent. A polygon is **regular** if its sides are congruent and its interior angles are congruent.

For example, Figure **1-4** shows two regular polygons, a square and an equilateral triangle.

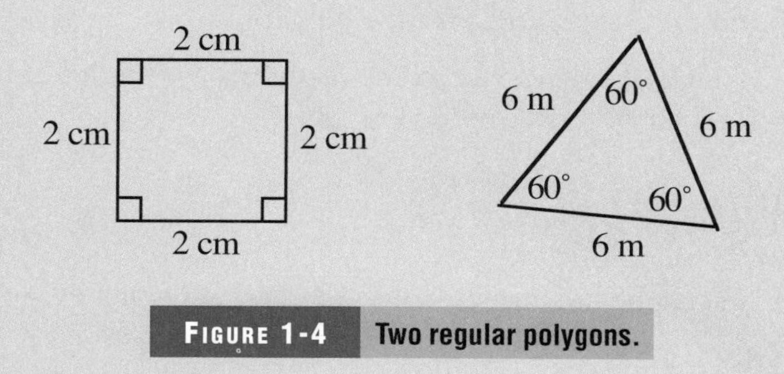

Figure 1-4 Two regular polygons.

An angle formed by two rays drawn from the center of a circle is a **central angle.**

When a regular polygon is **inscribed** in a circle, all vertices of the polygon lie on the circle. The central angles formed by rays drawn from the center of the circle to consecutive vertices of the polygon divide the polygon into congruent isosceles triangles.

For example, Figure **1-5** shows equilateral triangle ABC inscribed in a circle with center O. In this case, $\angle AOB$, $\angle AOC$, and $\angle BOC$ are central angles of $\triangle ABC$.

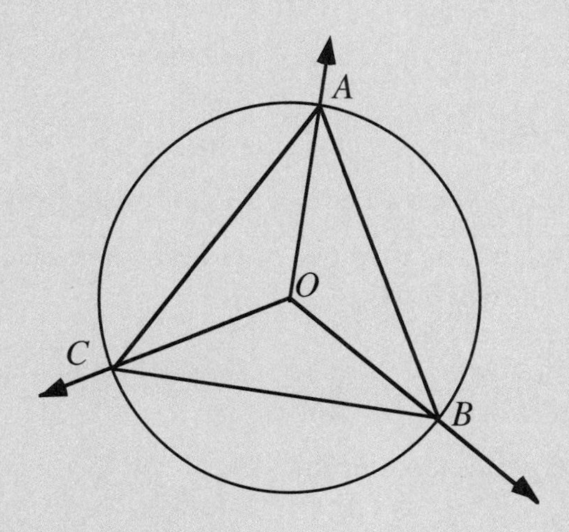

Figure 1-5 Inscribed equilateral triangle with central angles.

b. Are the polygons formed by the reflections in the exploration always regular polygons? Why or why not?

c. 1. What relationship exists between the number of sides of a regular polygon and the measure of its central angle?

 2. Express this relationship as an algebraic formula.

d. How many central angles are there in any regular polygon?

e. Identify the congruent isosceles triangles in Figure **1-5.**

f. What is the relationship between the vertex angles of the isosceles triangles and the central angles of the polygon?

g. What is the relationship between the base angles of the isosceles triangles and the interior angles of the polygon?

Warm-Up

1. Determine the measure of the central angle for a regular polygon with:

 a. 4 sides

 b. 6 sides

 c. 15 sides

2. Describe the number of sides in a regular polygon with a central angle measure of:

 a. $45°$

 b. $24°$

 c. $32\frac{8}{11}°$

Assignment

1.1 a. Describe the measure of the central angle for a regular polygon with n sides.

 b. Describe the number of sides in a regular polygon with a central angle measure of $0°$.

1.2 Explain how to draw each of the following figures using only a ruler and two hinged mirrors.

 a. two perpendicular lines

 b. a $120°$ angle

 c. a regular hexagon with sides 5 cm long

1.3 A carpenter wishes to make a tabletop in the shape of a regular hexagon. The edge of the table consists of six pieces like those shown below. The two longest sides of each edge piece are parallel to each other.

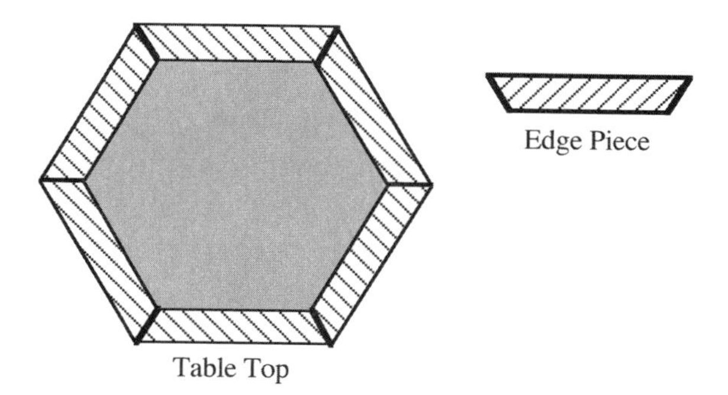

a. Determine the measure of each interior angle in an edge piece.

b. Identify the type of polygon represented by an edge piece. Is it a regular polygon? Explain your response.

c. If the tabletop was a regular octagon, how would the measures of the angles in the edge pieces change? Explain your response.

* * * * *

1.4 Determine the measure of a central angle for each of the following:

a. a regular pentagon

b. a regular octagon

c. a regular decagon

d. a regular n-gon

1.5 The following diagram shows square $ABCD$ inscribed in a circle with center O. In this case, the measure of central angle AOB is 90°, while the measure of angle OAB is 45°.

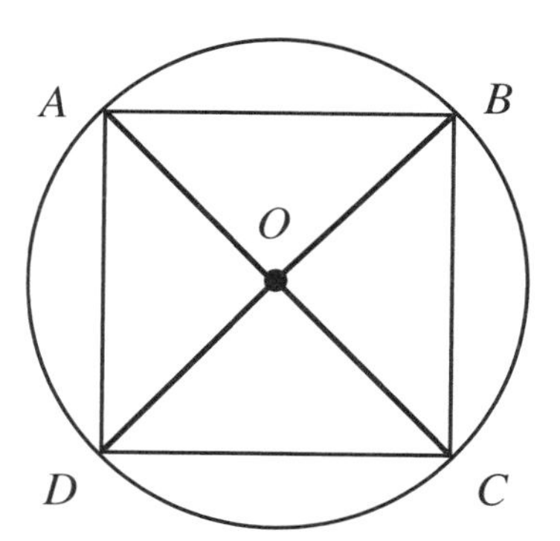

What is the measure of angle OAB if the inscribed polygon is:

a. a regular pentagon?

b. a regular octagon?

c. a regular decagon?

d. a regular n-gon?

1.6 **a.** Find the measure of the interior angles in each of the following:

1. a regular pentagon

2. a regular octagon

3. a regular decagon

4. a regular n-gon

b. Determine the sum of the measures of the interior angles for each regular polygon in Part **a.**

1.7 As mentioned in the mathematics note, the central angles of a regular polygon divide the polygon into congruent isosceles triangles. Describe how you could use the area of these triangles to find the area of each of the following:

a. a regular pentagon

b. a regular octagon

c. a regular decagon

d. a regular n-gon

When you look into your model kaleidoscope, the images you see are caused by light rays reflecting from the confetti, striking the hinged mirrors, then bouncing off the mirrors into your eyes. As you change the positions of the mirrors, the paths of the light rays also change. In this activity, you explore the paths that light rays follow in a reflection.

Exploration

a. Draw an x-axis and a y-axis on a sheet of graph paper with the origin (0,0) near the center of the sheet. Label the origin as point A and a point on the positive x-axis as point B.

b. As shown in Figure **1-6,** place a mirror tightly against one edge of a block of fiberboard and perpendicular to the broad face of the block.

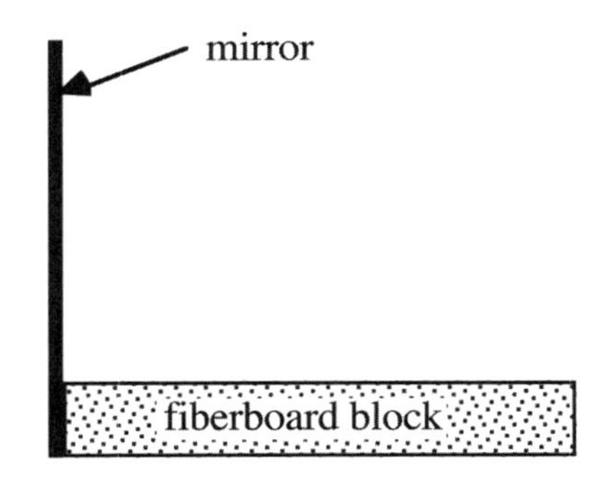

FIGURE 1-6 **Light-ray experiment (side view).**

c. Carefully fold the graph paper along the x-axis. Place the folded sheet on top of the fiberboard block with the x-axis tightly against the mirror, as shown in Figure **1-7.**

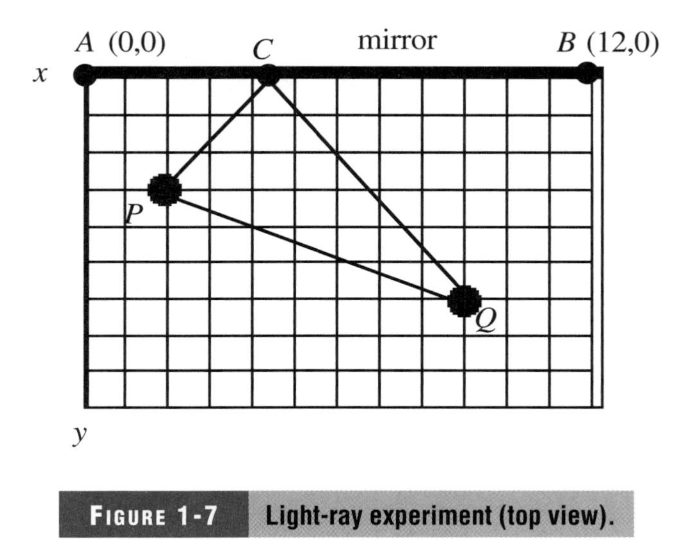

FIGURE 1-7 **Light-ray experiment (top view).**

d. Choose two points that fit the description below.

1. The x-coordinates are at least 3 units apart.
2. The y-coordinates are different and between –3 and –7.

e. 1. Label the point with the lesser x-coordinate as P and the other point as Q.

2. Place one pushpin through P and another through Q.
3. Sight through P toward the mirror with one eye closed. Looking at the reflection of Q, move your head until P aligns with the image of Q.
4. Mark a point C on the x-axis where P, C, and the reflection of Q are collinear (on the same line).

f. Place a rubber band around the pushpins. Using the point of a pencil, pull the side of the rubber band closer to the mirror until the pencil is at C. Check the position of C again to make sure P, C, and the reflection of Q are collinear. The side of the rubber band you stretched shows the path that light rays follow from Q to the mirror to P.

g. 1. Remove your graph paper from the fiberboard block and unfold it. Draw $\overline{PC}$ and $\overline{CQ}$ These segments show the path of light as it travels from the pushpin at Q to your eye at P by reflecting off the mirror.

2. Measure $\angle QCB$ and $\angle PCA$. Record these angle measures. **Note:** Save your graph paper for use in the assignment and in Activity **3.**

science note

Light rays reflecting off a flat surface form rays and angles as shown in Figure **1-8.**

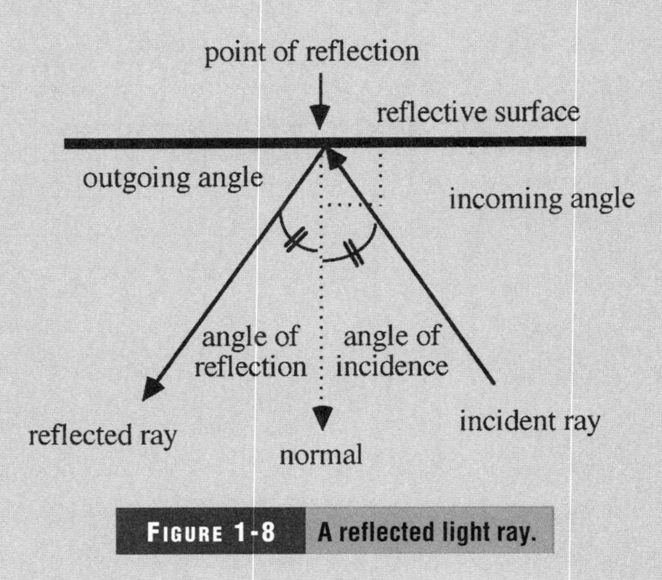

FIGURE 1-8 A reflected light ray.

The **incident ray** models the path that a light ray follows from the object to the reflective surface, while the **reflected ray** models the path of the light ray away from the reflective surface.

The **incoming angle** is the angle between the reflective surface and the incident (incoming) ray. The **outgoing angle** is the angle between the surface and the reflected (outgoing) ray.

The **normal** of the reflecting surface is the perpendicular line to the surface at the **point of reflection.** The **angle of incidence** is the angle formed by the normal and the incident ray, while the **angle of reflection** is the angle formed by the normal and the reflected ray.

Discussion

a. Using terms from the Science Note, describe the path traveled by a light ray that passes through Q and strikes the mirror before reaching your eye.

b. Make a conjecture about the relationship between the measures of the incoming angle and the outgoing angle.

c. Compare the angle measures you recorded with others in your group. Do any of these measurements contradict your conjecture? If so, do you still believe that your conjecture is correct? Explain your response.

d. Describe several ways in which an error in measurement could occur in the exploration. How might these errors affect your conclusions?

e. Suggest another method for confirming your conjecture in Part **c.**

mathematics note

If the sum of the measures of two angles is 90°, then the two angles are **complementary**. In Figure **1-9,** for example, $\angle BAC$ and $\angle HIG$ are complementary angles because 30° + 60° = 90°.

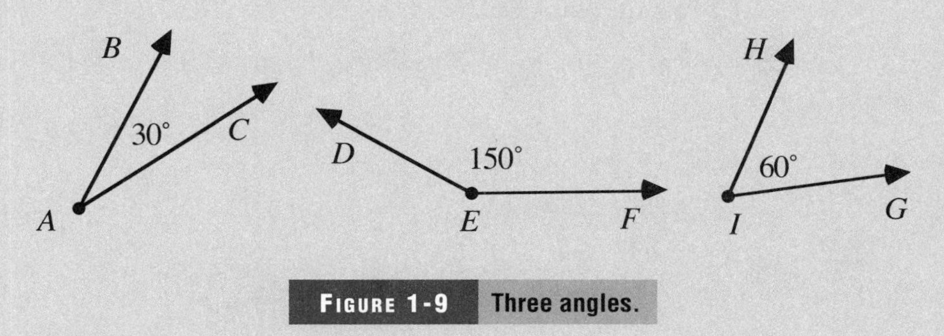

FIGURE 1-9 Three angles.

If the sum of the measures of two angles is 180°, then the two angles are **supplementary.** In Figure **1-9,** $\angle BAC$ and $\angle DEF$ are supplementary angles because 30° + 150° = 180°.

f. Identify the pairs of angles in Figure **1-8** that are complementary.

Warm-Up

1. Identify each set of angle measures as supplementary, complementary, or neither. Justify your answers.

   a. 42°, 48°

   b. 63°, 127°

   c. 36°, 144°

   d. 120°, 40°, 20°

2. Determine the supplement and complement of each angle measure below:

   a. 40°

   b. $m°$, where $m < 90$

Assignment

2.1 Use your graph from the exploration to complete Parts **a–c** below.

a. **1.** Draw and label a normal on the graph at the point where the light rays were reflected.

2. Measure and label the angle of incidence and the angle of reflection.

b. Use the graph to make a conjecture about the relationship between each of the following pairs of angles:

1. the angle of incidence and the angle of reflection

2. the incoming angle and the angle of incidence

3. the outgoing angle and the angle of reflection.

c. Write an argument to convince a classmate that your conjectures are correct.

2.2 **a.** Consider a light ray bouncing off a mirror. Draw and label the normal to the surface at the point of reflection.

b. Use a protractor to draw a light ray bouncing off the mirror with an angle of incidence of 55°.

c. Label all angles and give their measures.

2.3 **a.** Prepare a labeled diagram that shows what happens when a ray of sunlight reflects off the surface of a watch.

b. Write a summary of the mathematical ideas represented in the diagram.

* * * * *

2.4 Using mathematical terms, describe what happens when a driver adjusts the side mirror on a car.

2.5 Reflections occur not only in mirrors, but also in other situations. In the game of pool, players use a cue stick to strike a white ball (the cue ball). When a player hits the cue ball correctly, it strikes one of the other balls and knocks it into one of six holes, or pockets, on the table. In a bank shot, a ball bounces off a side rail before falling into a pocket. The path of a ball bouncing off a side rail is like the path of light reflecting off a mirror.

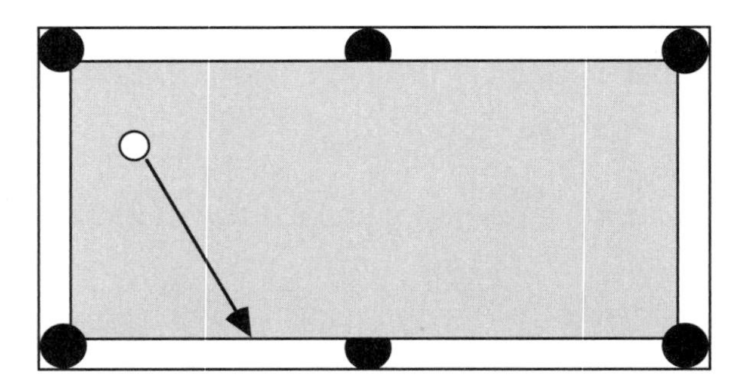

Suppose a pool ball is hit along the path shown in the diagram. Will the ball fall into the upper right corner pocket after a single bounce off the side rail? Explain your response.

2.6 Light rays passing through glass are bent towards the normal. This bending of light rays is called **refraction.** For example, a stick in water appears bent because of refraction. The light ray enters and exits the glass as shown below.

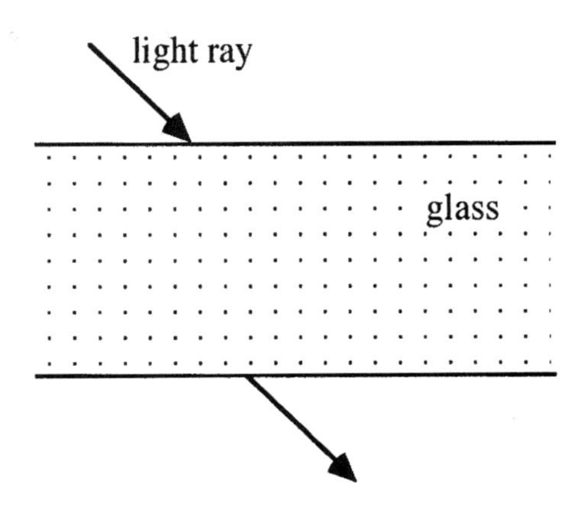

a. Copy the diagram above and draw the path of light from the entry point to the exit point.

b. Draw and label the normals at the entry and exit points.

c. In your drawing from Parts **a** and **b**, identify and label all pairs of angles that appear to be congruent.

Research Project

1. Describe how to determine the length of the smallest mirror that would allow every member of your family to see a complete reflection from head to toe. Include a diagram with your report.

2. Write a report about periscopes that answers the following questions.

   a. What is a periscope?

   b. In what types of situations are periscopes useful?

   c. How does a periscope work? (Include a diagram in your report.)

   d. How can you make a simple periscope using a tube and two mirrors? (Include a model with your report.)

ACTIVITY 3

When you look in a mirror, your reflection sometimes appears to be behind the mirror's surface. This illusion, often called a **virtual image,** is created by light rays reflecting off the mirror. In this activity, you explore the relationship between the position of an object and the apparent position of its reflection in a mirror.

Exploration 1

a. Unfold your sheet of graph paper from the exploration in Activity **2** and lay it flat. Position a tinted plastic reflector along the x-axis with points P and Q on your side of the reflector.

mathematics note

The reflection of an object is its **image.** The object itself is the **preimage.** If point A is the preimage, then the image of a point A can be represented as A' (read "A prime").

b. 1. Find the reflection of point Q in the reflector.

2. Place your pencil behind the reflector and mark the point on the graph paper where the reflection of Q appears to be. This point is the image of Q. Label it Q'.

3. Remove the reflector and draw $\overline{PQ'}$. As shown in Figure **1-10,** points P, C, and Q' should be collinear.

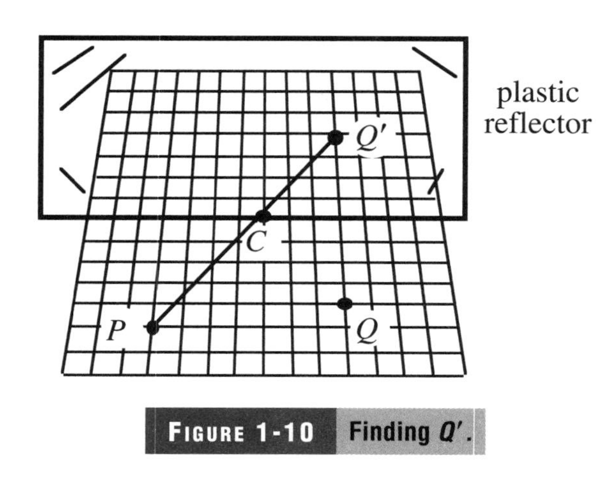

FIGURE 1-10 **Finding Q'.**

c. 1. Use the plastic reflector to mark the image of point P on your graph paper. Label this point P'.

   2. Remove the reflector and draw $\overline{QP'}$.

d. The **distance from a point to a line** is the distance along a path perpendicular to the line. Measure the distance from the x-axis to each of the following points:

   1. Q and Q'.

   2. P and P'.

e. Make a conjecture about the relationship between the distance from an object to the mirror line and the distance from its image to the mirror line.

Discussion 1

a. In Activity **2,** you pushed pins through two layers of folded graph paper at points P and Q. How do the locations of the pinholes in the second layer compare with the locations of P' and Q'?

b. How is the distance from Q to the x-axis related to the distance from Q' to the x-axis?

c. 1. Where do $\overline{PQ'}$ and $\overline{QP'}$ intersect?

   2. What does this tell you about the paths traveled by reflected light?

d. Does the class data support the conjecture you made in Part **e** of Exploration **1**? Explain your response.

Exploration 2

In this exploration, you use technology to model the process described in Exploration **1.** Most geometry utilities have reflection tools for finding the images of objects. To use this feature, you must first define a mirror line and the points to be reflected.

a. 1. Construct a mirror line segment, $\overline{AB}$.

   2. Construct two points, P and Q, on the same side of $\overline{AB}$.

   3. Reflect points P and Q in $\overline{AB}$ and label the images P' and Q', respectively.

   4. Construct $\overline{PQ'}$ and $\overline{QP'}$.

   5. Construct a point C at the intersection of $\overline{AB}$ and $\overline{PQ'}$.

   6. Measure $\angle PCA$ and $\angle QCB$.

7. Construct $\overline{PP'}$ and $\overline{QQ'}$.

8. Label the intersection of $\overline{AB}$ and $\overline{PP'}$ as point D and the intersection of $\overline{AB}$ and $\overline{QQ'}$ as point E. Your construction should now resemble the one in Figure **1-11** below.

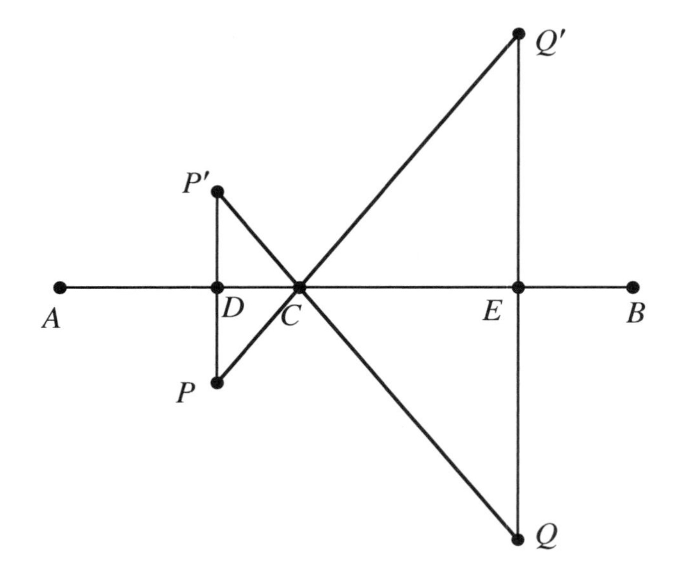

FIGURE 1-11 Reflection modeled on a geometry utility.

9. Measure $\angle PDA$ and $\angle QEB$.

10. Measure the distances from $\overline{AB}$ to points P, P', Q, and Q'.

11. Measure $\overline{EQ}$ and $\overline{EQ'}$.

b. Use your measurements in Part **a** to make a conjecture about the relationship between $\overline{AB}$ and $\overline{QQ'}$.

c. Select and move various points on your construction. Note any relationships you observe among the measurements of angles and segments as you move the points.

d. Complete Steps **1–3** below using your construction from Part **a.**

1. Construct a point S anywhere on $\overline{AB}$.

2. Measure the total distance traveled when moving from Q to S and then from S to P.

3. By moving S along $\overline{AB}$, find the point where the total distance traveled in Step **2** is shortest.

mathematics note

The **perpendicular bisector** of a segment is the line that is perpendicular ($\perp$) to the segment and divides the segment into two congruent parts.

In Figure **1-12,** for example, line m is the perpendicular bisector of $\overline{CC'}$ because line m and $\overline{CC'}$ are perpendicular and $\overline{CM} \cong \overline{C'M}$.

A **reflection** in a line is a pairing of points in a plane so that the **line of reflection** (or **mirror line)** is the perpendicular bisector of every segment connecting a point in the preimage to its corresponding point in the image. Every point on the line of reflection is its own image.

In Figure **1-12,** parallelogram $C'D'E'F'$ is the image of parallelogram $CDEF$. Line m is the line of reflection because it is the perpendicular bisector of each segment joining a point in the preimage to its corresponding point in the image.

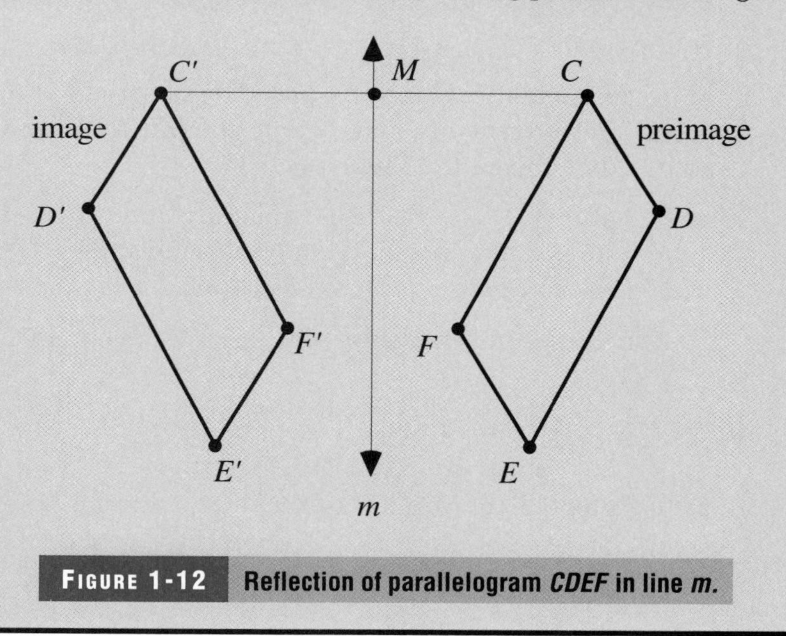

FIGURE 1-12 **Reflection of parallelogram *CDEF* in line *m*.**

Discussion 2

a. 1. Make a conjecture about the relationship between $\overline{AB}$ and $\overline{PP'}$ in Figure **1-11.**

   2. Do your measurements in Exploration **2** support this conjecture?

b. What conjecture can you make about the path that results in the shortest total distance in Part **c** of Exploration **2** and the point of reflection?

c. Imagine that $\overline{AB}$ in Figure **1-11** is on the x-axis.

   1. What does the measure of $\angle QEB$ tell you about the x-coordinates of points Q and Q'?

2. What do the lengths of $\overline{EQ}$ and $\overline{EQ'}$ tell you about the y-coordinates of Q and Q'?

3. Which segments would you measure to compare the y-coordinates of points P and P'?

d. 1. Describe the relationship between the coordinates of point Q and its image Q'.

2. Describe the relationship between the coordinates of point P and its image P'.

3. Are these relationships also true for each preimage and image in Exploration **1**?

e. What generalization might you make about the relationship between the coordinates of a point in the preimage and the coordinates of its image under a reflection in each of the following lines:

1. the x-axis?

2. the y-axis?

f. Many mathematical ideas are based on observed patterns. When conjectures based on patterns are stated in a general form and proved, they become accepted mathematical **theorems.**

1. In Activity **2,** you made a conjecture about the relationship between the measures of the incoming and outgoing angles. Do your measurements in Exploration **2** support this conjecture?

2. If so, could this conjecture now become a theorem?

Warm-Up

1. Determine the coordinates of the image of each point when reflected in the x-axis.

   a. (4,7)

   b. (–3,6)

   c. (a,b)

2. Determine the coordinates of the image of each point when reflected in the y-axis.

   a. (10,6)

   b. (–11,–4)

   c. (a,b)

3. On a coordinate grid, draw the shortest path from point $A(2,4)$ to point $B(7,2)$ that touches the x-axis.

Assignment

3.1 **a.** Plot three points on a coordinate grid so that one point has all positive coordinates, one point has all negative coordinates, and one point has one positive and one negative coordinate. Label these points A, B, and C.

b. Plot the reflections of A, B and C in the y-axis. Label the image points A', B', and C', respectively.

c. List the coordinates of each point and its image.

d. Consider a point D with coordinates (x,y). If D is reflected in the y-axis, what are the coordinates of D'?

3.2 Use your graph paper from the exploration in Activity **2** to complete Parts **a** and **b** below.

a. Describe the shortest path from Q' to P.

b. How does the length of this path compare to the length of the path that light travels from Q to P? Explain your response.

3.3 A family wants to build the shortest possible trail from their house to the stream and then to the barn. The diagram below shows the distances between these locations.

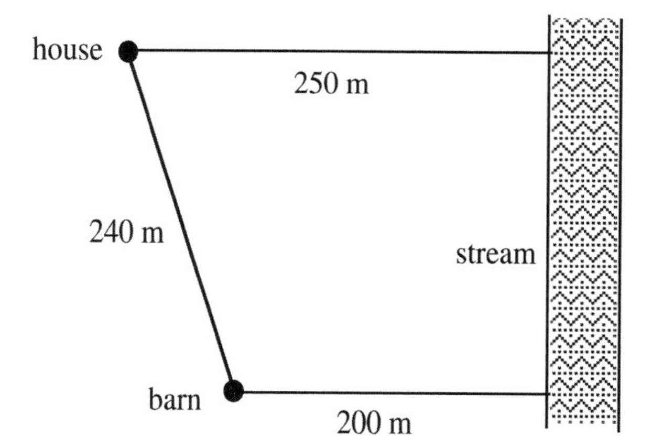

a. Make a scale drawing of this situation.

b. Use your drawing to determine where the trail should reach the stream to make the shortest trail from the house to the stream to the barn.

c. Explain how you used the properties of reflections to determine your solution.

* * * * *

3.4 The diagram below shows a square tile with its lower left-hand corner at the origin of an xy-coordinate system. Sketch a copy of this diagram on a sheet of graph paper.

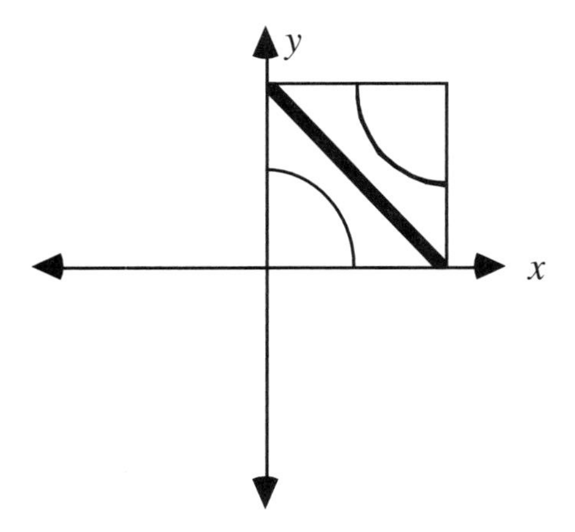

a. Sketch the image of the tile reflected in the x-axis.

b. Sketch the image of your response to Part **a** reflected in the y-axis.

3.5 The diagram below shows a section of an oil pipeline along with two nearby wells. To transport oil from the wells to the pipeline, the company plans to build a new pumping station somewhere on the line. If the company wants to minimize the amount of pipe needed to connect the two wells to the pipeline, where should it locate the pumping station?

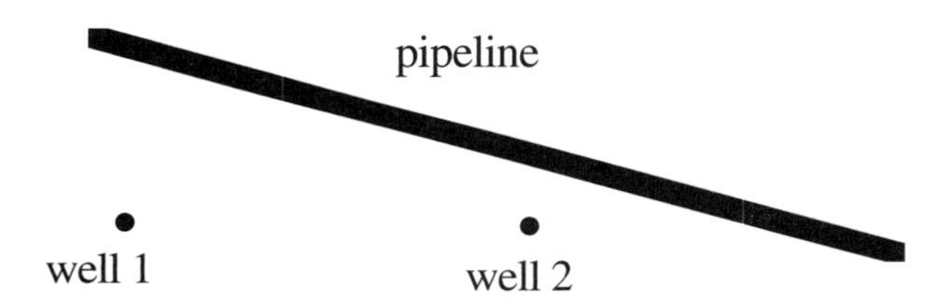

3.6 The diagram below shows the top of a pool table along with a cue ball.

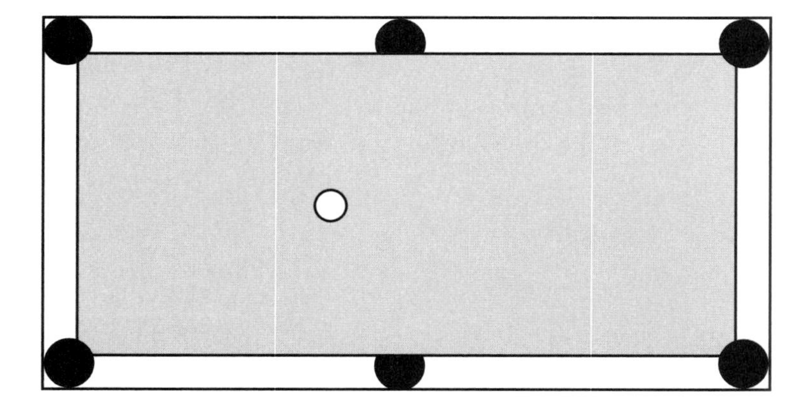

a. Trace a path that banks the cue ball off exactly one side and places it in a pocket.

b. Describe how you determined the path you chose in Part **a.**

c. Find another path to the same pocket, using a different side of the table to bank the ball.

3.7 In a hockey game between the Saints and the Tornadoes, six players are positioned as shown in the diagram below. Each circle that contains a letter S represents a member of the Saints; each circle that contains a T represents a member of the Tornadoes.

Draw all the paths that show a successful pass from the Saint on the left to one of the other two Saints. Each pass must reflect off one of the boards (sides). Explain why your pass is possible.

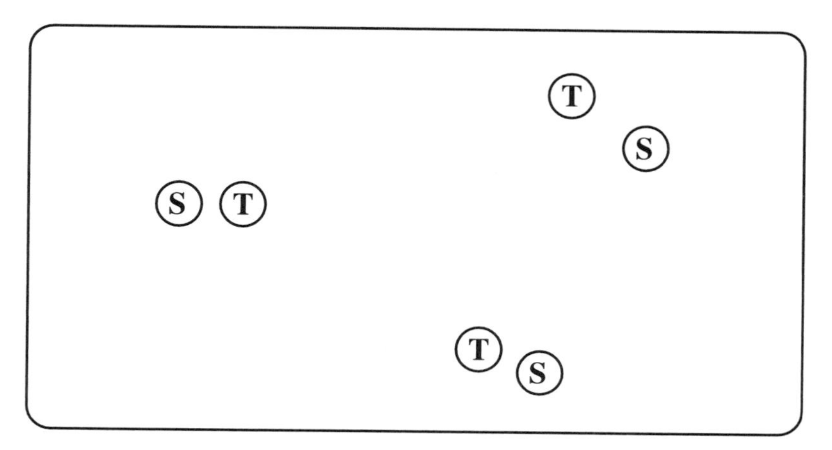

In the previous activities, you examined how light reflects off a single flat mirror. The kaleidoscope you built in the introduction, however, used two mirrors. In this situation, light reflects off one mirror, then the other. In the following exploration, you investigate the virtual images produced by light reflecting off two mirrors.

Exploration 1

a. On a sheet of graph paper, draw two perpendicular line segments and a point Q, as shown in Figure **1-13** on the next page.

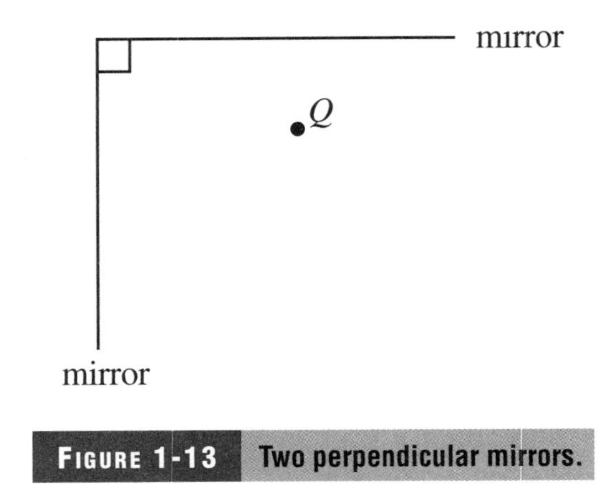

FIGURE 1-13 **Two perpendicular mirrors.**

b. If hinged mirrors like those used in Activity **1** were placed along the line segments, how many images of point Q would you see in the mirrors? Record your prediction.

c. Use two hinged mirrors to test your prediction in Part **b.** Record how many images of point Q you actually observe.

d. To discover why this number of images occurs, use your diagram from Part **a** to complete Steps **1–6** below.

1. Reflect Q in one of the line segments and label the image Q'_1.
2. Reflect Q in the other line segment and label this image Q'_2.
3. Place the hinged mirrors on the segments again. Observe that two of the virtual images of Q in the mirrors correspond to the two images of Q found in Steps **1** and **2.**
4. Remove the hinged mirrors. Reflect Q'_1 in the other line segment and label its image Q'' (read "Q double-prime").
5. Repeat Step **4** using Q'_2 to locate Q''_2. What do you observe about the positions of Q'' and Q''_2?
6. Place the hinged mirrors back on the line segments and observe the virtual image that corresponds to Q''. **Note:** Save your diagram for use in Exploration **2.**

Discussion 1

a. How did the number of images you observed in Part **c** of Exploration **1** compare with your prediction in Part **b**?

b. Explain why the two mirrors in Exploration **1** produce three virtual images.

c. In Exploration **1,** you labeled the image of a single reflection Q', and the image of a double reflection Q''. How would you label the image of a triple reflection?

d. How do your observations in Part **d** of Exploration **1** help explain the patterns you saw in the kaleidoscope?

Exploration 2

In this exploration, you use the properties of single reflections to investigate the path of light in a double reflection.

a. Add a point E to your diagram from Exploration **1,** as shown in Figure **1-14** below. In this diagram, point E represents the location of your eye.

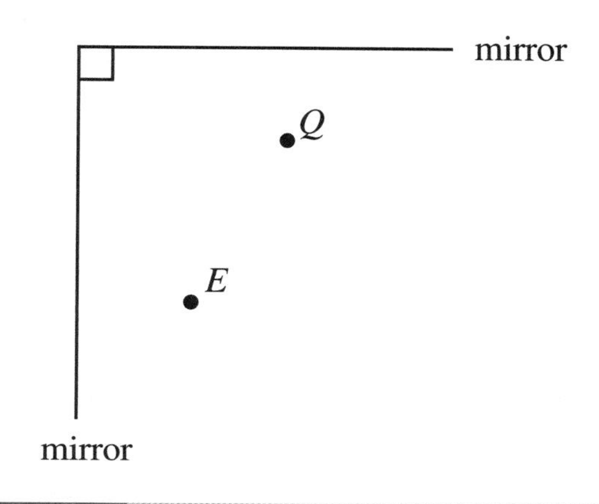

FIGURE 1-14 **Perpendicular mirrors with points *E* and *Q*.**

b. To find the path that light travels in a double reflection from Q to E, complete Steps **1–4** below.

1. Use a straightedge to connect E and Q''.
2. Label the point $\overline{EQ''}$ where intersects the mirror line segment as C_2.
3. Use a straightedge to connect C_2 and Q_1'.
4. Label the point where $\overline{C_2Q_1'}$ intersects the other mirror line segment as C_1.

c. Draw the path from Q to C_1, then to C_2, and finally to E. **Note:** Save your diagram for use in the assignment.

Discussion 2

a. What does the path drawn in Part **c** of Exploration **2** represent?

b. What do the points C_1 and C_2 represent?

c. Using light rays, explain why the virtual image that corresponds to Q'' appears where it does in the mirror.

Warm-Up

1. For each point P below, determine the coordinates of P', a reflection of P in the x-axis, and the coordinates of P'', a reflection of P' in the y-axis.

   a. (2,–5)

   b. (4,6)

   c. (–3,1)

   d. (a,b)

2. **a.** On a coordinate grid, draw the shortest path from $A(3,-2)$ to $B(2,-6)$ that touches both the x- and y-axes.

   b. Determine the measures of the incoming and outgoing angles on the graph that you drew in Part **a.** Describe the relationships among the angles.

Assignment

4.1 The diagram below shows two perpendicular mirrors and the points Q and E. On a copy of this diagram, draw the path that light travels in a double reflection from Q to E.

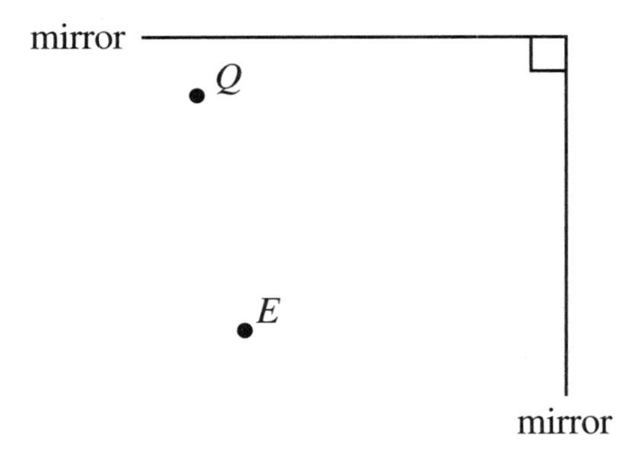

4.2 Use the diagram of two perpendicular mirrors that you created in Exploration **2** to complete Parts **a–e** below.

   a. Label the intersection of the two mirror line segments as point $Z(0,0)$ and graph two more points: $A(0,-4)$ and $B(4,0)$.

   b. Use a protractor to measure $\angle ZC_2C_1$ to the nearest degree. Record the measurement on your graph paper and label the angle as either outgoing or incoming.

   c. Explain how the measurements of the remaining angles can be determined by knowing only the measure of $\angle ZC_2C_1$.

   d. Label the remaining three angles as incoming or outgoing and record their measures.

e. **1.** Calculate the sum of the measures of the two incoming and two outgoing angles.

2. Use the sum of the four angles to make a conjecture about the path of a light ray in a double reflection or the path of a pool ball in a double bank shot.

4.3 To model a pair of mirrors, draw two perpendicular segments on a sheet of graph paper as in Exploration **2**. Label the intersection of the two segments point $Z(0,0)$ and graph two more points: $A(0,-4)$ and $B(4,0)$. Find the path that light would travel from point $O(4,-1)$ to point $E(3,-7)$ if it reflected off both mirrors. Label all points, angles, and segments that correspond to those found in Exploration **2**. Identify the incoming and outgoing angles and give their measures.

4.4 **a.** On a sheet of blank paper, use a protractor to draw two line segments representing mirrors hinged at 70°.

b. Label two points between the mirrors: point O, representing an object, and point E, representing the perspective of an eye.

c. Find the locations of the images of O. Label these points O' and O''.

d. Sketch the path of light from O to E in a double reflection.

e. Measure one of the incoming or outgoing angles and record this measurement on your drawing.

f. Determine the measures of the remaining three angles and record these measures on your drawing. Label all angles either as incoming or outgoing.

g. Calculate the sum of the measures of all four angles. Does this sum support the conjecture you made in Problem **4.2**?

4.5 A full-size pool table measures approximately 126 cm × 255 cm.

a. Make a scale drawing of a pool table, including the six pockets.

b. Mark the location of a ball somewhere on your scale drawing, then draw the path of a shot that requires the ball to strike at least two side rails before reaching a pocket.

c. Label the appropriate points (with measurements in centimeters), so that a pool player could:

1. locate the starting position of the ball on an actual pool table.

2. locate the point where the ball must hit the first side rail to make the shot.

d. If possible, test your calculations on a real pool table, and write an account of your test.

* * * * *

4.6 Some large radio telescopes use several reflecting surfaces positioned in special ways. The diagram below shows three such surfaces in a radio telescope built in Arecibo, Puerto Rico, in 1963. On a copy of this diagram, draw the path of each reflected radio wave and explain why these paths occur.

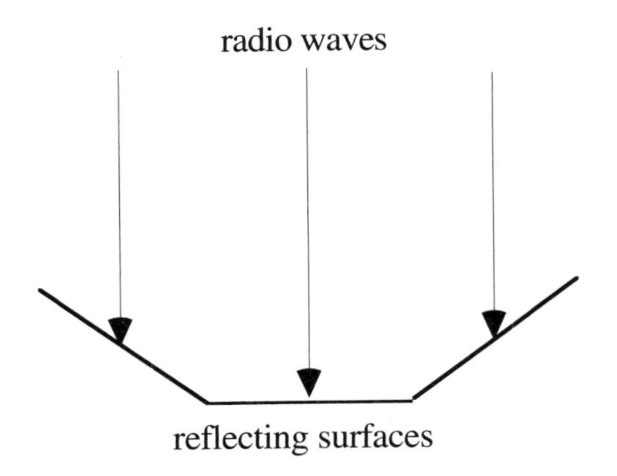

4.7 The diagram below shows three hinged mirrors positioned in the shape of an equilateral triangular prism. A hole in the center of one mirror allows a laser beam to enter the prism.

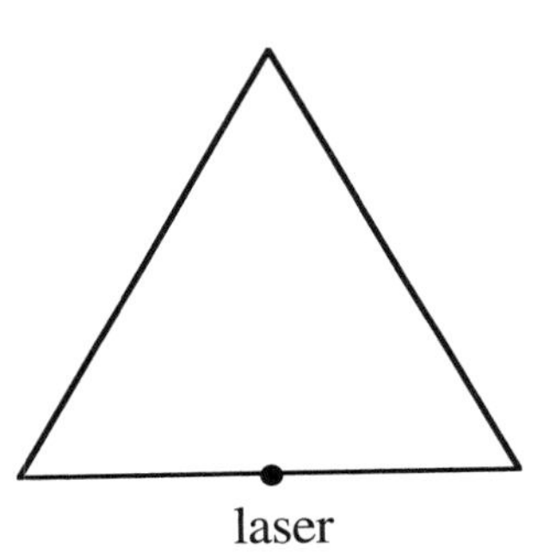

a. Draw a path for the laser beam that allows it to reflect off each of the other two mirrors exactly once and pass back through its starting point.

b. Determine the measures of every incoming and outgoing angle and the measures of every angle of incidence and angle of reflection.

c. Identify the shapes formed by the lines of reflection. How are these shapes related to the original triangle?

Summary Assessment

1. Most miniature golf courses have holes requiring a player to hit the ball off at least one wall to score a hole-in-one. An example is shown in the diagram below.

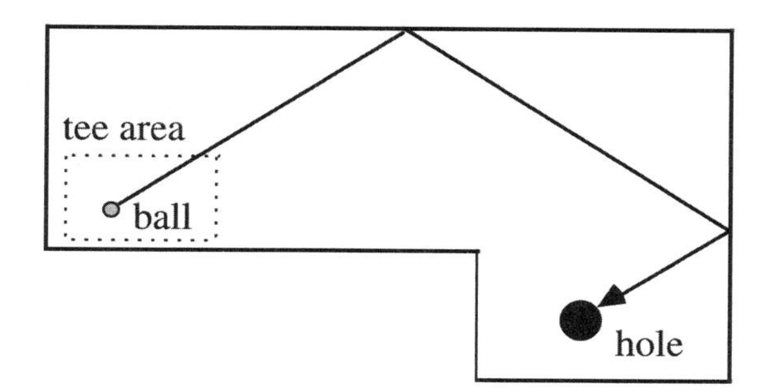

Design and draw some miniature golf holes according to the following three rules.

- The drawing must be to scale, with all dimensions indicated.
- Only line segments may be used for walls.
- A tee area must be provided.

As you design holes, sketch some possible paths for a hole-in-one. In your final drawing for each hole, however, do not reveal your winning strategy. Design one of each of the following types of holes.

a. A hole that looks simple, but where a hole-in-one is probably impossible.

b. A hole that looks difficult, but has a simple path for the ball.

c. A hole that has many possible paths.

d. A hole that requires a player to bank the ball off exactly three walls to get a hole-in-one.

2. To test your designs, trade drawings with a classmate. Try to sketch the path of a hole-in-one in each of your classmate's drawings.

3. After your designs have been tested, present one of them to the rest of the class. Use mathematical ideas and the language of this module to explain your design.

Module Summary

* A **polygon** is a union of coplanar segments intersecting only at endpoints. At most, two segments intersect at any one endpoint and each segment intersects exactly two other segments. Each segment in a polygon is a **side;** each endpoint is a **vertex** (plural **vertices).**

* A polygon is **equiangular** if its interior angles are congruent. A polygon is **equilateral** if its sides are congruent. A polygon is **regular** if its sides are congruent and its interior angles are congruent.

* An angle formed by two rays drawn from the center of a circle is a **central angle.**

* When a regular polygon is **inscribed** in a circle, all vertices of the polygon lie on the circle. The central angles formed by rays drawn from the center of the circle to consecutive vertices of the polygon divide the polygon into congruent isosceles triangles.

* The measure of a central angle of a regular polygon with n sides is:

$$\frac{360^\circ}{n}$$

* The measure of each **interior angle** of a regular polygon can be determined using the following formula, where n represents the number of sides:

$$180^\circ - \frac{360^\circ}{n}$$

* The sum of the measures of the interior angles of a regular polygon can be determined using the following formula, where n represents the number of sides:

$$\left(180^\circ - \frac{360^\circ}{n}\right)(n) = 180^\circ n - 360^\circ$$

* The **incident ray** models the path that a light ray follows from the object to the reflective surface, while the **reflected ray** models the path of the light ray away from the reflective surface.

* The **incoming angle** is the angle between the reflective surface and the incident (incoming) ray. The **outgoing angle** is the angle between the surface and the reflected (outgoing) ray.

* The **normal** of the reflecting surface is the perpendicular line to the surface at the **point of reflection.** The **angle of incidence** is the angle formed by the normal and the incident ray, while the **angle of reflection** is the angle formed by the normal and the reflected ray.

* If the sum of the measures of two angles is 90°, then the two angles are **complementary.**

* If the sum of the measures of two angles is 180°, then the two angles are **supplementary.**

* The incoming angle and the angle of incidence are **complementary;** in other words, the sum of their measures is 90°. The same is true for the outgoing angle and the angle of reflection.

* The **distance from a point to a line** is the distance along a path perpendicular to the line.

* The reflection of an object is its **image.** The object itself is the **preimage.** If point *A* is the preimage, then the image of a point *A* can be represented as *A*′ (read "A prime").

* The **perpendicular bisector** of a segment is the line that is perpendicular (⊥) to the segment and divides the segment into two congruent parts.

* A **reflection** in a line is a pairing of points in a plane so that the **line of reflection** is the perpendicular bisector of each segment connecting a preimage point to its corresponding image point. Every point on the line of reflection is its own image.

* When conjectures based on patterns are generalized and shown to be true for all cases, they become accepted mathematical **theorems.**

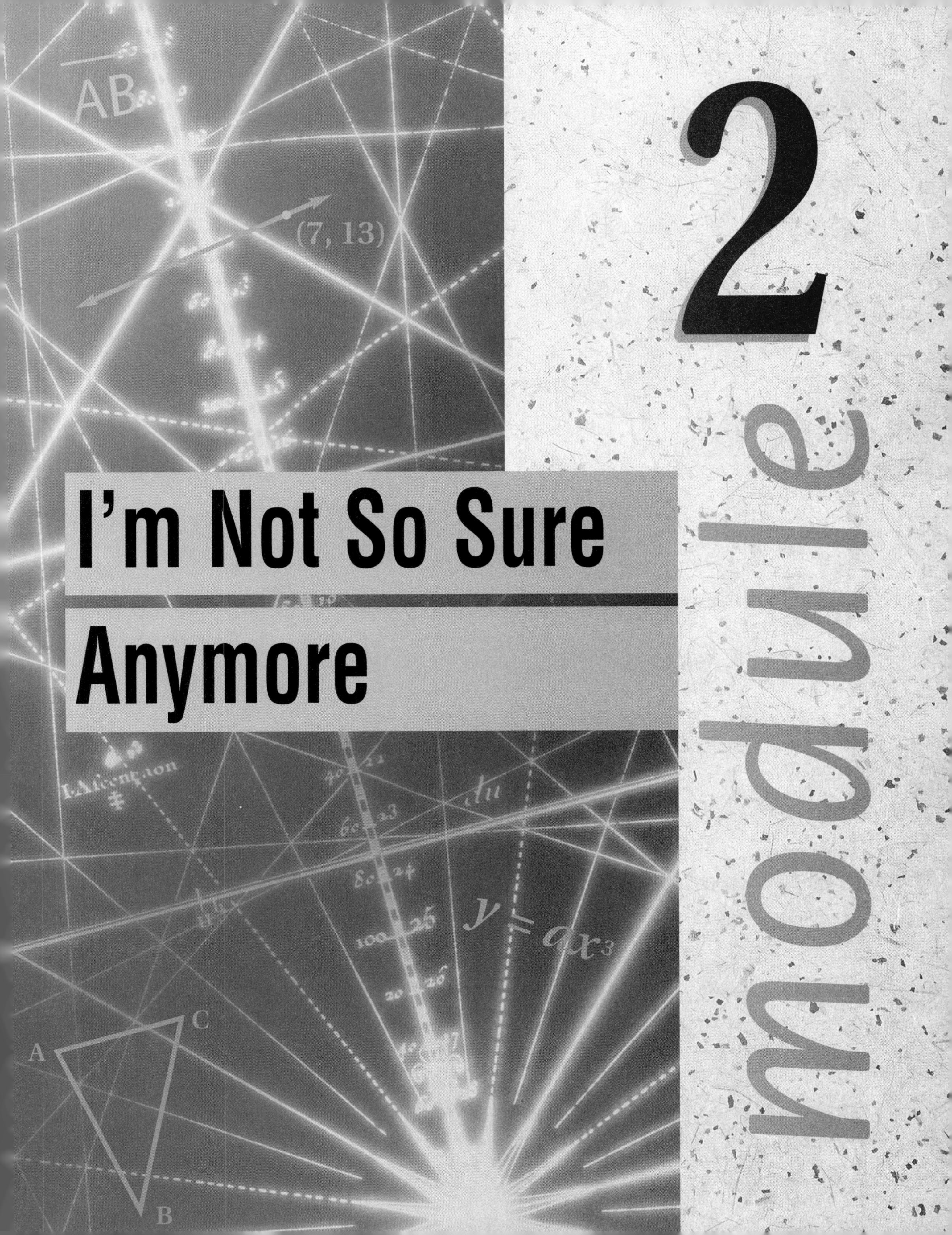

Module 2

I'm Not So Sure Anymore

Introduction

Sarah looked at the clock. The drawing was five minutes away. She clutched the week's lottery ticket in both hands, trying to convince herself that it was a winner. She knew that the probability of winning the jackpot was extremely low. Still, she had hope. After all, she'd bought her ticket at the Yummy Mart, where three other winning tickets had been sold, and she'd chosen lucky numbers, numbers that had shown up in many previous drawings.

As the numbers appeared on the television screen, Sarah moved to the edge of her chair. Her first number matched. So did the second. Her heart raced. The next two numbers also matched. As the last number was being drawn, the lights flickered and the screen went blank. A power outage!

Was the power restored in time for Sarah to see the fifth number? Did she win? And what were the rules of the game she was playing? Although you can't answer all of these questions, you might be able to determine the probability that Sarah is holding the winning ticket.

Exploration

In this exploration, you investigate a simple lottery game in which the prizes are small. In the Apple Lottery, players win red, green, or yellow apples. A sample ticket is shown in Figure **2-1.**

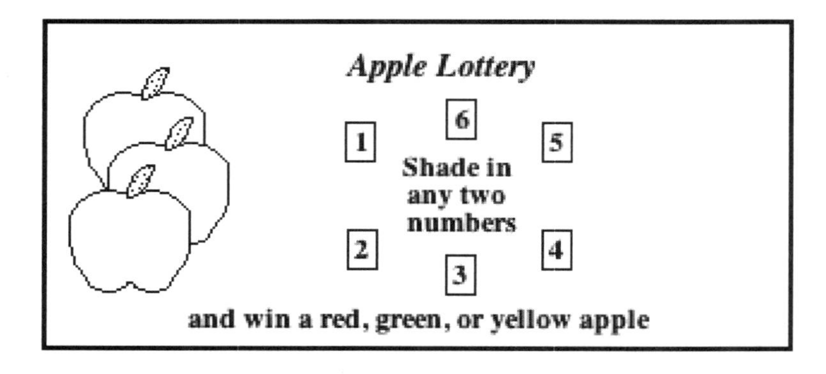

FIGURE 2-1 A ticket for the Apple Lottery.

All lottery games have rules, often printed on the back of the ticket. Figure **2-2** shows the back of an Apple Lottery ticket.

How to Play

- Shade two different numbers from 1 to 6 on the front of the ticket.

How to Win

Apple Lottery officials randomly draw two different numbers from 1 to 6.

- Win a yellow apple by matching 2 numbers.
- Win a green apple by matching 1 number.
- Win a red apple by matching 0 numbers.

FIGURE 2-2 The back of an Apple Lottery ticket.

a. When numbers are chosen at random, there is no way to predict which numbers will be chosen. Suggest a method that Apple Lottery officials might use to draw two different numbers from 1 to 6 at random.

b. In the Apple Lottery, there are three different **events**—winning a red apple, winning a green apple, and winning a yellow apple.

   Predict the number of each type of apple you would win if you played the Apple Lottery 1000 times. Record your predictions.

c. Pick two numbers from 1 to 6 that you would shade on an Apple Lottery ticket. Record these numbers.

d. Recall that a simulation is a model of a real-world occurrence. The results of a simulation are often used to make predictions.

   Use the following steps to simulate the Apple Lottery officials drawing two numbers.

   1. Place 6 objects in a container. Each object should be marked with a different number from 1 to 6.
   2. Shake the container. Without looking, draw two of the numbered objects.

e. Compare the numbers drawn in Part **d** with the two numbers you picked in Part **c.** Record the type of apple won.

f. Repeat Parts **d** and **e** 24 more times.

mathematics note

One way of predicting the likelihood of an event is to perform many trials under controlled conditions. The results of these trials provide the **experimental** (or **empirical**) **probability** of the event occurring. The experimental probability of an event can be calculated using the following ratio:

$$\frac{\text{number of times event occurs}}{\text{total number of trials}}$$

For example, suppose that you counted 60 heads in 100 trials of a coin toss. The experimental probability of obtaining a head on any one toss is:

$$\frac{60}{100} = \frac{3}{5}$$

g. Using your results from Part **f**, determine the experimental probability of each of the following events:

1. winning a red apple
2. winning a yellow apple
3. winning a green apple
4. winning an apple of any color.

h. Combine your results from Part **f** with those of the rest of the class. Use the combined results to determine the experimental probability of each of the following events:

1. winning a red apple
2. winning a yellow apple
3. winning a green apple
4. winning an apple of any color.

i. 1. Predict how many apples of each color you would win in 1000 games of the Apple Lottery.

2. Compare your response to the prediction made in Part **b** of the exploration.

Discussion

a. Compare the experimental probabilities found in Parts **g** and **h** of the exploration. Which do you believe give better estimates of the true chances of winning? Explain your response.

b. Explain why the experimental probability of winning an apple in the Apple Lottery is 1.

c. 1. What other methods could you use to generate two random numbers for the Apple Lottery?

   2. Do these methods guarantee that two different numbers will be generated?

   3. What problem might occur when using a simulation that can generate identical numbers?

   4. How could you modify the simulation to ensure that the two numbers are different?

d. What advantages might there be in using technology to simulate the Apple Lottery?

When using experimental probability to make predictions, the larger the number of trials you use, the better the estimate you get of the true likelihood of an event. In the following exploration, you use technology to help you simulate the results of many games of the Apple Lottery.

Exploration

a. Select two numbers from 1 to 6 for a new Apple Lottery ticket. Record these numbers.

b. When Apple Lottery officials draw two numbers, these might or might not match your numbers. The first column in Table **2-1** on the next page lists all the possible pairs of numbers in the Apple Lottery. This is the **sample space** for the lottery.

   Make a copy of Table **2-1.** For each possible pair of numbers, record the number of matching digits and the color of the apple you would win with your ticket.

c. Simulate the Apple Lottery by completing the following steps.

   1. Randomly generate the first number.

   2. Randomly generate the second number.

   3. If the second number is the same as the first, generate another number. Repeat until you obtain a number different from the first.

d. Use Table **2-1** to determine which apple you won.

TABLE 2-1 ■ *Apple Lottery Sample Space*

Pair of Numbers	Number of Matching Digits	Color of Apple Won
1, 2		
1, 3		
1, 4		
1, 5		
1, 6		
2, 3		
2, 4		
2, 5		
2, 6		
3, 4		
3, 5		
3, 6		
4, 5		
4, 6		
5, 6		

e. Repeat Parts **c** and **d** 99 more times, recording the number of times you won each color of apple.

f. Use the results of your 100 trials to determine the experimental probability of each of the following events:

1. winning a red apple
2. winning a yellow apple
3. winning a green apple

g. Combine your results from Part **f** with those of the rest of the class. Use this data to determine the probability of each of the following events:

1. winning a red apple
2. winning a yellow apple
3. winning a green apple

mathematics note

The set of all possible outcomes for an experiment is the **sample space.**

An **event** is a subset of the sample space.

If each outcome in a sample space has the same chance of occurring, then the **theoretical probability** of an event can be calculated using the following ratio:

$$\frac{\text{number of outcomes in the event}}{\text{total number of outcomes in the sample space}}$$

For example, you can represent the sample space for tossing two fair coins as {HH, TH, HT, TT}, where H stands for head and T stands for tail. The event of getting one tail when tossing two coins consists of 2 outcomes: TH and HT. Because the total number of outcomes in the sample space is 4, the theoretical probability of getting one tail is:

$$\frac{2}{4} = \frac{1}{2}$$

h. Use the information in Table **2-1** to determine the theoretical probability of each of the following events:

1. winning a red apple
2. winning a yellow apple
3. winning a green apple
4. winning an apple of any color

Note: Save your results for use in Problem **3.1.**

Discussion

a. Compare the theoretical probabilities of the events in the Apple Lottery with the experimental probabilities you determined in Part **f** of the exploration.

b. Compare the experimental probabilities determined using the class results in Part **h** with their corresponding theoretical probabilities.

c. How does the pair of numbers you selected for your Apple Lottery ticket affect the theoretical probability of winning each type of apple?

Warm-Up

1. Complete the following table, expressing all fractions in their simplest form.

Percentage	Decimal	Fraction
		1/4
	0.12	
8%		
	1.5	
0.3%		
		5/8

2. Describe the differences between experimental probability and theoretical probability. Give an example of each.
3. **a.** What is the sample space for tossing two coins?
   b. Determine the theoretical probability of obtaining each possible outcome when tossing two coins.
   c. What is the sum of the probabilities in Part **b**?
4. A bag contains 20 red marbles, 16 green marbles, and 12 blue marbles. If you select one marble at random from the bag, what is the probability that the marble is green?

Assignment

1.1 Explain why picking a new ticket in the Apple Lottery does not change the theoretical probability of winning a particular type of apple.

1.2 Judging from the theoretical probabilities, how many apples of each color do you think you would win after playing the Apple Lottery 1000 times?

1.3 Time has expired at the divisional basketball championship. The game is tied and Charrette is at the foul line. During the season, she made 4 out of every 5 of her free throws.

One way to simulate this situation is to use a spinner, as shown in the diagram on the right.

a. What does one spin represent in this simulation?

b. Use a pencil and a paper clip to simulate the arrow in the spinner. On a copy of the diagram above, spin the paper clip to determine whether Charrette makes or misses the free throw. If the paper clip lands on a boundary segment, spin again.

c. Record the results of 30 trials. Find the experimental probability of Charrette making the free throw.

d. Compare the experimental and theoretical probabilities of Charrette making the free throw.

1.4 Describe the sample space for each of the following situations.

a. At the end of the school year, a student receives a letter grade for a science class.

b. Two ordinary dice are rolled and the numbers added. For example, if one die shows a 6 and the other shows a 2, the result is 8.

1.5 Camie has asked Alicia to play a game of cards. This game involves two piles of four cards each. The first pile contains the ace, king, queen, and jack of diamonds. The second pile contains the ace, king, queen, and jack of spades. The object of the game is to select a card from the first pile, then match it with a card from the second pile.

a. Determine the sample space for this game.

b. What is the theoretical probability of obtaining a winning combination of cards?

c. Does this game seem fair? Explain your response.

d. If all eight cards were shuffled together in one pile, would the sample space and theoretical probabilities remain the same? Explain your response.

* * * * *

1.6 A football coach wants to know the probability of winning the coin toss in the next three games if the team captain calls heads each time.

a. One player decides to use a simulation to predict the probability of this event. The table below shows the results of 250 trials of tossing three coins.

Three Heads	Two Heads	One Head	No Heads
29	109	91	21

Use these results to determine the experimental probability of getting three heads.

b. Another player tells the coach that he can determine the probability of getting three heads using the following sample space:

{HHH, HHT, HTH, THH, HTT, THT, TTH, TTT}

Use this sample space to determine the theoretical probability of getting three heads.

c. Do the results of the simulation agree with the theoretical probability? Explain your response.

1.7 In another version of the Apple Lottery, players choose two different numbers from 1 to 5. After lottery officials randomly select two different numbers from 1 to 5, prizes are awarded as in the original Apple Lottery.

a. Determine the sample space for this version of the Apple Lottery.

b. What is the theoretical probability of winning a red apple? a yellow apple? a green apple?

c. Devise a way to simulate playing this game 100 times.

1. Describe your simulation.
2. Run the simulation 100 times and record the results.
3. Using this data, what is the experimental probability of winning a red apple? a yellow apple? a green apple?

d. Do the results of the simulation agree with the theoretical probabilities you calculated in Part **b**? Explain your response.

e. In which version of the Apple Lottery are you more likely to win a yellow apple? Explain your response.

Research Project

A new game called the Match Lottery has the same rules as the Apple Lottery, except that the second number drawn need not be different from the first. In the Match Lottery, for example, players may select the numbers 3, 3.

Write a report on the Match Lottery that includes the following:

a. a description of the sample space

b. an explanation of how the difference in rules affects its simulation

c. the results of at least 100 trials in which the lottery ticket chosen has two different numbers

d. the results of at least 100 trials in which the lottery ticket chosen has two identical numbers

e. the experimental probabilities of winning each prize

f. the theoretical probabilities of winning each prize

g. an explanation of whether or not the results of the simulations support the theoretical probabilities

h. an explanation of whether or not any tickets have a better chance of winning a yellow apple than other tickets.

ACTIVITY 2

To calculate the probability of winning a lottery, you must determine the number of outcomes in the sample space. Even though the sample space for the Apple Lottery is relatively small, other lotteries may have more than a million possible outcomes.

Exploration

By counting the number of outcomes in small sample spaces, you might observe some patterns that could help you determine the size of large sample spaces.

In one simple lottery, for example, players select 1 number from the set {1, 2, 3}. The sample space for this lottery contains 3 singles:

1	2	3

If players must select 2 different numbers from the set {1, 2, 3}, the sample space contains 3 pairs:

1, 2	1, 3	2, 3

If players must select 3 different numbers from this set, the sample space contains 1 triple:

1, 2, 3

The numbers of outcomes in these sample spaces are recorded in the third row of Table **2-2** below. (Because this lottery has only three available numbers, there are no quadruples or quintuples.)

TABLE 2-2 ■ ***Size of Sample Space for Different Lotteries***

Numbers for the Lottery	No. of Singles	No. of Pairs	No. of Triples	No. of Quadruples	No. of Quintuples
{1}	1	0	0	0	0
{1, 2}	2	1	0	0	0
{1, 2, 3}	3	3	1	0	0
{1, 2, 3, 4}					
⋮	⋮	⋮	⋮	⋮	⋮
{1, 2, 3, . . . , 50}	50				

a. Create a spreadsheet with headings like those in Table **2-2.**

b. Consider a lottery in which players pick from the set {1, 2, 3, 4}. As you complete Steps **1–4,** record your responses in the spreadsheet.

   1. If players select 1 number from the set, how many singles are there in the sample space?
   2. If players select 2 different numbers from the set, how many pairs are there in the sample space?
   3. If players select 3 different numbers from the set, how many triples are there in the sample space?
   4. If players select 4 different numbers from the set, how many quadruples are there in the sample space?

c. Continue to determine the size of the sample spaces for other sets of lottery numbers. As you work, look for patterns that will allow you to quickly fill in all the cells of the spreadsheet.

   Note: Save your completed table for use later in this module.

Discussion

a. What patterns do you observe in the spreadsheet?

b. How did you complete the spreadsheet?

c. What does the number in each cell represent?

d. How would you use the spreadsheet to determine the theoretical probability of winning a lottery in which 3 different numbers are picked from the set {1, 2, 3, . . . , 20}?

Warm-Up

1. What is the theoretical probability of rolling each of the following using a fair, six-sided die?

   a. a three

   b. a six

   c. an even number

   d. an even or an odd number

   e. an even and an odd number

2. What is the sample space for rolling a pair of six-sided dice?

3. After analyzing its customer records, a rental-car company found that approximately 2% of its customers were involved in accidents. What is the probability that a customer chosen at random was not involved in an accident?

Assignment

2.1 Using your spreadsheet from the exploration, determine the number of quadruples you can select from 40 available numbers.

2.2 In one state lottery, players choose 4 different numbers from a set of 24. To win the jackpot, a player must match all 4 numbers.

a. Use your spreadsheet to determine the probability of winning the jackpot with one ticket.

b. What is the probability of winning the jackpot with 10 different tickets for the same drawing?

2.3 In the Double Pick Lottery, players pick a number from 1 to 4 from a white panel and a number from 1 to 2 on a black panel. Lottery officials randomly draw one ball from a container of four white balls and one ball from a container of two black balls. To win a prize, players must match the numbers on both the white and black balls.

A ticket for the Double Pick Lottery is shown below.

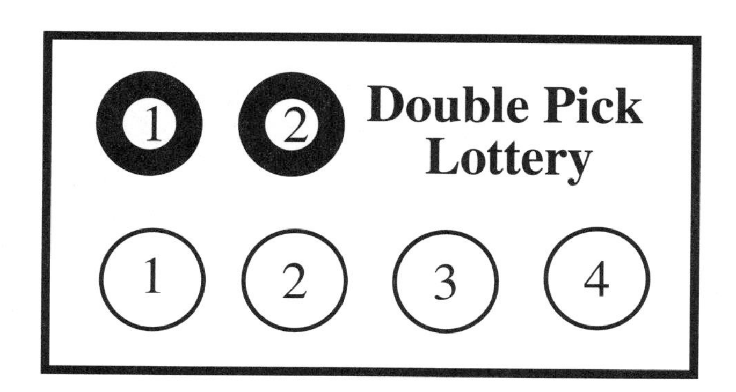

a. List the sample space for this game and determine the number of possible outcomes.

b. Describe how to determine the size of the sample space using the spreadsheet created in the exploration.

2.4 Another popular lottery game involves picking five numbers from 1 to 35 on a white panel and one number from 1 to 35 on a black panel. Lottery officials draw five balls from a container of 35 white balls and one ball from a container of 35 black balls. To win the lottery, players must match all five white balls and the black ball.

a. Determine the size of the sample space when selecting five numbers from a set of 35.

b. Determine the size of the sample space for selecting one number from a set of 35.

c. Using the method you described in Problem **2.3b,** determine the size of the sample space for this game.

d. Determine the theoretical probability of matching the five white balls and one black ball.

2.5 Determine the number of different groups of 5 that there are in your math class.

* * * * *

2.6 In Lottery A, officials randomly draw six numbers from the set $\{1, 2, 3, \ldots, 20\}$. In Lottery B, officials randomly draw eight numbers from the set $\{1, 2, 3, \ldots, 18\}$.

Josh thinks that he is more likely to match all the numbers in Lottery B than in Lottery A because the set of available numbers is smaller. Do you agree with Josh? Explain your response.

2.7 A drawer contains an assortment of 5 different pairs of gloves (a total of 10 single gloves). If you randomly select two gloves from the drawer, what are your chances of getting a matching pair? Explain your response.

2.8 In one state lottery, players pick five numbers from the set $\{1, 2, 3, \ldots, 45\}$ and one number from the set $\{1, 2, 3, \ldots, 45\}$.

a. Determine the size of the sample space for randomly selecting five numbers from the set $\{1, 2, 3, \ldots, 45\}$.

b. Determine the size of the sample space for randomly selecting one number from the set $\{1, 2, 3, \ldots, 45\}$.

c. Determine the size of the sample space for making both selections in Parts **a** and **b.**

d. Determine the theoretical probability that a player will pick the same six numbers as the lottery officials on a single ticket.

2.9 In another lottery game, officials randomly select four numbers from the set {1, 2, 3, . . . , 12} and a fifth number from a different set. The probability that a player will pick the same five numbers as lottery officials on a single ticket is 1/2970. How many numbers are there in the second set?

ACTIVITY 3

In many lotteries, the cost of playing is relatively small, even though the potential winnings could be very large. Typically, the probability of winning a large prize with any one ticket is low. Will playing the game many times increase your chances? In the following activity, you learn how much a lottery player can reasonably expect to win.

Exploration

The Apple Lottery has decided to change its prizes. In the new version of the game, players that match neither of the two numbers win nothing, players that match exactly one of the numbers receive $1.00, and players that match both of the numbers receive $3.00.

The cost of a New Apple Lottery ticket is $1.00. In the following exploration, you examine how much a player might expect to win at this game.

a. Create a spreadsheet with headings like those in Table **2-3** below.

TABLE 2-3 ■ *Experimental Results for New Apple Lottery*

Event	Prize	No. of Wins	Total Winnings
two matches	$3.00		
one match	$1.00		
no matches	$0.00		
	Sum	20	

b. Play the New Apple Lottery 20 times. Determine the number of times you won each prize and enter your results in the appropriate column of the spreadsheet.

c. Determine the total winnings for each row in the spreadsheet.

d. Find the sum of the winnings for all three events.

e. Calculate the mean amount won per game.

f. Determine the experimental probability of winning each prize in the New Apple Lottery. Record these probabilities in a spreadsheet with headings like those in Table **2-4** below.

Table 2-4 ■ *Experimental Probabilities for New Apple Lottery*

Event	Prize	Experimental Probability	Expected Winnings
two matches	$3.00		
one match	$1.00		
no matches	$0.00		
	Sum		

g. 1. Multiply the value of each prize by its experimental probability and enter the product in the expected winnings column of Table **2-4.**

2. Find the sum of the experimental probabilities and the sum of the expected winnings for the three events.

3. Compare the sum of the expected winnings to the mean amount won per game calculated in Part **e.**

Discussion

a. Compare the mean amount you won per game with others in the class.

b. Why does the sum of the expected winnings determined in Part **g** of the exploration equal the mean amount won per game?

c. On average, how much do you think you would win or lose by playing the New Apple Lottery?

mathematics note

The mean value of an experiment is the **expected value.** Expected value can be calculated by adding the products of the value of each event and its corresponding theoretical probability.

For example, consider a game in which players predict heads or tails, then flip a coin. If the prediction matches the result of the coin toss, the player wins $1.00. If the prediction does not match, the player wins $0.00. The products of the value of each event and its corresponding theoretical probability are shown in Figure **2-3.**

Event	Value	Theoretical Probability	Product
match	$1.00	1/2	$0.50
no match	$0.00	1/2	$0.00
	Sum	1	$0.50

FIGURE 2-3 Expected value of a coin game.

Because the sum of the products is $0.50, the expected value of the game is $0.50.

A **fair game** is one in which the expected value equals the cost of playing. For example, if you paid $0.50 to play the coin game described above, the game would be mathematically fair.

d. If the coin game described in the mathematics note cost $1.00 to play, how might the prizes be changed to make it a fair game?

e. Judging from your experimental results, do you believe that the New Apple Lottery is a fair game? Explain your response.

f. Why do you think most lotteries are not fair games?

Warm-Up

1. **a.** What number is 72% of 3010?

   b. Sixteen percent of what number is 240?

   c. Fifteen is 300% of what number?

   d. Four-fifths of what number is 60?

   e. What number is 7/8 of 88?

2. The following table shows the probabilities of all the possible outcomes of an event. Use this information to calculate the expected value in this situation.

Outcome (x)	Probability $P(x)$
10	1/6
4	1/3
2	1/2

3. The theoretical probability of success in a certain event is 30%. Predict how many successes will occur in each of the following:

   a. 10 trials

   b. 40 trials

   c. n trials

Assignment

3.1 To determine if the New Apple Lottery is a fair game, you must analyze it using expected value.

a. Create and complete a spreadsheet with headings like those in the table below.

Event	Value	Theoretical Probability	Product
two matches	$3.00		
one match	$1.00		
no matches	$0.00		
	Sum		

b. Explain why the New Apple Lottery is not a fair game.

c. Change the values of the prizes to make the lottery a fair game.

d. Are there other prize values that make this a fair game? Explain your response. *Hint:* Use the spreadsheet to help you examine possible prize values.

3.2 In one state lottery, players select five numbers from 1 through 37. Tickets cost $1.00 each. The table below shows the values of the prizes in this lottery.

No. of Matches	Prize	Probability of Winning with One Ticket
5	$20,000.00	$\frac{1}{435{,}897}$
4	$200.00	$\frac{160}{435{,}897}$
3	$5.00	$\frac{4960}{435{,}897}$

a. If a player buys one ticket, what is the expected value of the game? Describe how you determined your response.

b. Can players make the lottery a fair game by buying more than one ticket? Explain your response.

3.3 In a carnival game, players pay 10 cents for one roll of a 20-sided die. Each side of the die shows a different number from 1 to 20. The number rolled is the value of the prize in cents.

a. Find the theoretical probability of rolling each of the following:

1. 20

2. 15

b. Use expected value to determine if this is a fair game.

3.4 A basketball player has an 80% chance of making a free throw. Determine the number of shots you would expect the player to make in:

a. 30 attempts

b. 500 attempts

c. n attempts

3.5 Imagine that you have purchased one ticket for a benefit raffle. A total of 750 tickets have been sold at $2 each. From these tickets, one winner will be chosen at random. The prize is worth $300.

a. Determine the probability that you will win the $300 prize.

b. What is the expected value of this raffle for one ticket?

c. Is the raffle a fair game? Explain your response.

3.6 A typical roulette wheel has 38 compartments, each of which has an equal chance of being selected during one spin of the wheel.

a. If a player wins $30 for selecting the right compartment, what is the expected value of the game?

b. For this to be a fair game, how much should it cost to play? Explain your response.

* * * * *

3.7 As part of its annual fund drive, the local hospital sells 400 raffle tickets for $5.00 each. From these tickets, one winner will be chosen at random to receive a prize of $100.00. If you buy one ticket, what is the expected value for the raffle? Explain your response.

3.8 In the Red and Blue Lottery, players choose four numbers from 1 to 20 on a red panel and one number from 1 to 20 on a blue panel. Tickets cost $1.00 each. The table below shows the probability of winning the two smaller prizes in the game.

No. of Matches	Prize	Probability of Winning with One Ticket
four red, one blue		$\frac{1}{96,900}$
three red, one blue	$200.00	$\frac{16}{24,225}$
two red, one blue	$5.00	$\frac{12}{1615}$

a. Describe how to determine the probability of matching four numbers on the red panel and one number on the blue panel.

b. If the expected value for one play is approximately $0.70, what is the value of the prize for matching four red numbers and one blue number?

c. If the lottery commission sells 100,000 tickets for one game, how much money can it expect to make?

Summary Assessment

Your state legislature has decided to start a new lottery. Earnings from the game will fund the construction of an amusement park. To attract an innovative and appealing design, the governor has agreed to pay 10% of all lottery profits to the creator of the new game.

Design a new lottery for your state. Your proposal to the state gaming commission should include:

- a description of how to play the lottery and the cost to play (you might wish to include a sketch of a sample lottery ticket)
- a list of prizes and a description of how each prize is won
- the theoretical probability of winning each prize
- the expected value of the lottery for one ticket and for 1 million tickets
- the amount you expect to earn for one ticket and for 1 million tickets
- a summary of the experimental results obtained from a simulation of your lottery.

Show all calculations and explain how your experimental results support the theoretical probabilities and expected values.

Module Summary

* One way of predicting the likelihood of an event is to perform many trials under controlled conditions. The results of these trials provide the **experimental** (or **empirical**) **probability** of the event occurring. The experimental probability of an event can be calculated using the following ratio:

$$\frac{\text{number of times event occurs}}{\text{total number of trials}}$$

* The set of all possible outcomes for an experiment is the **sample space.**
* An **event** is a subset of the sample space.
* If each outcome in a sample space has the same chance of occurring, then the **theoretical probability** of an event can be calculated using the following ratio:

$$\frac{\text{number of outcomes in the event}}{\text{total number of outcomes in the sample space}}$$

* The mean value of an experiment is the **expected value.** Expected value can be calculated by adding the products of the value of each event and its corresponding theoretical probability.
* A **fair game** is one in which the expected value equals the cost of playing.

Module 3

Yesterday's Food Is Walking and Talking Today

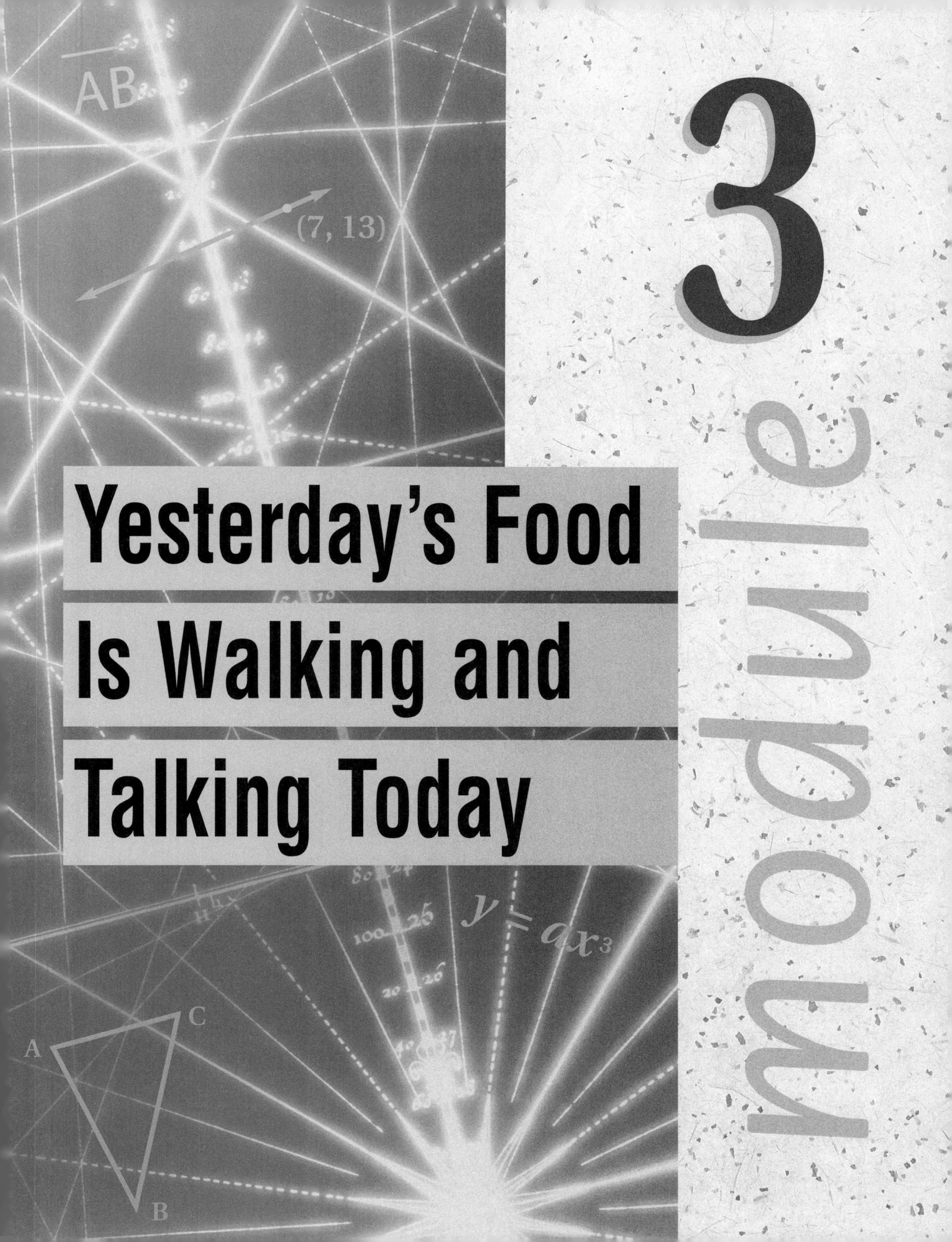

Introduction

Eating provides your body with fuel in the form of calories. In this module, you examine the number of calories the body needs to perform some typical activities.

Exploration

A **calorie** is a measure of heat energy. One way to determine the number of calories in a food is to measure the amount of heat released when that food is burned. In the following exploration, you use this technique to estimate the number of calories in a nut.

Note: You must wear eye protection throughout this experiment. Put on a pair of goggles *before* beginning the exploration.

a. Arrange the equipment as shown in Figure **3-1** below. Bend the paper clip to form a free-standing cradle. The bottom of the water can should be no more than 5 cm above the nut.

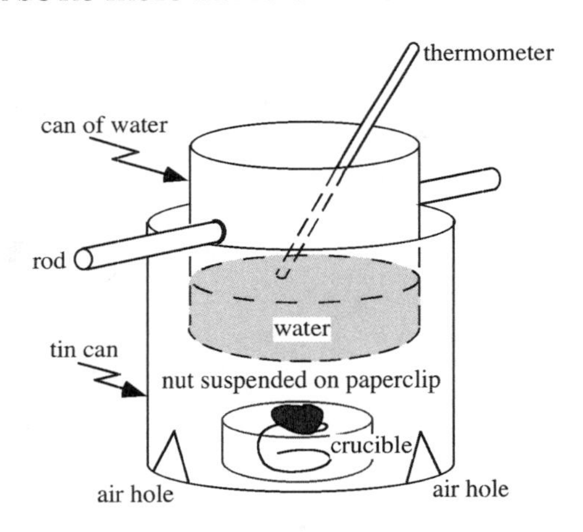

Figure 3-1 Experiment for estimating calories in a nut.

b. Make a table with headings like those in Table **3-1** on the next page and record the types of nuts you plan to test.

c. Measure and record each of the following:

1. the initial temperature of the water in degrees Celsius (°C)
2. the volume of the water in milliliters (mL)
3. the total mass of the nut, crucible, and paper clip in grams (g).

Table 3-1 ■ *Data for Calorie Experiment*					
Type of Nut	Initial Temperature (°C)	Maximum Temperature (°C)	Initial Mass (g)	Final Mass (g)	Volume of Water (mL)

d. 1. Ignite the nut. As the nut burns, observe the change in water temperature.

2. Allow the nut to burn completely. Record the maximum temperature of the water.

e. Determine the total mass of the ash, crucible, and paper clip. The difference between this value and the mass measured in Part **c** is the change in mass (the number of grams that burned).

f. Repeat Parts **c–e** for several different types of nuts.

science note

A **calorie (cal)** is the amount of energy required to raise the temperature of one milliliter (1 mL) of water one degree Celsius (1°C).

A **kilocalorie (kcal),** 1000 cal, is the amount of energy needed to raise the temperature of one liter (1 L) of water 1°C.

A **dietary calorie** (typically referred to as a Calorie with a capital C) is equal to 1 kcal. The calorie-per-gram rating on most food labels refers to dietary calories.

g. Create a table with headings like those in Table **3-2** below.

Table 3-2 ■ *Kilocalories in Different Kinds of Nuts*					
Type of Nut	Change in Temperature (°C)	Change in Mass (g)	Volume of Water (mL)	Calories per Gram	Kcal per Gram

h. Use the data you recorded in Table **3-1** and the definitions described in the science note to complete Table **3-2.** In this case, the number of calories per gram in each type of nut can be calculated using the following formula:

$$\text{calories per gram} = \frac{\text{volume of water (mL)} \bullet \text{change in temperature (°C)}}{\text{change in mass (g)}}$$

Discussion

a. Do all types of nuts appear to contain about the same number of kilocalories per gram?

b. Compare your results with the calorie-per-gram rating on a package of nuts.

c. If a nut failed to burn completely, would the experiment produce faulty data? Explain your response.

d. What types of experimental errors might have affected your data?

e. How would using a different quantity of water change the results of the experiment?

The human body uses calories at varying rates, depending on the level of activity. Calorie consumption also depends on a person's size, physical condition, and other factors. Table **3-3** shows the number of kilocalories used per minute during a variety of activities.

TABLE 3-3 ■ ***Kilocalories Used Per Minute Per Kilogram of Body Mass***

Activity	$\frac{\text{kcal}}{\text{min} \bullet \text{kg}}$	Activity	$\frac{\text{kcal}}{\text{min} \bullet \text{kg}}$	Activity	$\frac{\text{kcal}}{\text{min} \bullet \text{kg}}$
archery	0.065	drawing	0.036	painting	0.034
badminton	0.097	eating	0.023	racquetball	0.178
basketball	0.138	football	0.132	running	
card playing	0.025	golf	0.085	7.2 min/km	0.135
carpentry	0.052	gymnastics	0.066	5.6 min/km	0.193
circuit training		jumping rope	0.162	5.0 min/km	0.208
Universal	0.116	judo	0.195	3.7 min/km	0.252
Nautilus	0.092	lying at ease	0.022	sitting quietly	0.021
free weights	0.086	music playing		stock clerking	0.054
cycling		cello	0.041	swimming	
slow	0.064	drums	0.066	backstroke	0.169
medium	0.100	flute	0.035	crawl	0.156
fast	0.169	organ	0.053	table tennis	0.068
dancing		piano	0.040	typing	0.027
aerobic	0.135	trumpet	0.031	walking	0.080
normal	0.075	woodwind	0.032	writing	0.029

SOURCES: McArdle, et al., *Exercise Physiology*; Sharkey, *Physiology of Fitness*.

Discussion 1

a. What types of activities burn calories at a high rate?

b. What types of activities burn calories at a low rate?

c. When would your body burn no calories at all?

d. The units for the values in Table **3-3** are

$$\frac{\text{kcal}}{\text{min} \bullet \text{kg}}$$

Describe how these units can help you determine the number of kilocalories a 60-kg person burns while lying at ease for 30 min.

e. A 60-kg person playing basketball for x minutes burns 500 kcal. This can be represented by the equation $500 = 8.28x$.

1. Both sides of this equation must have the same units: kilocalories. Explain why the expression $8.28x$ represents kilocalories.

2. Describe how to determine x, the number of minutes spent playing basketball.

mathematics note

An equation of the form $y = mx$ can be solved for x by dividing each side of the equation by m.

For example, if $10 = 7x$, divide each side of the equation by 7. This results in the equation

$$\frac{10}{7} = x$$

The solution, therefore, is 10/7.

Exploration

a. Choose one activity from Table **3-3** that requires a high amount of energy, one that requires a moderate amount of energy, and one that requires a low amount of energy.

b. Create a table with headings like those Table **3-4** on the next page. Record the names of your chosen activities.

Table 3-4 ■ *Time Required to Burn Kilocalories for Three Activities*			
Energy Required	**High**	**Moderate**	**Low**
Activity			
Time to Burn 100 kcal			
Time to Burn 200 kcal			
Time to Burn 300 kcal			
Time to Burn 400 kcal			
Time to Burn 500 kcal			

c. For each activity you chose, calculate the time required for a 60-kg person to burn 100 kcal, 200 kcal, 300 kcal, 400 kcal, and 500 kcal. Record the answers in your table.

d. Graph a scatterplot of the data in Table **3-4** on a single set of axes. Represent time on the x-axis and energy used on the y-axis.

mathematics note

An equation of the form $y = mx$ represents a line that passes through the origin where m is the **slope** of the line. The slope is the ratio of the change in vertical distance to the change in horizontal distance between any two points on the line.

The slope of a line containing two points with coordinates (x_1,y_1) and (x_2,y_2) is

$$m = \frac{y_2 - y_1}{x_2 - x_1}$$

where $y_2 - y_1$ is the change in the vertical distance and $x_2 - x_1$ is the change in the horizontal distance. If $x_1 = x_2$, the line is vertical and has no slope.

For example, the graph in Figure **3-2** shows the energy used by a 80-kg person playing cards. This graph can be represented by an equation of the form $y = mx$, where y represents energy used in kilocalories and x represents time in minutes.

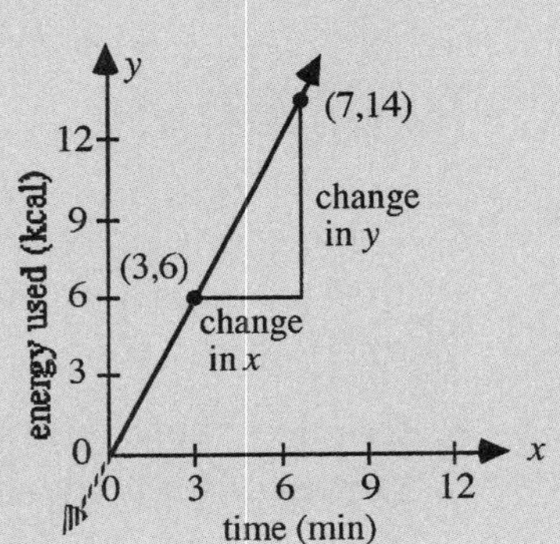

Figure 3-2 The slope of a line.

Using the points (7,14) and (3,6), the change in the vertical distance is 14 – 6; the change in the horizontal distance is 7 – 3. Therefore, the slope of the line is:

$$m = \frac{14 - 6}{7 - 3} = \frac{8}{4} = 2$$

Since the line passes through the origin and its slope is 2, the equation of the line is $y = 2x$.

e. For each activity in Table **3-4,** find an equation that expresses y in terms of x, where y represents energy used in kilocalories and x represents time in minutes.

f. Graph your equations from Part **e** on the same set of axes as the scatterplots from Part **d.**

Discussion 2

a. What common point is contained by all the graphs in Part **f** of the exploration?

b. What type of activities have graphs that are closest to vertical?

c. What type of activities have graphs that are closest to horizontal?

d. In Figure **3-2,** the line $y = 2x$ is used to represent the energy consumed over time by a 80-kg person playing cards.

   1. Describe what a vertical change of 6 and a horizontal change of 3 means in terms of playing cards.

   2. In this situation, the slope of the line $y = 2x$ is the measure of a rate. Describe this rate.

e. 1. Identify the slope of each equation you wrote in Part **e** of the exploration.

   2. Explain how the values in Table **3-4** can be used to determine the slope of each equation.

   3. Describe the rates represented by the slopes of these equations.

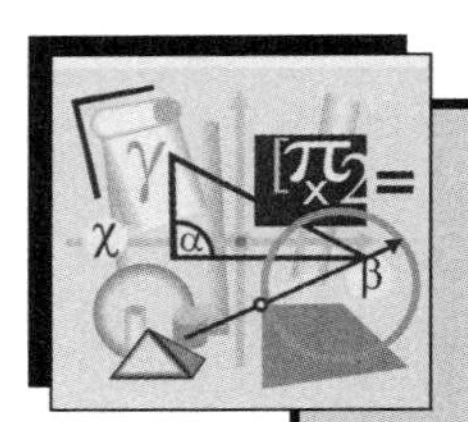

mathematics note

A **relation** between two variables is a set of ordered pairs of the form (x,y).

The **domain** of a relation is the set of first elements in the ordered pairs (the x-values). The **range** of a relation is the set of second elements in the ordered pairs (the y-values).

A **function** is a relation in which each element of the domain is paired with an element of the range and each element of the domain occurs in only one ordered pair. A function may be described by a rule or equation.

In mathematics, functions usually involve domains and ranges that are sets of real numbers. When a function is written without specifying the domain, you can assume that the domain comes from the set of real numbers. The range can be determined by finding the y-value that corresponds with each number in the domain.

For example, consider the function defined by the equation $y = 2x + 1$. In this case, the domain is the set of all real numbers. Each x-value is paired with only one y-value: a number that is 1 greater than twice the x-value. The range is also the set of all real numbers.

f. **1.** What is the domain of the relation described by each equation you wrote in Part **e** of the exploration?

2. What is the range of each relation?

g. **1.** When the equation $y = 2x$ is used to represent the energy consumed over time by an 80-kg person playing cards, what values of the domain make sense?

2. What values of the range correspond with these values of the domain?

Warm-Up

1. Use dimensional analysis to complete each of the following.

   a. ______ hr = 50 min = ______ sec

   b. 121 km = ______ m = ______ cm = ______ mm

   c. 60 mi/hr = ______ km/hr = ______ km/sec = ______ m/sec

   d. 2.4 L/hr = ______ mL/min

2. Solve each equation for the indicated variable.

a. $4x = 12$

b. $-3y = -15$

c. $-100 = 25x$

d. $y + 4 = -10$

e. $y - 3 = -20$

f. $y/-4 = -10$

3. Find the slope of the line through each of the following pairs of points.

a. (4,6) and (3,9)

b. (–3,9) and (5,–8)

c. (4,–6) and (3,–6)

d. (5,–8) and (5,–7)

e. (a,b) and (c,d)

4. List the domain and range for each relation below. Describe whether or not each relation is also a function.

a. {(2,3), (–3,6), (4,7), (1,6)}

b. {(–1,12), (3,4), (–1,3), (2,6)}

5. a. What is the slope of the line with the equation $y = -2$?

b. What is the slope of the line with the equation $x = 4$?

Assignment

1.1 a. How many kilocalories does a 57-kg person use playing racquetball for 23 min?

b. Tristin has a mass of 61 kg. If he plays football for 2 hr, how many kilocalories will he burn?

c. Write an equation that describes the number of kilocalories expended by a 58-kg person while playing golf for x minutes.

d. Identify the domain and range of the relation you described in Part **c.**

1.2 a. Sigrid has a mass of 58 kg. While practicing judo, she used 300 kcal of energy. How many minutes did she practice?

b. Miguel has a mass of 72 kg. His breakfast contained 320 kcal. How long will it take Miguel to use these kilocalories at his aerobics class?

c. A 60-kg person uses y kilocalories while typing. Write an equation that expresses the amount of time, x, spent typing.

1.3 **a.** While running for 30 min, Alexi burns 500 kcal. Draw and label a graph to represent this situation. Use the graph to estimate how many kilocalories Alexi had burned after 17 min of running.

b. While typing for 30 min, David burns 50 kcal. Draw and label a graph to represent this situation. Use the graph to estimate how many kilocalories David had used after 12 min of typing.

c. While swimming, Alexi burns 150 kcal in 12 min and David burns 300 kcal in 28 min. Draw one graph to represent this situation. Use the graph to determine who would burn more kilocalories in 1 hr of swimming. Explain your reasoning.

d. Which quantity represents the range of the relations described in Parts **a–c:** the number of minutes or the number of kilocalories? Explain your response.

1.4 **a.** Determine the slope for each change in vertical and horizontal distance shown in the table below.

Change in Vertical Distance	Change in Horizontal Distance	Slope
8	4	
4	8	
–8	4	
3	–12	

b. On a single set of axes, sketch the graphs of the lines that pass through the origin with the slopes in Part **a.**

1.5 Find the slope of the line through each of the following pairs of points.

a. (3,7) and (12,3)

b. (5,2) and (6,–4)

c. (12,–8) and (10,4)

d. (–7,–2) and (–3,2)

e. $\left(\frac{9}{7}, \frac{2}{5}\right)$ and $\left(-\frac{5}{7}, -\frac{3}{5}\right)$

1.6 The slopes of the lines you graphed in the exploration describe rates of energy usage in kilocalories per minute. Give an example of a rate which corresponds with each of the following:

a. a large positive value for slope

b. a small positive value for slope

c. a negative value for slope.

1.7 Use the following graph to complete Parts **a–c.**

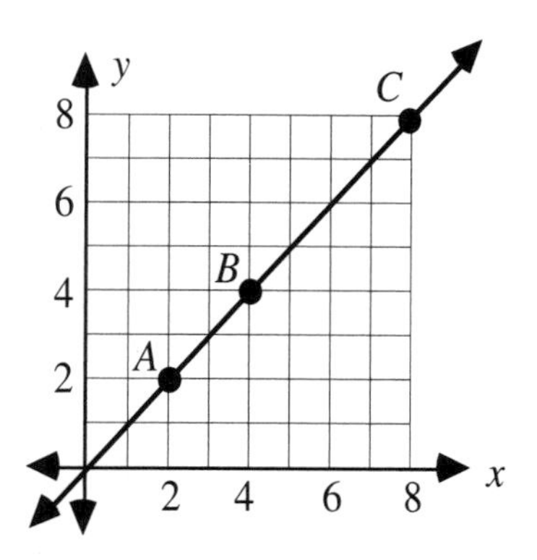

a. List the coordinates of points A, B, and C.

b. Find the change in vertical distance, the change in horizontal distance, and the slope (m) between:

1. points A and B

2. points B and C

3. points A and C.

c. Does the pair of points used to calculate the slope of a line affect the value of the slope? Explain your response.

1.8 **a.** Select one activity from Table **3-3.** Write an equation that describes the energy used over time by a 50-kg person performing this activity, where y represents energy in kilocalories and x represents time in minutes.

b. Graph the equation.

c. Identify the domain and range in this setting.

d. Find the slope of the line and describe what it represents in this situation.

e. Determine the number of kilocalories used when performing this activity for:

1. 30 min

2. 100 min

f. Describe how the slope of the line can be determined from your responses in Part **e.**

1.9 **a.** Draw the graph of a horizontal line and label the coordinates of any two points on the line.

b. Determine the slope of the line.

c. Draw the graph of a vertical line and label the coordinates of any two points on the line.

d. Determine the slope of the line.

mathematics note

A horizontal line has a slope of 0 and an equation of the form $y = c$. All the points on a horizontal line have the same y-coordinate, c.

A vertical line has no slope and an equation of the form $x = c$. All the points on a vertical line have the same x-coordinate, c.

e. **1.** Write the equation of the horizontal line in Part **a.**

2. Identify the domain and range for this relation.

f. **1.** Write the equation of the vertical line in Part **c.**

2. Identify the domain and range for this relation.

1.10 Sam's fast-food lunch contained 865 kcal. If his mass is 75 kg, how long would Sam have to jump rope to burn this amount of energy?

1.11 **a.** A sumo wrestler has a mass of 227 kg. Write an equation that describes the energy he uses over time while lying at ease. Let y represent number of kilocalories and x represent time in minutes.

b. Sam's mass is 75 kg. Write an equation that describes the energy he uses over time while lying at ease. As in Part **a,** let y represent number of kilocalories and x represent time in minutes.

c. Graph the two equations you wrote in Parts **a** and **b** on the same set of axes.

d. Which line appears closer to vertical? What does this observation indicate in this setting?

1.12 The slope of a line can be used to describe the average rate of change in one quantity with respect to another. For example, one familiar rate of change is speed, often expressed in kilometers per hour.

a. Rolando is climbing a mountain. At 10:00 A.M., he stood at an elevation of 1000 m. By 2:00 P.M., he had reached an elevation of 1220 m. Determine Rolando's average rate of change in elevation in meters per hour.

b. In 1980, the city of Tucson, Arizona, had a population of 534,000. By 1990, its population had grown to 655,000. Find Tucson's average rate of change in population in people per year.

c. In 1950, the price of a pair of jeans was about $8.00. By 1990, the price had risen to about $32.00. Find the average rate of change in the price of jeans in dollars per year.

d. The graph below shows the change in a parachutist's altitude (in meters) during an interval of 2 sec. Use the graph to estimate the parachutist's average rate of change in altitude in meters per second.

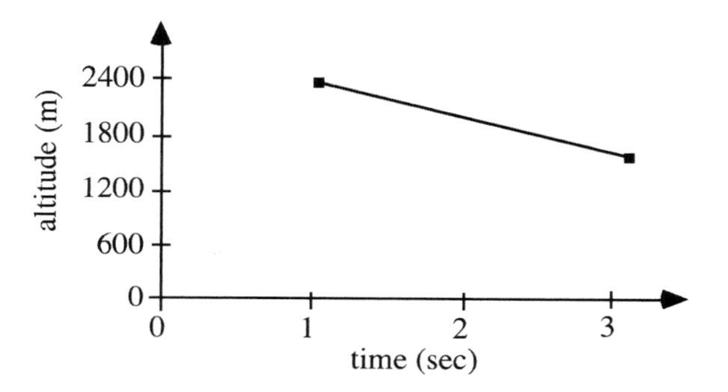

e. Identify the domain and range for the graph in Part **d.**

ACTIVITY 2

Many dietary specialists think of breakfast as the most important meal of the day. In this activity, you use linear equations to help plan an adequate breakfast for an active morning. Table **3-5** shows the number of kilocalories per serving in some typical breakfast foods.

TABLE 3-5 ■ *Kilocalories Per Serving for Common Breakfast Foods*

Food	kcal/item	Food	kcal/item
Toast, white	80	Croissant, egg, bacon, cheese	386
Toast, wheat	70	Biscuit, bacon, egg, cheese	483
Doughnut, plain	240	Biscuit with sausage	330
Cereal, with sugar	180	Cherry pie	260
Cereal, plain	120	Egg with muffin	340
Apple	60	English muffin with butter	186
Banana	80	Hotcakes with butter	500
Grapefruit	60	French toast	400
Orange juice	120	Fries	360
Egg, fried	120	Omelet	290
Egg, scrambled	80	Sausage, one patty	200
Egg, substitute	90	Milk, 2%	112
Milk, whole	160	Milk, chocolate	192
Yogurt, plain	120	Peanut butter and jam	500
Coffee	0	Soda pop	144

SOURCES: Gebhardt and Matthews, *Nutritive Value of Foods;* McArdle, et al., *Exercise Physiology;* Page and Raper, *Food and Your Weight.*

Exploration

a. Use the information in Tables **3-3** and **3-5** to design a breakfast that will supply a 62-kg person with the number of kilocalories necessary to play racquetball for 1 hr.

b. Make a table that shows the kilocalories remaining from the meal at the end of each 5-min interval of racquetball.

c. Create a scatterplot of the data from Part **b.** Let the time in minutes be the domain of the relation and the energy remaining be the range.

d. Determine the slope of the data.

e. Determine the coordinates of the point where the data intersects the y-axis.

mathematics note

The y-coordinate of the point where a line intersects the y-axis is known as the **y-intercept.**

The equation of a line with slope m and y-intercept b can be written in the form $y = mx + b$. This is the **slope-intercept** form of the equation of a line.

For example, Figure **3-3** shows a graph of the equation $y = -2x + 4$. This line has a slope of −2 and a y-intercept of 4. It intersects the y-axis at the point (0,4).

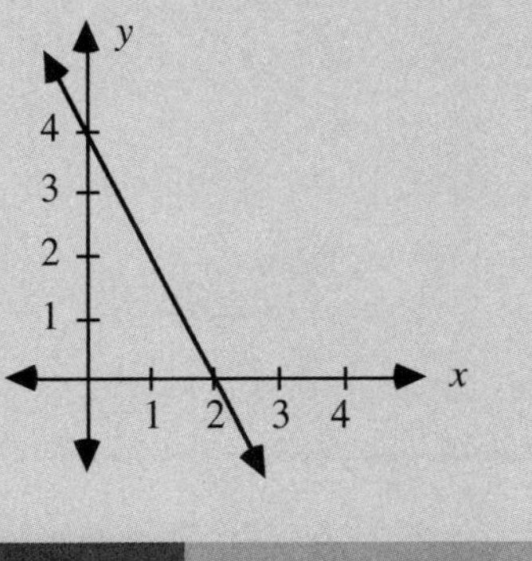

FIGURE 3-3 Graph of $y = -2x + 4$.

f. On the same set of axes as the scatterplot in Part **c**, graph the equation $y = mx + b$, where m is the slope of data and b is the y-intercept.

g. Repeat Parts **b–f** for a 62-kg person who ate a breakfast of 800 kcal.

Discussion

a. In Part **f** of the exploration, how did the scatterplot compare with the graph of the equation in the form $y = mx + b$?

b. Describe what the variables y and x represent in the exploration.

c. What information besides the slope do you need to identify a specific line?

d. Compare the slopes of the equations in Parts **f** and **g** of the exploration.

mathematics note

Two lines that have equal slopes are **parallel.**

As shown in Figure **3-4,** for example, the graphs of the lines $y = 2x$ and $y = 2x + 3$ are parallel.

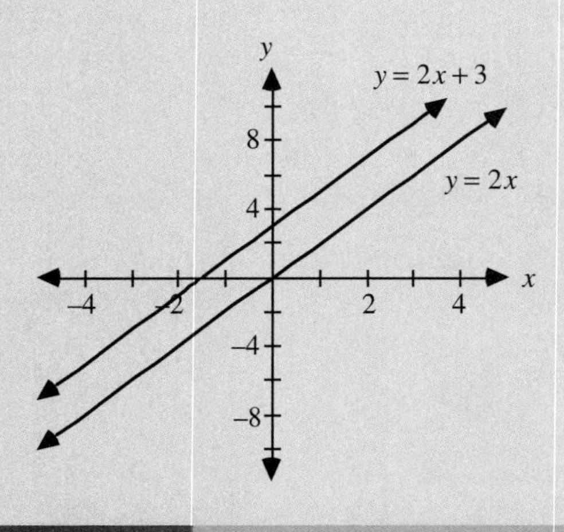

FIGURE 3-4 Graph of $y = 2x$ and $y = 2x + 3$.

Although vertical lines have no slope, any two vertical lines are also parallel.

e. Given the equation of a line in the form $y = mx + b$, describe how to determine its slope and y-intercept.

f. Given the slope and y-intercept of a line, describe how to write an equation of the line.

Warm-Up

1. Identify the slope and y-intercept of each of the following lines.

   a. $y = 3x + 1$

   b. $y = -2x + 5$

   c. $y = (2/3)x - 5$

   d. $y = -1x - 3$

2. Write an equation in slope-intercept form for each of the following:

   a. the line with a slope of 7 and y-intercept of -3

   b. the line that crosses the y-axis at $(0,-5)$ and has a slope of $1/4$

   c. the line with a slope of $-2/5$ and y-intercept of 7

3. Identify each of the following pairs of lines as parallel or not parallel. Justify your responses.

   a. $y = 3x - 5$ and $y = 3x + 2$

   b. $y = 0.25x + 1$ and $y = 0.75x + 1$

   c. $2y = -4x + 6$ and $4y = -8x + 20$

Assignment

2.1 Imagine that a 50-kg person plans to dance aerobically for 1 hr.

   a. Use the information in Tables **3-3** and **3-5** to design a breakfast that will provide enough energy for this activity.

   b. Write an equation in slope-intercept form that describes the number of kilocalories remaining from the meal in Part **a** at the end of each minute of dancing.

   c. Write an equation in slope-intercept form that describes the number of kilocalories remaining from a 600-kcal meal at the end of each minute of dancing.

   d. Sketch the graphs of both equations on a single set of axes.

2.2 a. Identify the y-intercept of a nonvertical line that passes through the origin (0,0).

   b. Write an equation for the line with a slope of 3 and a y-intercept of 4.

   c. Write an equation for the line that crosses the y-axis at (0,5) and has a slope of −2.

   d. Write an equation for the line with a slope of 7/3 and a y-intercept of 2/5.

   e. Write an equation for the line that crosses the y-axis at (0,−3) and has a slope of 2/5.

2.3 The following two equations were rewritten in slope-intercept form by solving for y in terms of x.

$$\begin{aligned} y - 5 &= 7x \\ y - 5 + 5 &= 7x + 5 \\ y &= 7x + 5 \end{aligned}$$

$$\begin{aligned} y + 5x &= 7x \\ y + 5x + (-5x) &= 7x + (-5x) \\ y &= 7x + (-5x) \\ y &= 2x \end{aligned}$$

   Use similar methods to solve each of the following equations for y.

   a. $y + 3 = 2x$

   b. $y - 5 = 3x + 2$

   c. $y + 6x = 2x - 7$

   d. $3x + 4y = 7$

   e. $2x - 3y = 6$

2.4 The following two equations were rewritten in slope-intercept form by multiplying both sides of each equation by the same quantity.

$$\frac{y}{3} = 4x \qquad\qquad 4y = 16x$$

$$3 \bullet \frac{y}{3} = 3 \bullet 4x \qquad\qquad \frac{1}{4} \bullet 4y = \frac{1}{4} \bullet 16x$$

$$y = 12x \qquad\qquad y = 4x$$

Use a similar method to solve each of the following equations for y.

a. $\frac{y}{-5} = 2x$

b. $7y = 4x$

c. $-2y = 8x$

2.5 As shown in the graph below, the points with coordinates (2,2), (6,4), and (x,y) are on the same line. In this case, the coordinates (x,y) represent any point on the line.

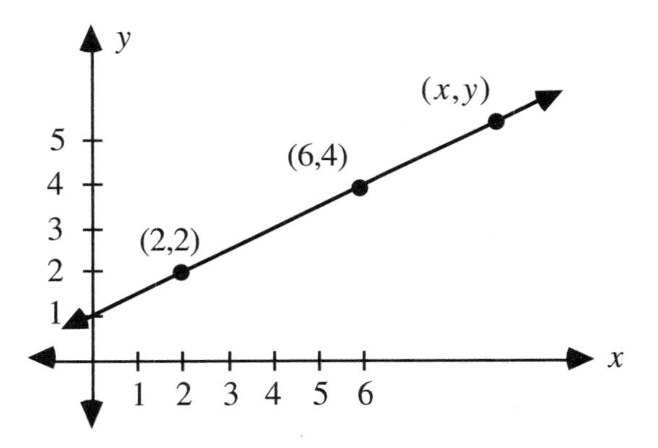

a. Calculate the slope of the line using the points (2,2) and (6,4).

b. Calculate the slope of the line using the points (2,2) and (x,y).

c. Write a mathematical equation that describes the relationship between the two slopes calculated in Parts **a** and **b**.

2.6 As shown in the following graph, the points with coordinates (x,y), (x_1,y_1), and (x_2,y_2) are on the same line. In this case, the coordinates (x,y) represent any point on the line.

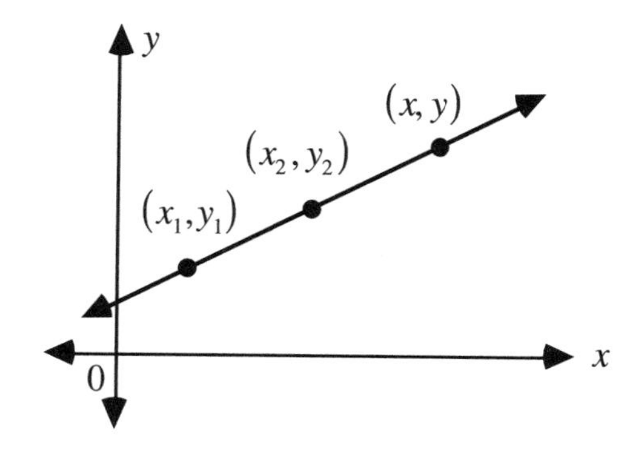

a. Write a representation for the slope of the line using the points (x_1,y_1), and (x_2,y_2).

b. Write a representation for the slope of the line using the points (x,y) and (x_1,y_1).

c. What relationship exists between the two representations you wrote in Parts **a** and **b**?

d. Write a mathematical equation that describes this relationship.

mathematics note

The equation of a line that passes through the point (x_1,y_1) and has a slope of m can be written in the form: $y - y_1 = m(x - x_1)$. This is the **point-slope form** of the equation of a line.

For example, the point-slope equation of a line that passes through the point (2,–4) and has slope of –7 is $y - (-4) = -7(x - 2)$.

2.7 **a.** Write an equation in point-slope form for each of the following lines.

1. The line that passes through (5,8) and has a slope of –3.
2. The line that passes through (2,10) and (12,5).
3. The line that passes through the origin and has a slope of 2/3.
4. The line that passes through (–6,4) and (–2,5).

b. Rewrite each equation from Part **a** in slope-intercept form.

* * * * *

2.8 Some equations do not represent lines. Using appropriate technology, graph the following equations and identify which ones are linear.

a. $y = 2x + 3$

b. $y = x^3 + 2$

c. $y = 3x^2$

d. $y = \frac{4}{x}$

e. $y = -\frac{1}{3}x - 2$

f. $y = \sqrt{x}$

g. $y = 5x - 2$

2.9 Ordered pairs do not always involve integer values. Even when ordered pairs contain decimal values, however, the slope and equation of a line can still be found using the methods described in this activity.

a. Find the slope of the line through each of the following pairs of points:

1. (6.4,8.2) and (1.9,7.5)

2. (9.00,0.12) and (5.00,–0.46)

b. Write equations in point-slope form for the lines in Part **a.**

c. Rewrite each equation from Part **b** in slope-intercept form.

In the previous activities, you examined nutritional information using a number of different methods, including graphs.

Exploration

After breakfast, Maurice and Janet enjoy a leisurely ride on their bicycles. As Janet rides, the number of kilocalories remaining from her meal can be described by the equation $y = -6x + 500$, where x represents time in minutes.

Because Maurice is heavier than Janet, he uses more energy while cycling. The equation that describes the number of kilocalories remaining from his breakfast is $y = -9x + 710$.

a. Describe what the slope and y-intercept of each equation represents in this situation.

b. Graph both equations on the same set of axes.

c. Estimate the coordinates of the point common to both lines.

d. Describe what the coordinates of the common point represent in terms of kilocalories and time.

mathematics note

Two lines with different slopes that lie in the same plane always intersect in a single point. The coordinates of the point of intersection satisfy the equations of both lines.

For example, Figure **3-5** shows the graphs of $y = 3x$ and $y = 0.5x$. The two lines intersect at (0,0). Since $0 = 3(0)$ and $0 = 0.5(0)$, the coordinates of the point of intersection satisfy both equations.

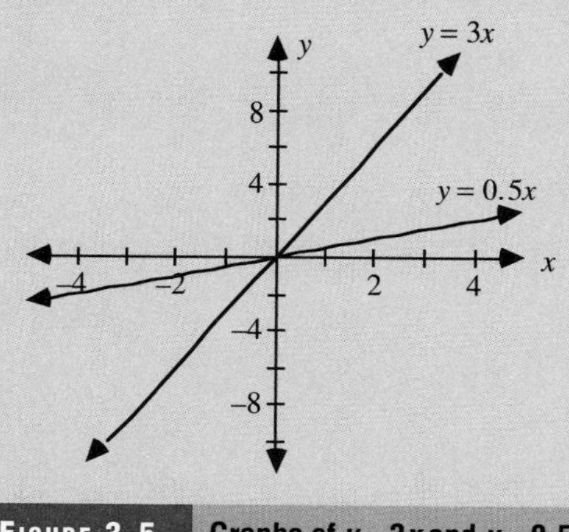

FIGURE 3-5 Graphs of $y = 3x$ and $y = 0.5x$.

Discussion

a. What information do the two equations in the exploration give about Janet and Maurice?

b. What would have to be true about these two equations if their graphs did not intersect?

c. Describe how to determine when Maurice and Janet had the same number of kilocalories remaining from breakfast.

d. What advantages are there to writing the equation of a line in slope-intercept form?

mathematics note

The **distributive property** of multiplication over addition is a key connection between the two operations. It can be described as follows:

$$a(b + c) = ab + ac \quad \text{or} \quad (b + c)a = ba + ca$$

For example,

$$7(b + c) = 7b + 7c \quad \text{or} \quad (b + c)7 = 7b + 7c$$

Similarly,

$$2(3 + 4) = 2 \bullet 3 + 2 \bullet 4 = 14 \quad \text{or} \quad (3 + 4)2 = 3 \bullet 2 + 4 \bullet 2 = 14$$

e. The following two equations were rewritten in slope-intercept form using the distributive property:

$$y = 2(x + 3)$$
$$y = 2 \bullet x + 2 \bullet 3$$
$$y = 2x + 6$$

$$y = -5(x - 3)$$
$$y = -5 \bullet x - (-5) \bullet 3$$
$$y = -5x - (-15)$$
$$y = -5x + 15$$

Use the distributive property to write each of the following equations in slope-intercept form:

1. $y = 5(x - 4)$
2. $y = -3(x + 2)$
3. $y = -7(x - 5)$

f. Using the distributive property, describe how to change an equation in point-slope form, $y - y_1 = m(x - x_1)$, to an equation in slope-intercept form, $y = mx + b$.

Warm-Up

1. Use the distributive property to expand each of the following expressions.

   a. $3(x - 2)$

   b. $0.5(x + 7)$

   c. $-2(x - 5)$

   d. $-\frac{5}{7}\left(x - \frac{2}{5}\right)$

   e. $1.6(x + 5.1)$

   f. $r(s - t)$

2. Use the distributive property to determine if the expressions $4(x + 3)$ and $2(2x + 6)$ are equivalent.

3. Identify the slope and y-intercept of each of the following lines.

   a. $y = (4/3)(x + 2)$

   b. $y = -0.2(x - 1.9)$

   c. $y + 7 = 2(x - 6)$

   d. $y - 4 = 0.2(x + 10)$

   e. $y - r = s(x - t)$

Assignment

3.1 It might require several steps to change some equations to slope-intercept form. For example, consider the following two equations:

$$\begin{aligned} y - 3 &= 2(x - 5) \\ y - 3 &= 2x - 10 \\ y &= 2x - 10 + 3 \\ y &= 2x - 7 \end{aligned}$$

$$\begin{aligned} \frac{y}{3} &= x - 1 \\ 3\left(\frac{y}{3}\right) &= 3(x - 1) \\ y &= 3x - 3 \end{aligned}$$

Use similar methods to rewrite each of the following equations in slope-intercept form.

a. $y - 5 = 2(x - 4)$

b. $y + 2 = 2x + 11$

c. $y + 7 = 2(8x - 3)$

d. $\frac{y}{5} = x + 2$

e. $2y = 6x + 4$

f. $\frac{y}{3} = 2x - 6$

3.2 a. The equation $y - 700 = -16(x + 5)$, where x represents time in minutes, describes the number of kilocalories remaining from Ricardo's breakfast during a cross-country race. Write this equation in slope-intercept form and sketch its graph. What does the slope represent in this situation?

b. During the Olympic decathlon competition, Perry burned kilocalories at a rate described by the equation $y - 94 = 2(x + 3)$, where x represents time in minutes. Write this equation in slope-intercept form and sketch its graph. What does the y-intercept represent in this situation?

c. Kelly is spending a rainy summer afternoon reading a mystery novel. While reading, she uses kilocalories at a rate described by the equation $3y - 150 = 5(x - 12)$, where x represents time in minutes. What can you tell about Kelly's energy usage from this equation?

3.3 In Olympic competition, wrestlers must compete in specific classes according to their mass in kilograms. Two athletes, Norjar and Ruiz, plan to wrestle in the same class. On June 12, Norjar had a mass of 78 kg. By June 16, his mass had decreased to 77 kg. Ruiz's mass on June 14 was 62 kg. By June 18, it had risen to 64 kg.

a. Write the dates and masses for Norjar as two ordered pairs. What is the slope of the line containing these points?

b. Write an equation for the line describing Norjar's change in mass in slope-intercept form.

c. Determine an equation that describes Ruiz's change in mass.

d. Graph the two equations from Parts **b** and **c** on the same set of axes.

e. What does the point common to both lines represent in this situation?

f. What are the coordinates of this common point?

g. If the mass of each wrestler continues to change at its previous rate, on what date will their masses be equal?

h. What is the value of their masses on the date the masses are equal?

3.4 **a.** Determine the slope of the line that passes through the points (4,8) and (6,14).

b. Use the point (4,8) and the slope from Part **a** to write an equation of the line in point-slope form.

c. Use the point (6,14) and the slope from Part **a** to write an equation of the line in point-slope form.

d. Are the two equations you wrote in Parts **b** and **c** equivalent? Justify your response.

3.5 Imagine that you are the project director for the next space shuttle flight. For an experiment on energy usage in space, mission specialists Kimberly and Manuel must have the same mass on launch day. To reach this target mass, Manuel has increased his daily activities, while Kimberly has increased her consumption of calories. As project director, you have received the data in the table below.

Astronaut	Day 5	Day 10	Day 15	Day 20
Kimberly	no data	63.0 kg	64.5 kg	66.0 kg
Manuel	74.0 kg	no data	72.0 kg	71.0 kg

If the mass of both astronauts continues to change at the rate for the previous 16 days, on what day can the launch proceed?

3.6 Four other astronauts also have been training for the launch described in Problem **3.5.** They are willing to change their caloric intake as necessary to substitute for Manuel or Kimberly. As project director, you must select one of them as an alternate. The table below shows the mass of each astronaut at some time during the previous 16 days.

Astronaut	Mass
Britte	69.0 kg on day 5
Kwasi	72.5 kg on day 15
Sergei	78.0 kg on day 20
Yukawa	62.5 kg on day 10

a. Using the mass of Manuel and Kimberly and the launch day found in Problem **3.5,** write an equation for each potential alternate that describes the change in mass required to meet the mission restrictions.

b. As project director, which astronaut would you select to serve as an alternate for this launch? Explain your decision.

3.7 Rolf and Tanya meet every morning to exercise. While warming up, Tanya uses 100 kcal of energy. She then burns 4.4 kcal/min during her walk. Rolf uses 60 kcal of energy during his warm-up and burns 15 kcal/min while running.

a. The equation $y = 4.4x + 100$, where x represents time in minutes, describes Tanya's energy usage in kilocalories. Write an equation that describes Rolf's energy usage in kilocalories.

b. Graph both equations in Part **a** on the same set of axes. Estimate the coordinates of the point of intersection and describe what these coordinates represent in this situation.

3.8 **a.** Find the coordinates of the point of intersection for each of the following pairs of equations.

1. $y = 4x - 2, \quad y = 2x - 6$

2. $y = 3(x + 5), \quad y = x - 9$

3. $y = \frac{1}{2}(x + 4), \quad y = 2(x - 3)$

4. $(y - 2) = 2(x - 4), \quad (y - 5) = (x - 6)$

b. Check each solution by verifying that the coordinates satisfy both equations.

* * * * *

3.9 Write an equation in slope-intercept form for the line that passes through the given point with the given slope.

a. $(4,3)$, $m = -1$

b. $(3,-1)$, $m = 0$

c. $(-4,-2)$, $m = 1/2$

3.10 Denali is climbing a cliff 300 m high. After 30 min, she has moved 75 m up the cliff.

a. Assuming that Denali continues to climb at a constant rate, write an equation that describes her distance from the bottom in meters in terms of time in hours.

b. Identify the slope of the equation in Part **a** and describe what it represents in this situation.

c. How long will it take Denali to reach the top of the cliff?

3.11 Find the coordinates of the point common to each pair of lines below.

a. $\begin{cases} y = x - 3 \\ 4x + y = 32 \end{cases}$

b. $\begin{cases} -3x + 6y = 4 \\ 2x + y = 4 \end{cases}$

c. $\begin{cases} 3x + y = 13 \\ 2x - 4y = 18 \end{cases}$

Summary Assessment

Rick has a mass of 66 kg. Before sitting down at his desk, he always eats breakfast and completes a morning workout. After eating a large breakfast, Rick exercises by running at the fast rate of 3.7 min/km. After eating a moderate breakfast, he exercises by bicycling at a slow rate.

For Rick, a large breakfast consists of hotcakes with butter, an omelet, a cup of 2% milk, and a glass of orange juice. This provides a total of 1022 kcal. A moderate breakfast consists of an omelet, a cup of 2% milk, and a glass of orange juice, for a total of 522 kcal.

1. On a single set of axes, create a graph of each of the following:
   a. the kilocalories remaining from the large breakfast while Rick runs at the fast rate of 3.7 min/km
   b. the kilocalories remaining from the moderate breakfast while Rick bicycles at a slow rate
2. a. Estimate the coordinates of the intersection of the two lines in Problem **1.**
   b. Describe what these coordinates represent in this situation.
3. After a certain number of minutes of running or biking, Rick will have the same number of kilocalories remaining from either breakfast. Determine how long Rick can perform his job as a writer using these remaining kilocalories.
4. The graph below shows Rick's energy usage in kilocalories while running fast and cycling slowly.

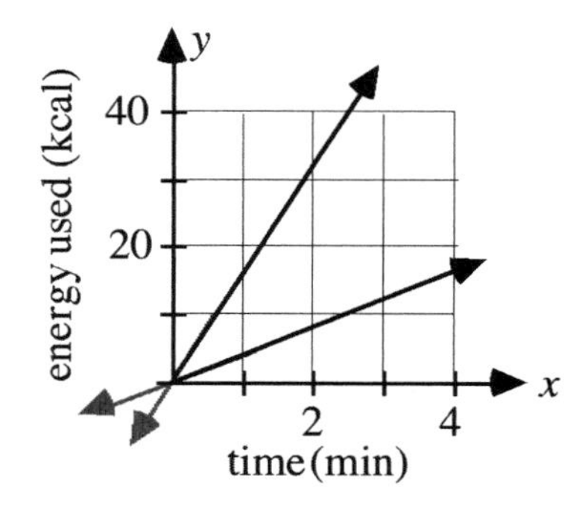

   a. Use the concepts of slope and rate to explain which line represents energy used while cycling and which line represents energy used while running.
   b. Describe how the graph can be used to approximate the slope of each line.
   c. Identify the domain and range of the relations that describe Rick's energy usage during both activities.

5. The following graph shows the number of kilocalories remaining after an entirely different breakfast and exercise routine for Rick.

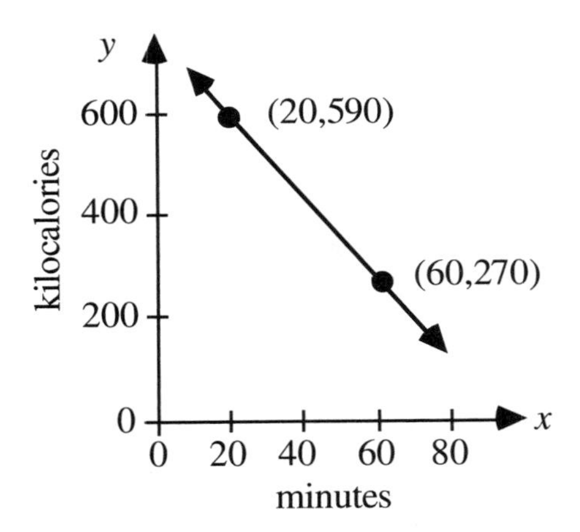

a. Write an equation in point-slope form that describes the kilocalories remaining from breakfast as Rick exercises.

b. Rewrite the equation in Part **a** so that it shows the number of kilocalories in Rick's breakfast.

c. Identify an exercise that would result in this rate of energy use for Rick.

Module Summary

* A **calorie** is the amount of energy required to raise the temperature of 1 mL of water 1°C.
* A **kilocalorie (kcal),** 1000 cal, is the amount of energy needed to raise the temperature of 1 L of water 1°C.
* A **dietary calorie** (normally referred to as a **Calorie** with a capital C) is equal to 1 kcal. The calorie-per-gram rating on most food labels measures dietary calories.
* To solve an equation of the form $y = mx$ for x, divide each side of the equation by m.
* An equation of the form $y = mx$ represents a line that passes through the origin where m is the **slope** of the line. The slope is the ratio of the change in vertical distance to the change in horizontal distance between any two points on the line.
* The slope of a line containing two points with coordinates (x_1, y_1) and (x_2, y_2) is

  $$m = \frac{y_2 - y_1}{x_2 - x_1}$$

  where $y_2 - y_1$ is the change in the vertical distance and $x_2 - x_1$ is the change in the horizontal distance. If $x_1 = x_2$, the line is vertical and has no slope.
* A **relation** between two variables is a set of ordered pairs of the form (x, y).

  The **domain** of a relation is the set of first elements in the ordered pairs (the x-values). The **range** of a relation is the set of second elements in the ordered pairs (the y-values).
* A **function** is a relation in which each element of the domain is paired with an element of the range and each element of the domain occurs in only one ordered pair. A function may be described by a rule or equation.
* A horizontal line has a slope of 0 and an equation of the form $y = c$. All the points on a horizontal line have the same y-coordinate, c.
* A vertical line has no slope and an equation of the form $x = c$. All the points on a vertical line have the same x-coordinate, c.
* The y-coordinate of the point where a line intersects the y-axis is known as the **y-intercept.**
* The equation of a line with slope m and y-intercept b can be written in the form $y = mx + b$. This is the **slope-intercept** form of the equation of a line.
* Two lines that have equal slopes are **parallel.** Although vertical lines have no slope, any two vertical lines are also parallel.

* The equation of a line that passes through the point (x_1, y_1) and has a slope of m can be written in the form: $y - y_1 = m(x - x_1)$. This is the **point-slope form** of the equation of a line.

* Two lines with different slopes that lie in the same plane always intersect in a single point. The coordinates of the point of intersection satisfy the equations of both lines.

* The **distributive property** of multiplication over addition is a key connection between the two operations. It can be described as follows:

$$a(b + c) = ab + ac \quad \text{or} \quad (b + c)a = ba + ca$$

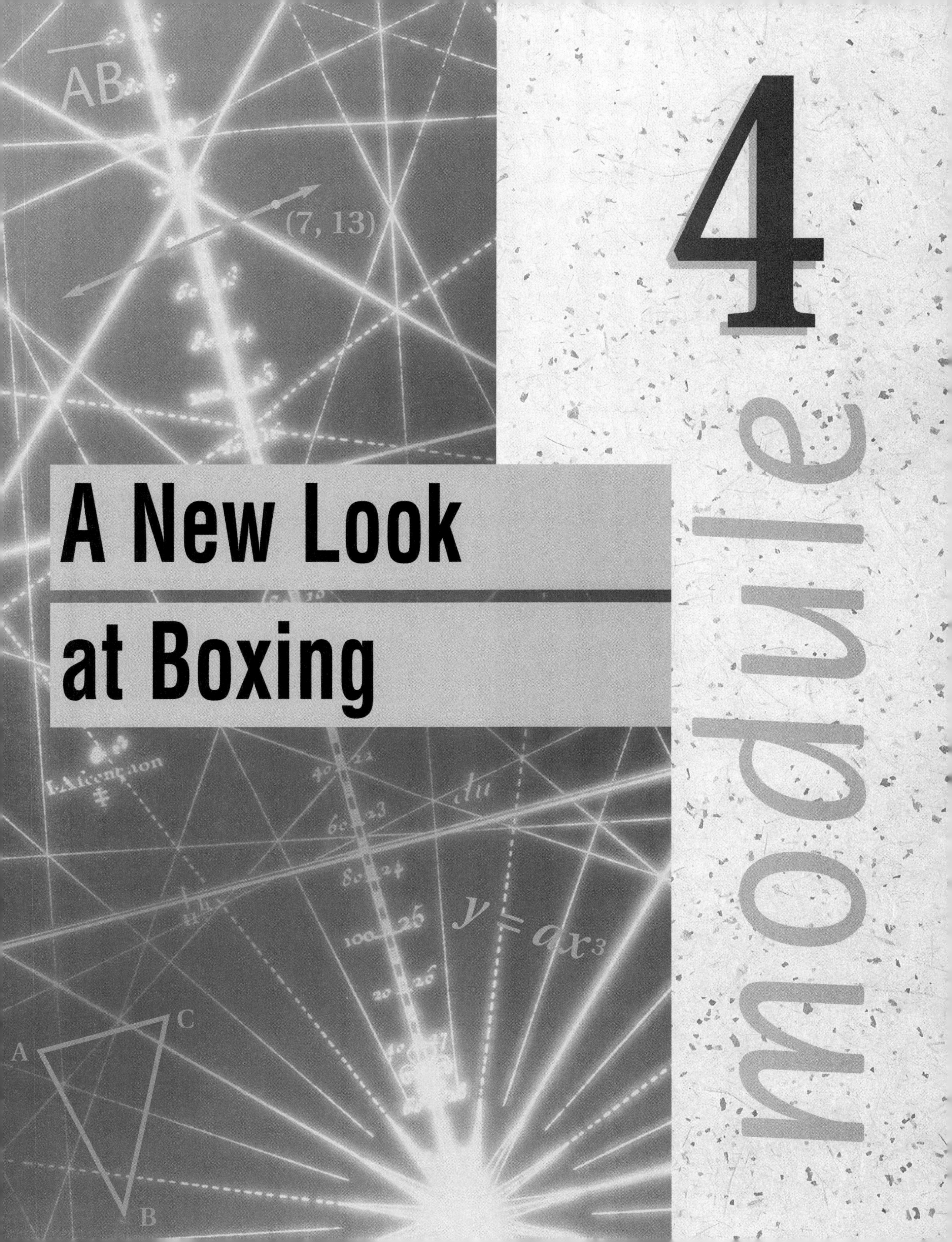
Module 4
A New Look at Boxing

Introduction

Gloria watches the clock: tick, tick, tick. Time always seems to drag when she's waiting for lunch. Finally, the bell rings. It's pizza time!

Friends, pop, breadsticks, and pizzas make Little Cheesers the most popular lunchtime hangout at Gloria's school. There's only one problem: time flies when she's having fun, and lunch is only 30 minutes long. As she heads for the door, Gloria asks for a box. She still has one slice of pizza left. On the way back to school, Gloria finishes her meal. Without a second thought, she tosses the box into the trash.

The cashier used a full-size box for Gloria's leftovers. A box big enough to hold a whole pizza might not be the best container for a single slice. If the box had been the right shape and size, less material would have been wasted. In this module, you will look at some different properties of boxes and explore how much material it takes to make them.

mathematics note

A **prism** is a three-dimensional figure determined by two congruent polygons in parallel planes whose corresponding vertices are connected by segments. The two congruent and parallel faces are the prism's **bases.** The parallelograms formed by joining the corresponding vertices of the bases are the prism's **lateral faces.**

For example, Figure **4-1a** shows a cereal box that, like many pizza boxes, is a prism with rectangular faces. Figure **4-1b** shows a box for a candy bar in the shape of a triangular prism.

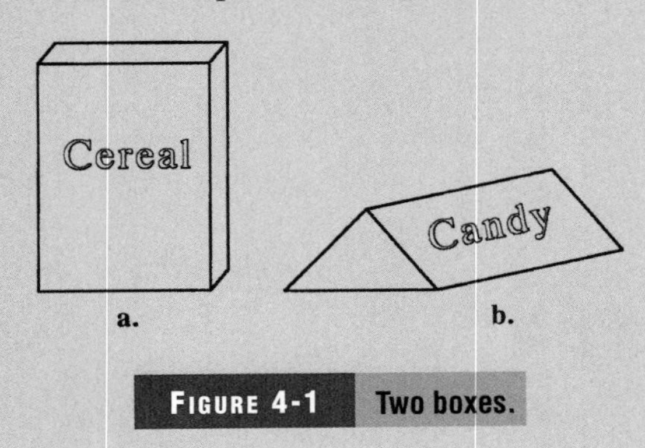

FIGURE 4-1 Two boxes.

Discussion

a. Explain why a cereal box is a prism.

b. Which faces of the prism in Figure **4-1b** are the bases?

c. Describe several examples of other objects that are prisms.

d. Is a tennis-ball container a prism? Explain your response.

The cardboard for the cereal box in Figure **4-1** was cut from a pattern. What does this pattern look like? In this activity, you examine a box and the pattern used to create it.

Exploration

Use a box similar to the cereal box in Figure **4-1** to complete the following steps.

a. Estimate the total area, in square centimeters, of all the sides of the box.

b. On a sheet of grid paper, make a scale drawing of the pattern you think the manufacturer used to create the box. Use dotted line segments to indicate folds. Cut out your paper pattern and fold it into a box.

c. Without tearing the cardboard, take the box apart and lay it flat. The box probably was constructed using glued tabs.

   A pattern with tabs is a **template.** A pattern without tabs is a **net.** Figure **4-2** shows both a net and a template for a cube.

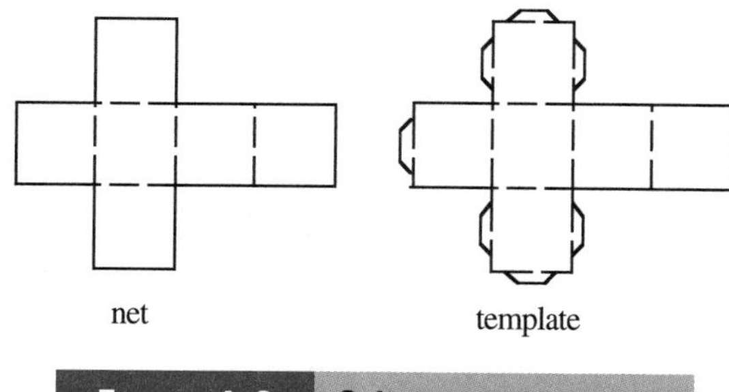

FIGURE 4-2 Cube net and template.

d. Find the area of the net for the box. Compare this area to the estimate you made in Part **a.**

e. Imagine that the template for the box was cut from a rectangle of cardboard. Record the dimensions of the smallest rectangle that will enclose the template.

Discussion

a. Does your folded box from Part **b** of the exploration resemble the original box?

b. How does your paper pattern from Part **b** of the exploration compare to the template for the box?

c. Without making any calculations, compare the area of the net to the area of the template.

d. Why might a box manufacturer be interested in the smallest rectangle that will enclose a template?

e. How do the areas of the net and the template compare to the actual surface area of the box?

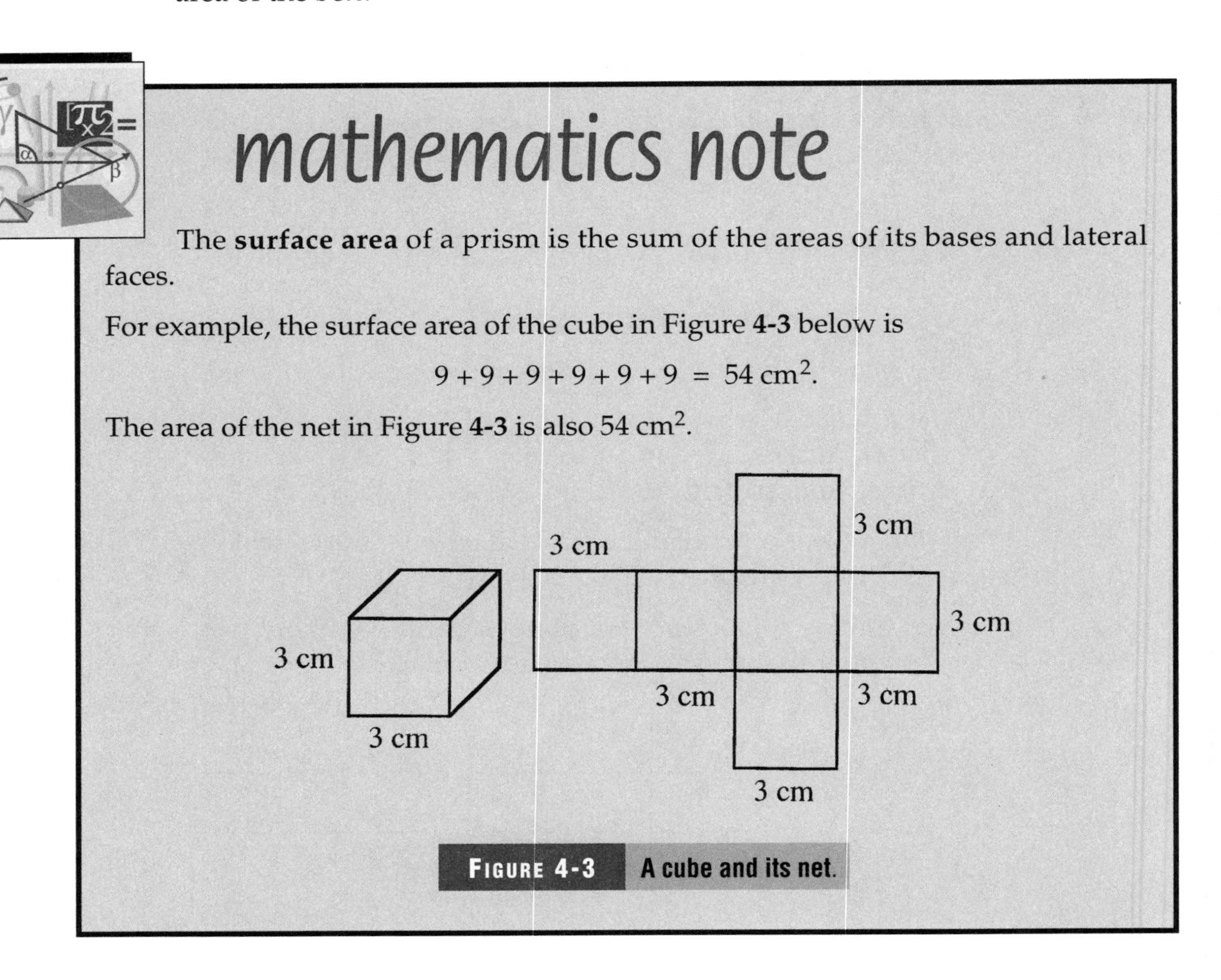

mathematics note

The **surface area** of a prism is the sum of the areas of its bases and lateral faces.

For example, the surface area of the cube in Figure **4-3** below is

$$9 + 9 + 9 + 9 + 9 + 9 = 54 \text{ cm}^2.$$

The area of the net in Figure **4-3** is also 54 cm^2.

FIGURE 4-3 A cube and its net.

f. Are all containers prisms? Use examples to support your answer.

Warm-Up

1. Which of the following objects are prisms? Identify the type of each prism. If the object is not a prism, explain why.

   a. 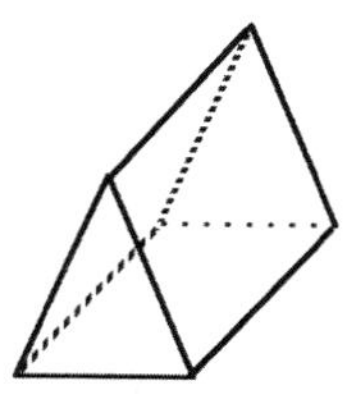

   b. 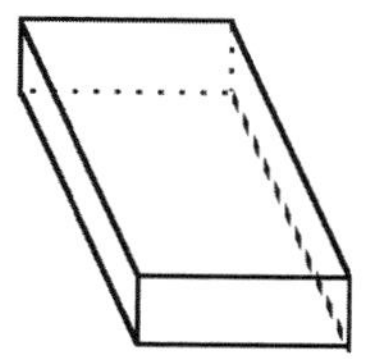

   c. 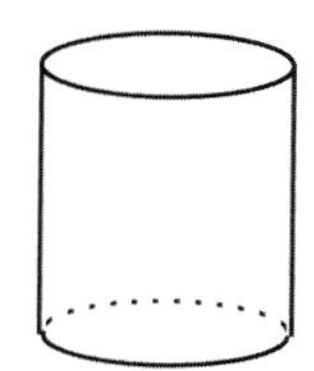

2. Find the area of each polygon below.

   a. 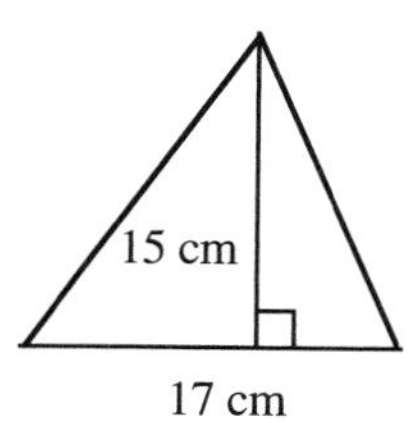

   b. 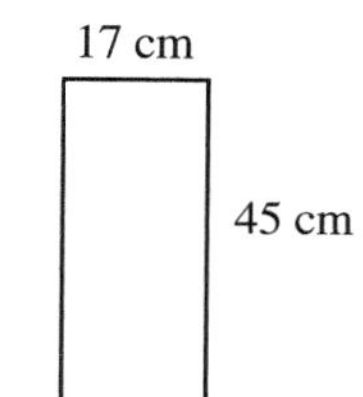

   c. 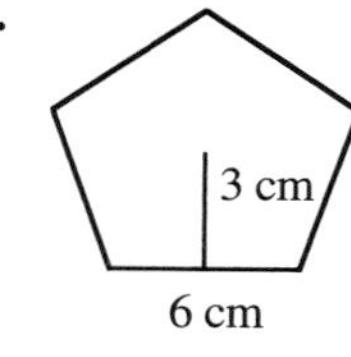

Assignment

1.1 The template shown below can be used to create an octagonal prism.

   a. Draw the corresponding net for the prism.

   b. Make a sketch of the three-dimensional figure.

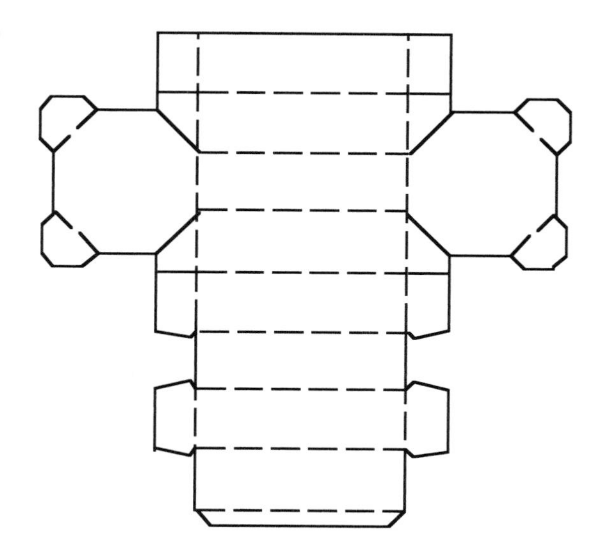

1.2 In Part **e** of the exploration, you recorded the dimensions of the smallest rectangle that would enclose the template for the box.

a. Find the area of this rectangle in square centimeters (cm^2).

b. Find the area of the template.

c. When the template is cut from the rectangle in Part **a**, what percentage of the cardboard is wasted?

d. Imagine that a box manufacturer makes 500,000 boxes by cutting templates from cardboard rectangles. If cardboard costs 14 cents per square meter, what is the cost of the wasted cardboard? Describe any assumptions you make in solving this problem.

1.3 **a.** Make a sketch of a container that is not a prism but has faces that are polygons.

b. Draw a possible template for this container.

c. Explain why this container is not a prism.

1.4 A sugar company would like to sell packages of 100 sugar cubes. Each cube is approximately 1 cm on a side.

a. Draw a net for a container which could be used to package 100 sugar cubes.

b. Explain how you could position several copies of your net so that the containers could be produced efficiently.

* * * * *

1.5 You are in charge of repainting the red background on all the stop signs in a large city. Before you can order paint, you must determine the area of a stop sign. Draw a regular octagon and describe how to find its area.

1.6 Gold bullion is often molded into blocks. The diagram on the right shows a type of block for which the cross section is an isosceles trapezoid. The trapezoid has a height of 4 cm and bases of 10 and 16 cm.

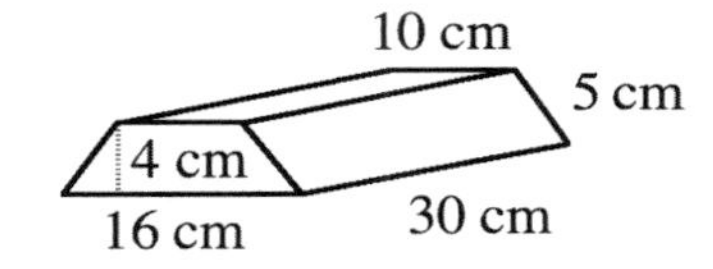

a. Draw a net that could be used to create a model of the block.

b. Use the net to find the surface area of the block.

Determining the shape that encloses the template helps minimize waste in box construction. But there's more. How will those shapes fit together? For example, a box template might be enclosed by a rectangle. To improve efficiency, a manufacturer might place these rectangles edge to edge on a large sheet of cardboard and cut many templates at once.

Figure **4-4** shows one way in which smaller rectangles can be arranged on a larger rectangle of cardboard. To cover an even larger sheet without gaps or overlaps, more of the smaller rectangles could be added.

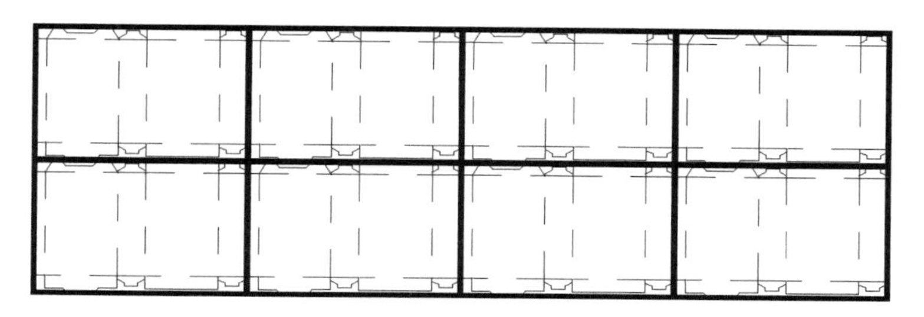

FIGURE 4-4 Cereal box templates.

mathematics note

When a shape is repeated to form a pattern that covers an entire plane without gaps or overlaps, it **tessellates** or **tiles** the plane. The pattern that covers the plane is a **tessellation** or **tiling.**

For example, Figure **4-5** shows two tessellations.

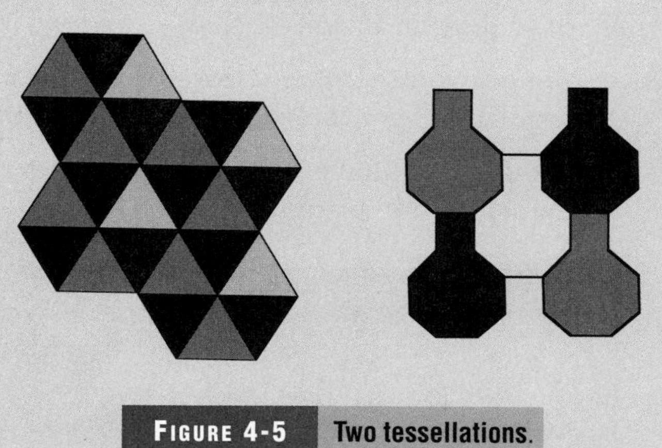

FIGURE 4-5 Two tessellations.

Exploration

Installing floor tiles is similar to covering a plane with regular polygons. Because squares fit together easily without gaps or overlaps, many floor tiles are square. However, it is also possible to tile a floor with other polygons.

a. Cut out templates of all the regular polygons, other than squares, with up to 12 sides. Determine which of these regular polygons can tile a plane. Use drawings to record your results.

b. On a sheet of paper, extend the sides of an equilateral triangle to form three equal exterior angles. In Figure **4-6** below, ∠1, ∠2, and ∠3 are the exterior angles and ∠4, ∠5, and ∠6 are the interior angles.

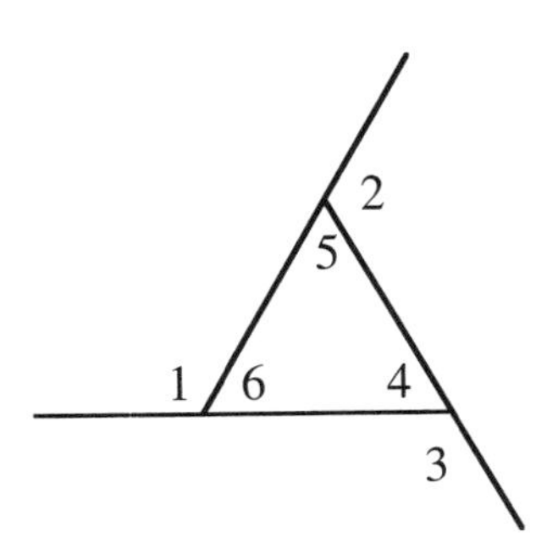

FIGURE 4-6 An equilateral triangle with exterior angles.

1. Without measuring, determine the sum of the measures of the exterior angles. *Hint:* Start at the vertex of ∠1 as shown in Figure **4-6** and visualize walking around the polygon (triangle) until you return to the starting point facing in the same direction. How many degrees did you turn during the walk?
2. Record the measure of a single exterior angle in a spreadsheet with headings like those in Table **4-1** below.
3. Use your response to Step **2** to determine the measure of an interior angle of the regular polygon and record the result in Table **4-1.**
4. Determine the number of these regular polygons that would "fit" at one vertex and record the result in Table **4-1.**

TABLE 4-1 ■ ***Measures of Angles of Regular Polygons***

No. of Sides in Polygon	Measure of Exterior Angle (x)	Measure of Interior Angle (m)	No. of Polygons that "Fit" at One Vertex ($360°/m$)
3			
4			
⋮			

c. Repeat Part **b** for all regular polygons with up to 12 sides.

Discussion

a. How can you use Table **4-1** to determine which regular polygons tessellate a plane?

b. Identify the regular polygons that tessellate a plane. Explain your answer.

c. Will the method of finding the sum of the measures of the exterior angles described in Part **b** of the exploration work for any regular polygon? Explain your response.

d. What is the sum of the measures of the exterior angles of any regular polygon?

e. What is the measure of an exterior angle of a regular polygon with n sides?

f. What is the measure of an interior angle of a regular polygon with n sides?

g. If you knew the number of degrees in an interior angle of a regular polygon, how could you determine the number of sides in the polygon?

Warm-Up

1. Determine the sum of the measures of the exterior angles for a regular polygon with:

   a. 3 sides

   b. 6 sides

   c. n sides

2. Determine the measure of an exterior angle for a regular polygon with:

   a. 5 sides

   b. 9 sides

   c. n sides

3. Determine the measure of an interior angle for a regular polygon with:

   a. 5 sides

   b. 9 sides

   c. n sides

Assignment

2.1 Consider a regular polygon with 24 sides.

   a. Find the measure of an interior angle of the polygon.

   b. Find the sum of the measures of the interior angles of the polygon.

2.2 Find the measure of an interior angle of a regular polygon with 102 sides.

2.3 Is there a regular polygon with more than six sides that will tile a plane? Explain your response.

2.4 Describe one of your tilings from Part **a** of the exploration so that someone unfamiliar with regular polygons and tessellations could reconstruct the pattern.

2.5 A box manufacturer wishes to cut templates from a roll of cardboard 400 cm wide and 6000 m long. The dimensions of the smallest rectangle that will enclose the template are 22.4 cm by 35.5 cm. How many templates can be cut from one roll?

2.6 **a.** The net shown below is just one of several possible nets of a cube. Draw three different cube nets.

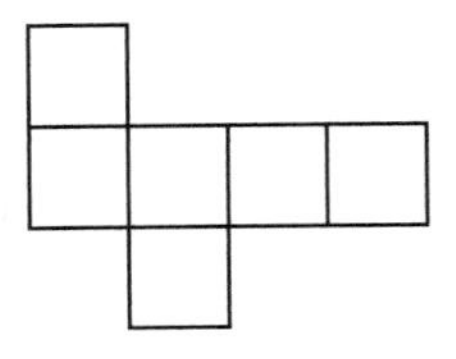

b. On a sheet of grid paper, find a cube net that tessellates a plane. Use at least six copies of the net to show that the pattern may be extended in all directions.

2.7 Although a regular pentagon will not tile the plane, there are pentagons that do form tessellations. The pentagon in the following diagram is equilateral but not equiangular.

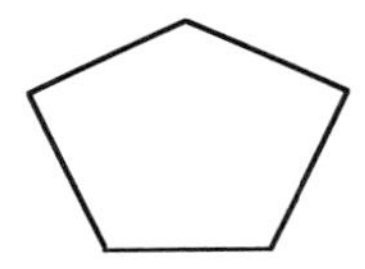

a. Trace this pentagon and determine whether it will tessellate the plane.

b. Design a pentagon different from the one above that tessellates the plane.

2.8 Do you think that all quadrilaterals will tessellate a plane? Explain your response.

2.9 **a.** Find the measures of an interior angle and an exterior angle of a 16-sided regular polygon.

b. Calculate the sum of the interior angles and the sum of the exterior angles of a 16-sided regular polygon.

c. If the measure of an interior angle of a regular polygon is 170°, how many sides does the polygon contain?

Research Project

Regular polygons can be arranged in many interesting patterns.

a. Find at least six ways in which a combination of regular polygons will tessellate a plane. In each tiling, use at least two different regular polygons.

b. Make a careful drawing of each of your patterns.

c. Describe each pattern in a few sentences.

d. Find at least two examples of tilings that use polygons other than squares and rectangles in your home or community.

Not all prisms have rectangular bases. Some have bases that are triangular. Others, such as the octagonal prisms shown in Figure **4-7,** have bases that are regular polygons.

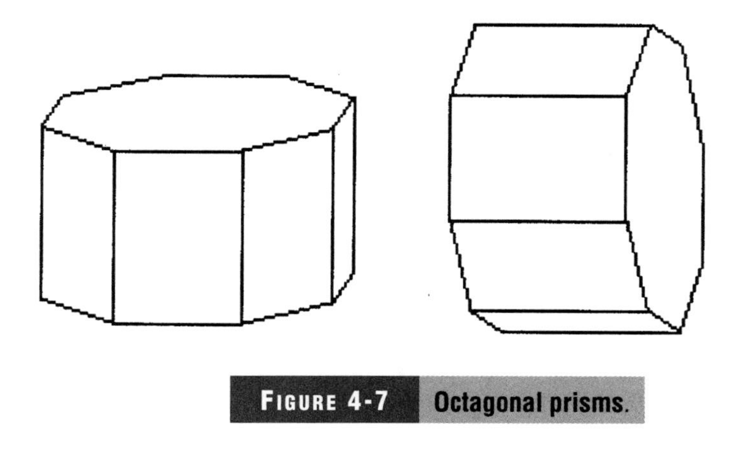

FIGURE 4-7 Octagonal prisms.

In this activity, you use your knowledge of the area of triangles and squares to develop a method for finding the area of regular polygons with five or more sides.

Exploration

a. Use a geometry utility to construct a regular pentagon by completing the following steps.

1. Construct a circle. Place five points on the circle. Use segments to connect the center of the circle to each of the five points. Each angle formed by two adjacent radii is a **central angle.**
2. Drag the points on the circle until the measures of all the central angles are equal.
3. Connect the points on the circle to form a regular pentagon.

b. Create a table with headings like those in Table **4-2** below.

TABLE 4-2 ■ *Triangles in Regular Polygons*

Polygon	No. of Triangles	Apothem (a)	Length of Side (s)	Area of Polygon
pentagon	5			
heptagon				
decagon				
n-gon				

c. Measure the perpendicular distance from the center of the polygon to one side. This distance is the length of the **apothem.** In Figure **4-8,** for example, $\overline{AG}$ is the apothem. Record this measure in the appropriate column in Table **4-2.**

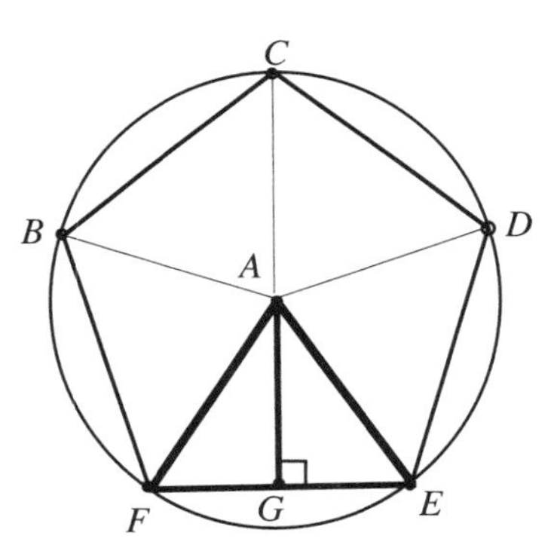

FIGURE 4-8 Constructing a regular pentagon.

d. Measure the length of one side of the polygon. Record this length in the appropriate column of Table **4-2.**

e. 1. Your construction of a polygon contains congruent triangles. Create a formula using the length of the apothem to find the area of one of these triangles.

2. Use the area of one congruent triangle to find the total area of the polygon. Record this area in the appropriate column of Table **4-2.**

f. Use the geometry utility to find the area of the polygon. Compare this value to the one you determined in Part **e.**

g. Repeat Parts **a–f** for a regular heptagon and a regular decagon.

h. Create a formula for finding the area of a regular n-gon. Enter it in the appropriate cell of Table **4-2.**

Discussion

a. As the number of sides of a polygon increases, what happens to the shape of the polygon?

b. How does the measure of the central angle of a polygon affect the shape of the polygon?

c. How do the areas of the polygons found using your formula compare to the areas of the same polygons found using the geometry utility?

d. The area of a regular polygon with n sides, apothem a, and side length s can be described by the following equation:

$$\text{Area} = \left(\frac{1}{2}as\right)n$$

Is this equation equivalent to the formula you developed in Part **h** of the exploration? Explain your response.

Warm-Up

1. Draw an appropriately labeled diagram for each of the following.

a. $\overline{AB}$

b. ray RS

c. line r

d. $\angle TAL$

e. obtuse $\angle FUN$

f. acute $\angle SUN$

2. **a.** Name the sides of $\angle SUN$ from Part **f** of Problem **1.**

b. Name the vertex of $\angle SUN$.

c. List two other ways of naming $\angle SUN$.

3. Determine the measure of the central angle for a regular polygon with:

   a. 5 sides

   b. 9 sides

   c. n sides

4. What is the geometric relationship between the apothem and a side of a regular polygon?

5. Determine the perimeter of a regular polygon with a side length of 12 cm and each of the following numbers of sides:

   a. 7

   b. 12

   c. n

6. The formula for the area A of a regular polygon is:

$$A = \frac{1}{2} a \bullet s \bullet n$$

   What does the expression $s \bullet n$ represent?

Assignment

3.1 The floor of Greg's new hot tub is shaped like a regular hexagon. He wants to install a tile floor. What measurements should he make?

3.2 Write a formula for finding the area of a regular polygon in terms of the apothem and the perimeter.

3.3 Use the net below to find the surface area of the corresponding hexagonal box.

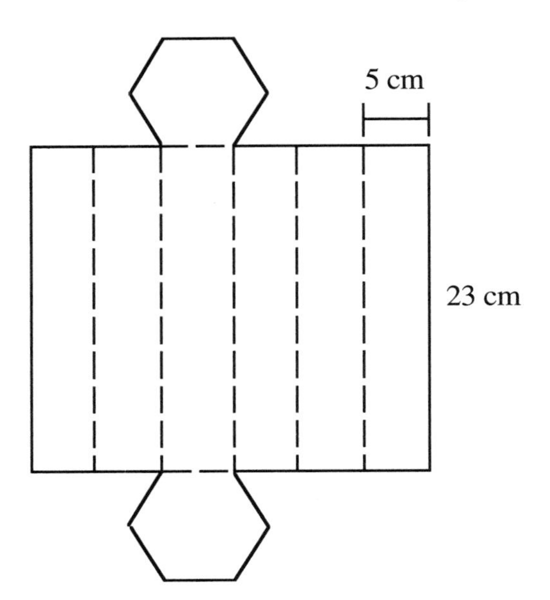

3.4 A product engineer has created the template below for a cardboard box.

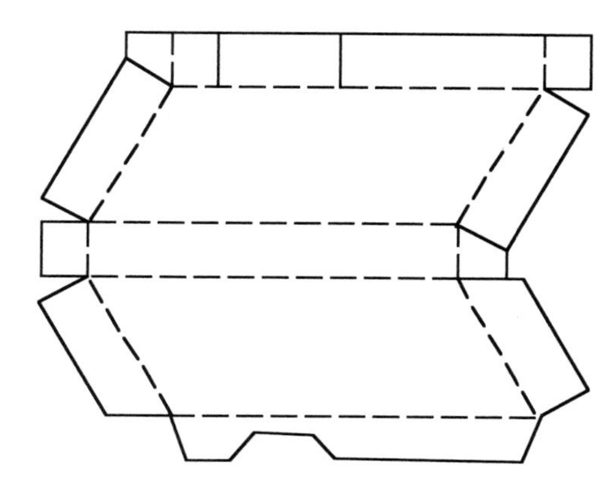

To hold down production costs, you must design a shape that encloses the template and minimizes waste. Prepare a presentation for the product engineer that includes:

a. the area of the template and the area of the shape

b. a sketch of the tessellation of the shape

c. the percentage of cardboard wasted when the template is cut from the shape.

3.5 Find a box that is not a rectangular prism. Carefully unfold the box and lay its template flat.

a. Draw the smallest shape that encloses the template and also tessellates a plane.

b. Sketch the tessellation of the shape.

c. Find the area of the shape from Part **a.**

d. Calculate the percentage of cardboard wasted when the template is cut from the shape.

3.6 A soccer ball can be modeled with 12 regular pentagons and 20 regular hexagons, each with a side length of approximately 4.5 cm. Find the approximate surface area of a soccer ball. *Hint:* You might need to draw a sample hexagon and pentagon and measure their apothems.

Summary Assessment

You have been asked to design and build an efficient box for one slice of pizza. The specifications and costs are listed below.

- A whole pizza has a diameter of 30 cm. Each pizza is cut into 8 equal slices.
- Cardboard costs 22 cents per square meter.
- The template must assemble into a closed container.
- The shape enclosing the template should both tessellate the plane and minimize waste.

Prepare a report describing your container, including the following:

1. a template
2. the area of the template
3. the shape that encloses the template and tessellates a plane
4. a sketch of the tessellation
5. the cost to make one template
6. the percentage of cardboard wasted in making one template
7. an attractive advertising logo sketched on a template
8. a model of the container.

Module Summary

- A **prism** is a solid determined by two congruent polygons in parallel planes whose corresponding vertices are connected by segments. The two congruent and parallel faces are the prism's **bases.** The parallelograms formed by joining the corresponding vertices of the bases are the prism's **lateral faces.**
- A **template** is a two-dimensional pattern with tabs that can be folded to make a three-dimensional solid.
- A **net** is a two-dimensional pattern without tabs that can be folded to make a three-dimensional solid.
- The **surface area** of a prism is the sum of the areas of its bases and lateral faces.
- When a shape is repeated to form a pattern that covers an entire plane without gaps or overlaps, it **tessellates** or **tiles** the plane. The pattern that covers the plane is a **tessellation** or **tiling.**
- The measure of an exterior angle of a regular polygon with n sides is $360°/n$.
- The measure of an interior angle of a regular polygon with n sides is:

$$180° - \frac{360°}{n}$$

- The **apothem** is the segment whose measure is the perpendicular distance from the center of a regular polygon to one of its sides.
- The area of a regular polygon with n sides, apothem a, and side length s can be described by the following equation:

$$\text{Area} = \left(\frac{1}{2}as\right)n$$

module 5

What Will We Do When the Well Runs Dry?

Introduction

What is a drink of fresh, clean water worth to you? Imagine a time when citizens pay $1.00 for a glass of water and $10.00 for a bath. At those prices, public fountains will disappear and green lawns will become rare luxuries. If this sounds far-fetched, think about the millions of people who already buy bottled water. Although humans can survive only a few days without water, we often take its availability for granted.

Discussion

a. Do you think that water will become as expensive as the introduction suggests? Why or why not?

b. Is there a water shortage in your area?

c. 1. What causes water shortages?

   2. Can these causes be avoided?

d. 1. Estimate the amount of water you use each day.

   2. How could you measure your daily water use?

ACTIVITY 1

How can you estimate the amount of water you use in one day? Before confronting any of the issues involved with water use and conservation, you must understand volume.

mathematics note

A **prism** is a three-dimensional figure determined by two congruent polygons in parallel planes whose corresponding vertices are connected by segments. The two congruent and parallel faces are the prism's **bases.** The parallelograms formed by joining the corresponding vertices of the bases are the prism's **lateral faces.**

Prisms are named by the polygonal shape of the two bases. The **height** of a prism is the perpendicular distance between the bases.

For example, Figure **5-1** shows a trapezoidal prism and a triangular prism.

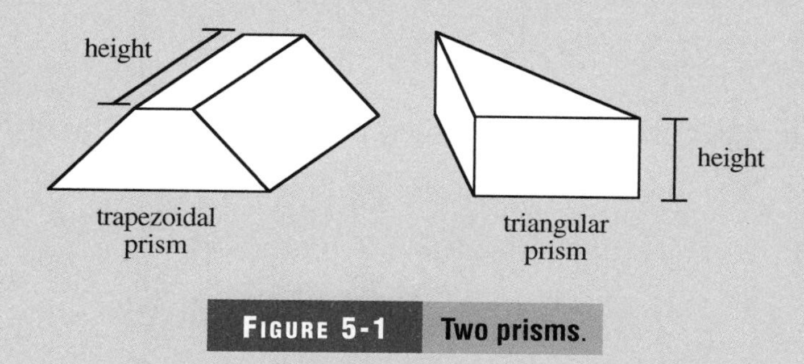

FIGURE 5-1 Two prisms.

The amount of space occupied by an object is its **volume.** Volume is measured in units such as cubic centimeters (cm^3) or liters (L).

The volume (V) of a prism may be found by multiplying the area of the polygonal base (B) by the height (h): $V = Bh$.

For example, if the area of the base of a triangular prism is 120 cm^3 and its height is 30 cm, then its volume is $V = Bh = (120)(30) = 3600$ cm^3.

Exploration 1

In this exploration, you determine the volume of a cube.

a. On a sheet of cardboard, draw a net for a cube with 10 cm × 10 cm faces.

b. Cut out, fold, and tape the net to form a cube.

c. Calculate the volume of the cube in each of the following units:

1. cubic centimeters (cm^3)
2. cubic decimeters (dm^3).

d. Determine a relationship between cubic centimeters and cubic decimeters.

e. Estimate the number of liters (L) of water that the cube will hold.

f. Because it would not be practical to pour water into your cardboard cube, check your estimate by completing Steps **1–3** below.

   1. Open one face of the cube.
   2. Fill the cube with rice. **Note:** Make sure that the edges of the cube are securely taped. To prevent spills, you may place the cube inside a bucket while pouring rice.
   3. Use a 1-L container to measure the amount of rice in the cube.

g. Determine a relationship between liters and each of the following units:

   1. cubic centimeters
   2. cubic decimeters.

Discussion 1

a. 1. Is the cube you created in Exploration **1** a prism? Why or why not?

   2. How can you distinguish between the bases of a cube and its lateral faces?

b. 1. How many bases does a prism have?

   2. How many lateral faces does a prism have?
   3. How many lateral edges are there in a prism?
   4. What is the total number of edges in a prism?

c. Describe the relationship between each of the following:

   1. a cubic centimeter and a cubic decimeter
   2. a liter and a cubic centimeter
   3. a liter and a cubic decimeter.

Exploration 2

In Exploration **1,** you estimated, then calculated, the volume of a prism. In many communities, however, water supplies are stored in reservoirs that do not have polygonal bases. In this exploration, you examine a method for estimating the volume of objects that are not prisms.

a. On a 10 cm × 10 cm sheet of graph paper, draw a closed geometric figure that is not a polygon, such as the one shown in Figure **5-2** below.

FIGURE 5-2 A closed figure.

b. To estimate the area of the figure, complete Steps **1–4** below.

1. Determine the area of each square on the graph paper.
2. Count the number of whole squares in the figure.
3. Count the number of partial squares in the figure and divide this number by 2.
4. Find the sum of your answers to Steps **2** and **3.** Multiply this sum by the area of one square determined in Step **1.**

c. Using bases shaped like your geometric figure from Part **a,** make a three-dimensional solid 10 cm high, such as the one shown in Figure **5-3.** Tape the edges of the solid as securely as possible.

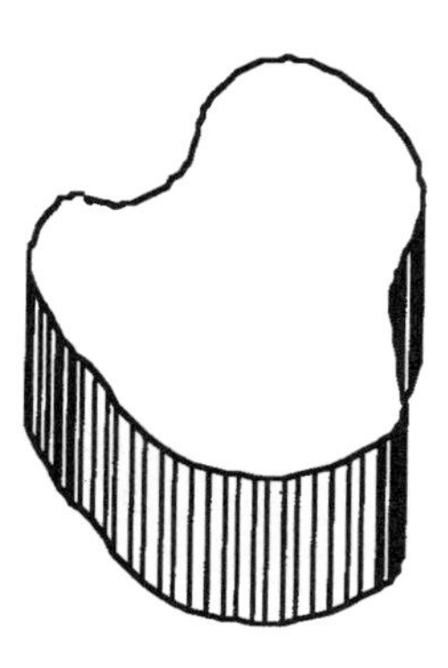

FIGURE 5-3 A three-dimensional solid.

d. Use the estimated area of the figure found in Part **b** to estimate the volume of the solid in each of the following units:

1. cubic centimeters
2. liters.

e. Check your estimate from Part **d** by opening your solid, filling it with rice, then measuring the amount of rice in the solid. **Note:** To prevent spills, you may place the solid inside a bucket while pouring rice.

Discussion 2

a. In Part **b** of Exploration **2,** you estimated the area of a figure by counting squares. What other methods could you use to determine the area of a figure that is not a polygon?

b. 1. How did you determine the volume of the solid in Part **d** of Exploration **2**?

2. How did this value compare to the amount of rice that filled the solid?

c. Describe how you could calculate the volume of a prism with bases shaped like each of the following:

1. triangles, rectangles, or trapezoids
2. polygons other than triangles, rectangles, or trapezoids.

Warm-Up

1. Convert each of the following measurements:

   a. 2 L = ______ cm^3 **b.** 500 cm^3 = ______ dm^3

   c. 257 dm^3 = ______ L **d.** 75 cm^3 = ______ L

   e. 4.5 L = ______ dm^3 **f.** x dm^3 = ______ cm^3

2. Use the pentagonal prism in the diagram below to identify these parts:

   a. the bases

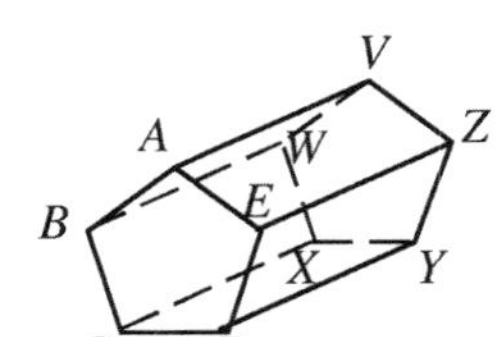

   b. a lateral face

   c. a lateral edge.

3. Determine the number of each of the following in a hexagonal prism:

   a. bases **b.** lateral faces

   c. lateral edges **d.** total edges.

Assignment

1.1 José has a bathtub that holds 250 L of water. Thaddeus has a tub that has inside measurements of 5 dm × 3 dm × 15 dm. Which tub holds more water? Justify your response.

1.2 A forced-air heating duct has dimensions 2 m × 6 dm × 50 cm.

   a. Make a scale drawing of this duct in centimeters.

   b. Determine its volume in cubic centimeters.

1.3 Determine the volume of each of the following objects:

   a. a water trough

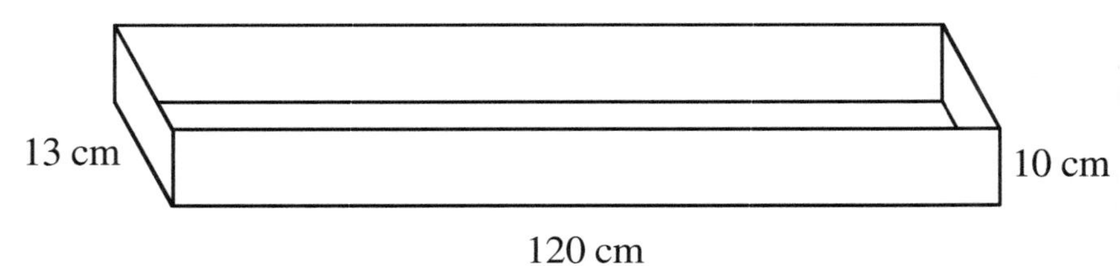

b. a toilet tank.

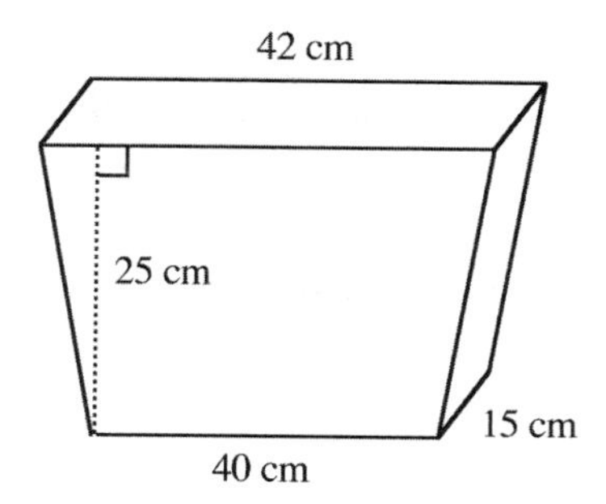

1.4 A Canadian town of 50,000 draws its water from the lake pictured below. The average depth of the lake is 15 m.

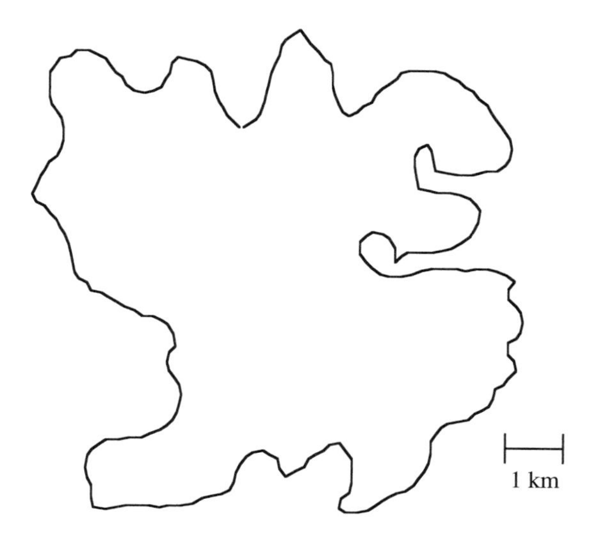

a. Estimate the volume of water in the lake and describe how you determined your estimate.

b. The average person in this town uses 380 L of water per day. If the lake is not replenished, how long will the water last?

1.5 The municipal reservoir for a U.S. city of 6 million people lies in a V-shaped valley. One end of the reservoir is dammed, and the other is faced by a steep rock wall. The body of water itself is 6 km long, 2 km wide, and has an average depth of 400 m.

a. Make a scale drawing of this reservoir in kilometers.

b. Determine its volume in liters.

c. The average person in this city uses 420 L of water per day. Assuming that the reservoir is not refilled, how long can it supply the city with water?

1.6 Cubic centimeters generally are used to measure the volume of solid materials. Health professionals also use these units to measure liquid volumes. In this setting, 1 cm^3 is referred to as 1 cc. What is the relationship between cubic centimeters and milliliters?

1.7 The following diagram shows the dimensions of a swimming pool with rectangular ends. How many liters of water does this pool hold?

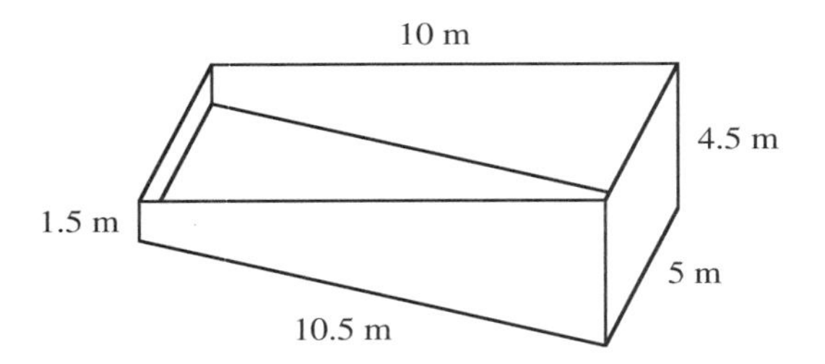

1.8 Construction companies often measure volume using cubic yards. How many cubic yards of concrete are needed to pave a driveway with the following dimensions: 20 ft × 15 ft × 6 in.?

1.9 The diagram below shows a small fish pond.

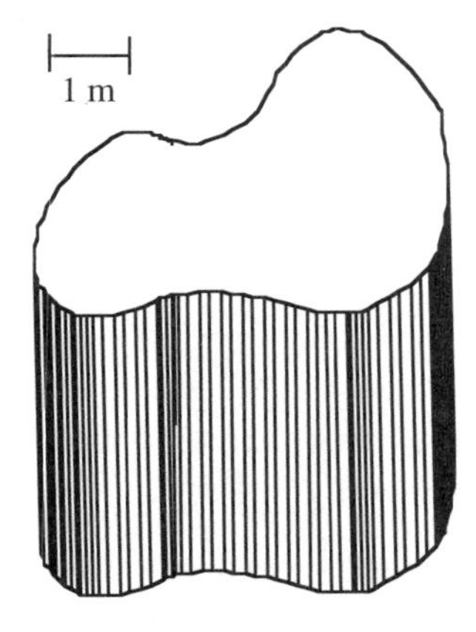

Determine the volume of the pond in each of the following units:

a. cubic meters **b.** liters.

How much water does a leaky faucet waste? How long does it take to fill a bathtub? How long would it take a broken water main to flood a basement? The answers to these questions depend partly on the water's rate of flow. In this activity, you use graphs to relate the rate of flow to the slope of a line. This activity extends the notions of lines found in "Yesterday's Food is Walking and Talking Today" to model a rate of flow.

Exploration

In this exploration, you measure the rate at which water flows through a funnel. **Note:** To prevent damage to papers, books, and electronic equipment, rice is used to simulate water.

a. Use cardboard to make a sturdy funnel with a volume of at least 2 L and an opening at the narrow end approximately 2 cm in diameter.

b. 1. Hold the funnel over a bucket and place one hand under the narrow end to block the flow of rice. Pour 2.0 L of rice into the funnel.

2. Simultaneously remove your hand from the narrow end of the funnel and start a timer. Determine the time (to the nearest 0.1 sec) required for the funnel to empty completely. Record the time in a table with headings like those in Table **5-1** below.

TABLE 5-1 ■ *Time Data*

Funnel Opening (cm)	Time for Trial 1	Time for Trial 2	Time for Trial 3
2			
3			
4			

c. Repeat Part **b** for two more trials.

d. To complete Table **5-1,** repeat Parts **a–c** using funnels with openings of 3 cm and 4 cm.

mathematics note

A **rate** compares the change in one quantity to the change in another quantity.

For example, the rate of flowing water compares a change in volume to a change in time. A rate of flow of 20 liters per minute may be written as 20 L/min.

e. Calculate the average time (to the nearest 0.1 sec) required for each size of funnel to empty.

f. Use these average times to determine the rate at which rice flowed from each funnel in the following units.

1. liters per second

2. liters per minute

3. liters per hour.

g. Use the rates from Part **f** to predict the volume (to the nearest 0.1 L) that could flow through each funnel in 1 min, 2 min, 5 min, and 10 min. Record your predictions in a table with headings like those in Table **5-2**.

TABLE 5-2 ■ *Time vs. Volume Data*

Time (min)	Volume (L)		
	2-cm Funnel	3-cm Funnel	4-cm Funnel
1			
2			
5			
10			

h. 1. Make a scatterplot of the predictions in Table **5-2** for the 2-cm funnel. Let x represent the time in minutes and y represent the volume in liters.

2. Find a line that fits the points as closely as possible. Draw the line on the same set of axes as the scatterplot.

3. Determine the slope of the line.

i. Use your line to estimate the volume that could flow through the funnel in 7 min and in 12 min. **Note:** Save your work in this exploration for use in the assignment.

Discussion

a. Compare the data you collected in Table **5-1** with that of others in the class. What might have caused the differences you observe?

b. What relationship did you observe between the size of the funnel opening and the rate of flow?

c. Do you think that the rates determined in Part **f** of the exploration are reliable? Explain your response.

d. Describe the relationship between the rate of flow and the slope of the line that you found in Part **h** of the exploration.

e. If a leaky faucet drips once every second and each drip has a volume of 0.50 mL, what volume of water will leak from the faucet in 1 day?

Warm-Up

1. Find the slope of the line that contains each of the following pairs of points:

   a. (5,2) and (7,8)

   b. (10,8) and (–3,13)

   c. (–2,5) and (6,5)

   d. (–1,–4) and (–1,5)

2. Create a graph of the line $y = (2/3)x - 7$. Identify its slope and y-intercept.

3. Graph a line with a slope of –6/5 and a y-intercept of 2. Write its equation in the form $y = mx + b$.

4. Write the equation of each line shown below:

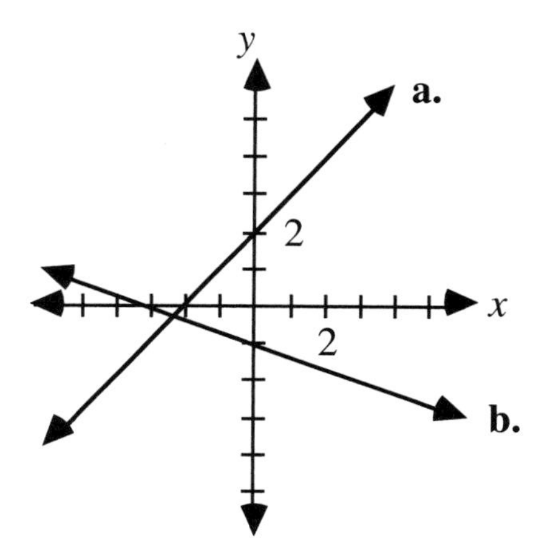

5. Write the equation of each line described below in the form $y = mx + b$.

   a. the line with slope –6 that passes through the point (3,–2)

   b. the line with slope 1/7 that passes through the point (–5,–4)

   c. the line that passes through the points (–6,4) and (3,10)

   d. the line that passes through the points (7,11) and (–2,23)

   e. the line that passes through the points (0,6) and (1,1)

   f. the horizontal line passing through the point (2,–4)

Assignment

2.1 Use your line from Part **h** of the exploration to complete the following.

a. **1.** Identify the y-intercept of the line.

2. What does the y-intercept represent in terms of the exploration?

b. Write an equation of the line in the form $y = mx + b$, where y represents volume in liters and x represents time in minutes.

c. Use your equation to predict the volume that could flow through the funnel in 7 min and in 12 min.

d. Compare these predictions with the ones you made in Part **i** of the exploration.

2.2 **a.** **1.** Make a scatterplot of the data in Table **5-2** for the 3-cm funnel.

2. Find a line that fits the data as closely as possible. Draw the line on the same set of axes as the scatterplot.

3. Write an equation of the line in the form $y = mx + b$, where y represents volume in liters and x represents time in minutes.

b. Repeat Part **a** for the data for the 4-cm funnel.

2.3 Graph the equations found in Problem **2.1b** and Problem **2.2a** and **b** on the same coordinate system. Describe any similarities or differences you observe and explain why they occur in terms of the exploration.

2.4 The table below shows the average time required to empty a 2.0-L water bottle using openings of different sizes.

Bottle Opening (cm)	Time to Empty (sec)
0.6	78.0
1.3	18.0
2.5	5.0

a. Use this data to determine the rate at which water flowed through each opening in the following units.

1. liters per second

2. liters per minute

3. liters per hour.

b. Write an equation of the form $y = mx + b$ to describe the flow of water through each opening, where y represents volume in liters and x represents time in minutes.

* * * * *

2.5 The All School Club is a service organization at Larry's school. When Larry became president of the club, he decided to start a membership drive. The campaign hopes to sign 4 new members per week. After 10 weeks, this should bring the club's total membership to 375 students. The following table shows the membership during the first five weeks of the campaign.

Week	Total Membership
1	335
2	339
3	343
4	347
5	351

a. 1. Draw a scatterplot of this data. Let x represent the week and y represent the total membership.

2. Draw a line that fits the data as closely as possible.

b. 1. Is the slope of the line positive or negative?

2. What does the slope indicate in terms of the membership drive?

c. 1. Identify the y-intercept of the line.

2. What does the y-intercept represent in terms of the membership drive?

2.6 Crickets make chirping sounds by rubbing their wings together. For some crickets, the relationship between the number of chirps per minute and the air temperature is very close to a line. When the air temperature is 20°C, these crickets chirp 124 times per minute. When the temperature is 26.6°C, they chirp 172 times per minute.

a. Graph this information on a scatterplot. Let x represent the temperature in degrees Celsius and y represent the number of chirps per minute.

b. Draw a line that fits the data as closely as possible.

c. Identify the y-intercept of this line.

d. Determine the slope of the line.

e. Write an equation of the line in the form $y = mx + b$.

f. Predict the temperature at which these crickets make 150 chirps per minute.

2.7 Lumber typically is sold in units called board feet. The table below shows the number of board feet contained in lengths of three common dimensions of lumber: 1×4, 2×4 and 2×12. (A 2×4 is approximately 2 in. thick and 4 in. wide.)

	Length				
Dimensions	**5 ft**	**10 ft**	**20 ft**	**30 ft**	**40 ft**
1×4	$1\frac{2}{3}$	$3\frac{1}{3}$	$6\frac{2}{3}$	10	$13\frac{1}{3}$
2×4	$3\frac{1}{3}$	$6\frac{2}{3}$	$13\frac{1}{3}$	20	$26\frac{2}{3}$
2×12	10	20	40	60	80

a. On a single coordinate system, create a scatterplot that shows the number of board feet in a piece of lumber versus its length for each of the following dimensions:

1. 1×4

2. 2×4

3. 2×12.

b. Describe the relationship between the length of a piece of lumber and the number of board feet it contains.

c. Draw a line that fits each scatterplot as closely as possible.

d. Write an equation for each line from Part **c** in the form $y = mx + b$.

e. Find the dimensions, including the length, of a piece of lumber that contains 1 board foot. Describe how you determined your response.

ACTIVITY 3

An aquifer is a water-filled layer of sand or gravel—a sort of underground deposit of water. The High Plains Aquifer, which underlies parts of eight states, is one of the largest known. It contains as much water as Lake Huron: about 4.24 quadrillion liters. For this reason, some geologists call it the "sixth Great Lake."

The geographical boundaries of the aquifer are shown in Figure **5-4** on the next page.

This region accounts for nearly 15% of the grain, 25% of the cotton, and almost 40% of the beef produced in the United States. Much of this production is due at least in part to the availability of water from the High Plains Aquifer.

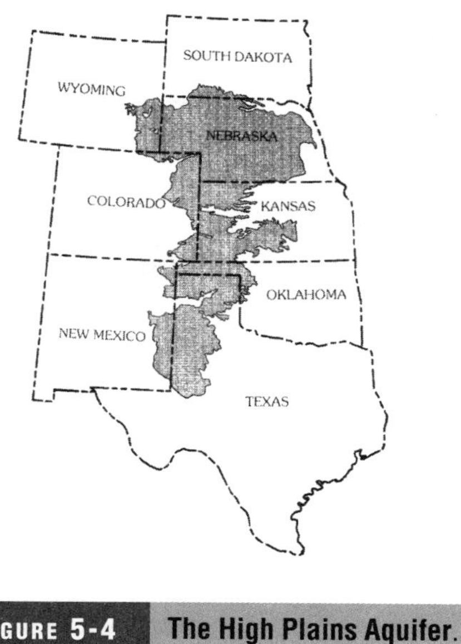

FIGURE 5-4 The High Plains Aquifer.

SOURCE: Dugan and Schild, *Water-Level Changes in the High Plains Aquifer.*

Although rain and snow help to replenish the aquifer, scientists predict that in some areas, it may be depleted in less than 100 years. To prevent this, many farmers are planting crops that require less water, while others are irrigating in ways that conserve the resource. Without irrigation, however, acres of productive farms would return to the original prairie.

Exploration

To monitor changes in the aquifer, researchers drilled wells in Chase County, Nebraska. They measured the distance from the surface of the ground to the water. As shown in Figure **5-5,** high-water readings were taken in June, and low-water readings were taken in September.

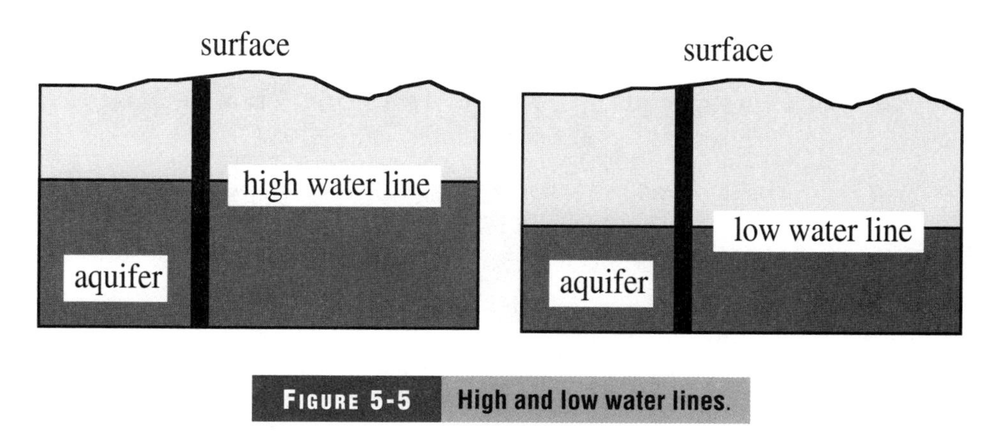

FIGURE 5-5 High and low water lines.

Table **5-3** below shows the distances from the surface to the high and low water lines from 1964 to 1978. The information in Table **5-3** seems to indicate that some sort of change is occurring in the aquifer. In this exploration, you determine whether or not this data can be reasonably modeled by a line.

TABLE 5-3 ■ ***Distance from Surface to Water Line (in meters)***

Year	High	Low	Year	High	Low
1964	17.1	18.1	1972	19.7	21.3
1965	17.2	18.1	1973	19.8	22.3
1966	17.1	18.2	1974	20.1	22.9
1967	17.4	18.2	1975	20.6	23.8
1968	17.7	19.4	1976	21.3	26.0
1969	18.1	19.8	1977	22.3	26.5
1970	18.9	20.7	1978	22.7	27.6
1971	19.4	21.3			

SOURCE: Dugan and Schild, *Water-Level Changes in the High Plains Aquifer.*

a. Enter the distances to the high-water level in a spreadsheet with headings like those in Table **5-4.** Note that the first column is headed "Years after 1964." This means that 1964 corresponds with 0, 1965 corresponds with 1, and so on.

TABLE 5-4 ■ ***Distances to High Water Level after 1964***

Years after 1964	Distance (m)
0	17.1
1	17.2
⋮	⋮
14	22.7

b. Create a scatterplot of the data from Part **a.** Let y represent the distance and x represent the number of years after 1964.

c. Mathematical models often use graphs or equations to describe relationships that arise in real-world situations. A mathematical model that consists of a line or its equation is a **linear model.**

1. Draw a linear model that fits the data from Part **a** as closely as possible.
2. Find the equation of the line.

d. 1. Add a third column to your spreadsheet with the heading "Predicted Distance."

2. Use the equation from Part **c** to predict the distance to the high-water level for each year in Table **5-3.**

3. Enter these predicted values in the appropriate column of the spreadsheet.

mathematics note

Figure **5-6** shows that a linear model might not fit every data point exactly. However, even when a line does not fit every point, it still can provide a reasonable model of the data.

A **residual** is the difference between an observed value and the predicted value. In Figure **5-6,** the residual for each data point is the difference between the y-coordinate of the data point and the corresponding y-value of the model. Because data points may be located above or below the line, the values of residuals may be positive or negative.

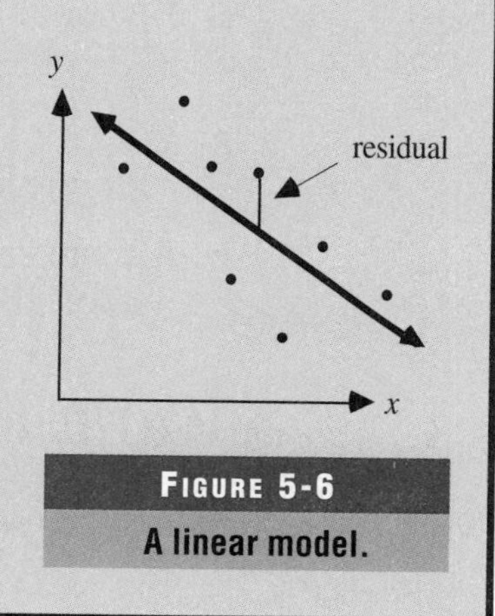

Figure 5-6
A linear model.

The **absolute value of a residual** is a measure of the distance from the data point to the linear model. In general, the smaller the sum of the absolute values of the residuals, the more closely a line approximates the data.

e. 1. Add a fourth column to your spreadsheet with the heading "Residuals."

2. Using your predicted distances from Part **d,** find and enter the residual for each data point.

3. Determine the sum of the residuals.

f. 1. Add a fifth column to your spreadsheet with the heading "Absolute Value of the Residuals."

2. Calculate and record the absolute value of each residual.

3. Determine the sum of the absolute values of the residuals.

g. Divide the sum of the absolute values of the residuals by the number of data points. This is the average distance from each data point to the model.

Discussion

a. Does the line you drew in Part **c** of the exploration fit the data exactly? Explain your response.

b. How could you use the average distance from each data point to the model to determine if a model fits reasonably well?

c. Does your line appear to be a good model for the data?

d. If the sum of the absolute values of the residuals is 0, then a linear model fits the data perfectly. Is this also true for the sum of the residuals? Use an example to justify your response.

e. Describe the slope of your linear model. What might this slope indicate about the aquifer in Chase County?

f. Do you think that water-level data has been recorded for enough years to support your response to Part **e** of the discussion? Why or why not?

g. What practices might be implemented to ensure that future generations can continue to draw water from the High Plains Aquifer?

h. Is there an aquifer in your area? If so, where would you go to find more information about it?

Warm-Up

1. a. Complete the data table below for the line $y = 2x + 5$.

x	y
−5	
	0
0	
	15
15	

b. Describe how you can identify the line's x- and y-intercepts using the completed table in Part **a**.

2. a. On a coordinate grid, plot the points $A(1,4)$, $B(6,6)$, and $C(8,9)$.

b. One line that approximates these points is $y = 0.7x + 3$. Graph this line.

c. Determine the residuals for A, B, and C.

Assignment

3.1 a. Create a scatterplot like the one in the exploration for the distances to the low water levels in Table **5-3.**

b. Draw a line that closely approximates the data.

c. Write an equation of the line in the form $y = mx + b$. Describe the method you used to find this equation.

d. Use your equation to predict the distances to the low-water levels of the aquifer from 1964 to 1978.

e. 1. Find the residual of each point in the scatterplot.

2. Calculate the sum of the absolute values of the residuals.

f. Explain whether or not your line is a good model for the data.

3.2 Imagine that you have a leaky pipe under the kitchen sink. To catch the water, you place a coffee can under the leak.

The following table shows the time that the can has been in place and the total mass of the can and water.

Time (min)	Total Mass (g)
5	160
10	350
15	470
20	570
25	790

If y represents the total mass in grams and x represents the time in minutes, which of the following equations more closely approximates this data? Support your choice by determining the sum of the absolute values of the residuals for each model.

$$y = 30x + 16$$

$$y = 33x + 15$$

3.3 When an inflated balloon is placed in a freezer, its volume decreases as the air inside it grows colder. When the balloon is removed from the freezer, its volume increases as it warms.

The table below shows some data comparing the temperature of the air in the balloon to its volume.

Temperature (°C)	Volume (mL)
10	500
20	520
30	531
40	558

a. Make a scatterplot of this data. Let y represent the volume in milliliters and x represent the temperature in degrees Celsius.

b. Draw a line that closely approximates the data.

c. Write an equation of the line in Part **b** in slope-intercept form.

d. **1.** Find the sum of the absolute values of the residuals.

2. Describe what the calculation from Part **d1** means in relationship to the linear model.

e. Predict the volume of the balloon at an air temperature of 100°C.

* * * * *

3.4 Jason is raising hamsters to sell to pet stores. As shown in the following table, he has 64 hamsters after 5 months.

Month (x)	Hamsters (y)
1	2
2	6
3	18
4	35
5	64

The local pet supplier buys hamsters only in lots of 200. To predict when he will have enough hamsters to sell, Jason decides to create a graph of the data in the table.

a. Make a scatterplot of Jason's data.

b. Draw a line that approximates the data.

c. Write an equation of the line in slope-intercept form.

d. Find the sum of the absolute values of the residuals.

e. Do you think Jason should use a linear model to predict when he will have 200 hamsters? If so, predict the time. If not, explain why not.

3.5 Over the past 80 years, Olympic swimmers have lowered the winning time in the women's 400-meter freestyle by more than 2 min. The table below shows the winning times in each race from 1924 to 1988, rounded to the nearest 0.01 min.

Year	Time	Year	Time	Year	Time
1924	6.04	1952	5.20	1972	4.32
1928	5.71	1956	4.91	1976	4.17
1932	5.48	1960	4.84	1980	4.15
1936	5.44	1964	4.72	1984	4.12
1948	5.30	1968	4.53	1988	4.06

a. 1. Graph this information on a scatterplot. Let x represent the number of years after 1920 and y represent time in minutes.

2. Draw a line that fits the data as closely as possible.

b. Write an equation of the line in the form $y = mx + b$.

c. Determine how well your model fits the data.

d. Use your model to predict the winning time in the 400-meter freestyle in 2000.

Brooke Bennett's actual winning time was 4:05.80, or approximately 4.10 min. How does this compare to your prediction?

e. Use your model to predict the winning time in the 400-meter freestyle in 2080. Do you think this prediction is realistic? Explain your response.

3.6 Another way to determine how well a linear model fits a specific data point is to use **percent error.** The percent error is the absolute value of the difference between the estimated value and the measured value, divided by the measured value, and expressed as a percentage:

$$\text{percent error} = \left|\frac{\text{estimated} - \text{measured}}{\text{measured}}\right| \bullet 100$$

For example, if a data point has coordinates (10,24) and the corresponding point on the linear model has coordinates (10,21), then the percent error can be calculated as follows:

$$\left|\frac{21-24}{24}\right| \bullet 100 = 12.5\%$$

If the measured value is 0, then percent error cannot be calculated.

a. Using the predicted distances to the high water levels from Part **d** of the exploration, find the percent error for your model for each of the following years:

1. 1964
2. 1970
3. 1975.

b. The equation $y = 0.7x + 17$ is one possible model for the distances to the low water levels in Table **5-3.** Find the percent error for this model for each of the following years:

1. 1965
2. 1970
3. 1975.

c. Do you think that percent error would be a good measure of fit for a set of data? Why or why not?

Research Project

On average, each resident of the United States uses about 420 L of water per day. How does your daily water use compare to this value? In the following research project, you analyze your own personal water use.

Create a table with headings like the one below. To complete the table, you will need to develop some innovative ways to measure water use. For example, how can you determine the volume of water used in a shower or bath? And how much water does it take to flush a toilet?

Use	Rate of Use	No. of Uses or Time Used	Daily Volume
washing machine			
dishwasher			
bathroom sink			
kitchen sink			
toilet			
shower or bath			
other			
other			
		Total	

Your report should include a description of the methods you used to determine each measurement, a comparison of your daily water usage to the national average, and a discussion of any differences you observe.

Summary Assessment

1. The diagram below shows four farms that share irrigation water from the same reservoir. The average depth of the reservoir is 8.0 m. Each farmer has 2 center-pivot irrigation sprinklers. Each sprinkler can pump more than 4000 L of water per minute.

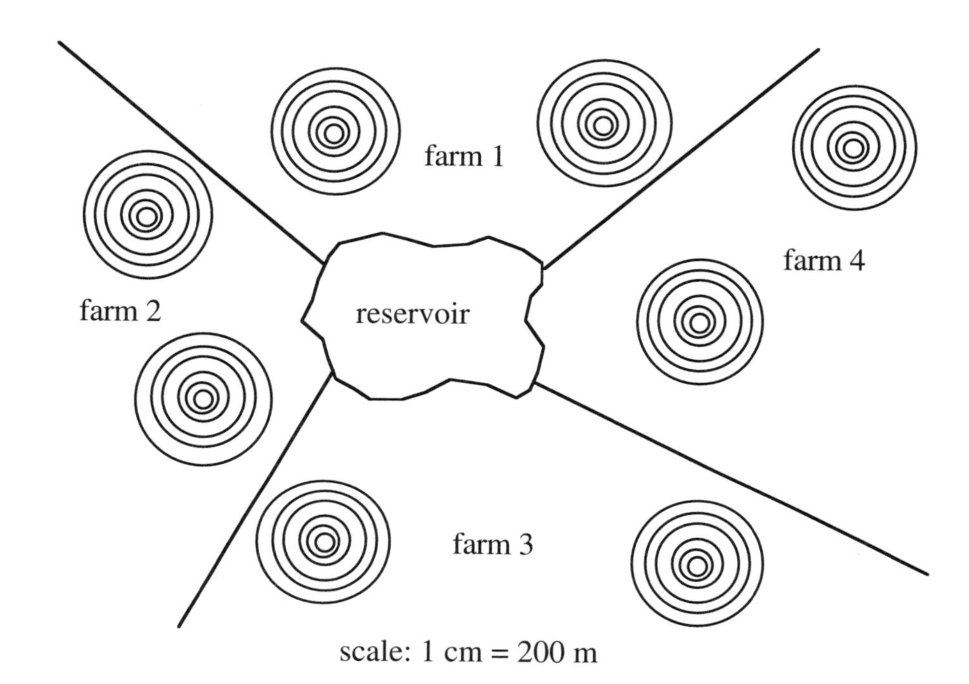

   a. During the 3-month growing season, the farmers plan to irrigate their fields for 16 hours a day, every day. Assuming that the reservoir is not refilled during the growing season, do they have enough water for their plan? Justify your response, showing all calculations.

   b. If the farmers do not modify their plan, for how many days can the reservoir supply them with water?

   c. What is the maximum number of hours per day the farmers can operate the sprinklers and still irrigate for the full 3 months?

2. The table below shows the volume of water flowing from a garden hose over time.

Time (min)	Volume (L)
0.00	0.0
1.00	15.0
2.00	29.0
3.00	48.0
4.00	65.0
5.00	73.0
6.00	94.0

a. Draw a scatterplot of the data. Let y represent volume in liters and x represent time in minutes.

b. Draw a line on the scatterplot that closely models the data points.

c. Write an equation for the line in the form $y = mx + b$.

d. Determine the average rate of flow in each of the following units:

1. liters per minute
2. liters per second
3. liters per hour.

e. How is the rate of flow in liters per minute related to the graph in Part **b**? Include mathematical terms and concepts in your response.

f. Assuming that the rate of flow remains constant, determine the volume of water which will flow from the hose in:

1. 15 min
2. 2 hr.

g. 1. Find the absolute value of the residual for each data point.

2. Determine the sum of the absolute values of the residuals.
3. Describe what this sum tells you about your model.

h. Another possible model for this data is the line $y = 14x + 2$. Compare the sum of the absolute values of the residuals found using this equation to the sum you calculated in Part **g.** Use the comparison to determine which equation is the better model.

Module Summary

* A **prism** is a three-dimensional figure determined by two congruent polygons in parallel planes whose corresponding vertices are connected by segments. The two congruent and parallel faces are the prism's **bases.** The parallelograms formed by joining the corresponding vertices of the bases are the prism's **lateral faces.**
* Prisms are named by the polygonal shape of the two bases. The **height** of a prism is the perpendicular distance between the bases.
* The amount of space occupied by an object is its **volume.** Volume is measured in units such as cubic centimeters (cm^3) or liters (L).
* The volume (V) of a prism may be found by multiplying the area of the polygonal base (B) by the height (h): $V = Bh$.
* A **rate** compares the change in one quantity to the change in another quantity.
* Mathematical models often use graphs or equations to describe relationships that arise in real-world situations. A mathematical model that consists of a line or its equation is a **linear model.**
* The difference between the y-coordinate of a data point and the corresponding y-value of a linear model is a **residual.** Because data points may be located above or below the line, the values of residuals may be positive or negative.
* The **absolute value of a residual** is a measure of the distance from the data point to the linear model. In general, the smaller the sum of the absolute values of the residuals, the more closely a line approximates the data.

6
module
Skeeters Are
Overrunning
the World
AB
(7, 13)
A
B
C

Introduction

At last count, more than 6.5 billion people inhabited the Earth. If each of us laid head to toe, we would make a chain of humanity long enough to wrap around the equator 300 times.

How many people can live on Earth without destroying the environment? How many people can our planet feed successfully? Several organizations studying the ever-increasing human population are concerned with just these questions.

Even though foretelling the future is never a sure bet, you can gather information about the past and present, find any existing patterns, and use these patterns to make predictions.

Graphs can be useful tools for determining patterns. For example, Figure **6-1** shows the world population since 1650.

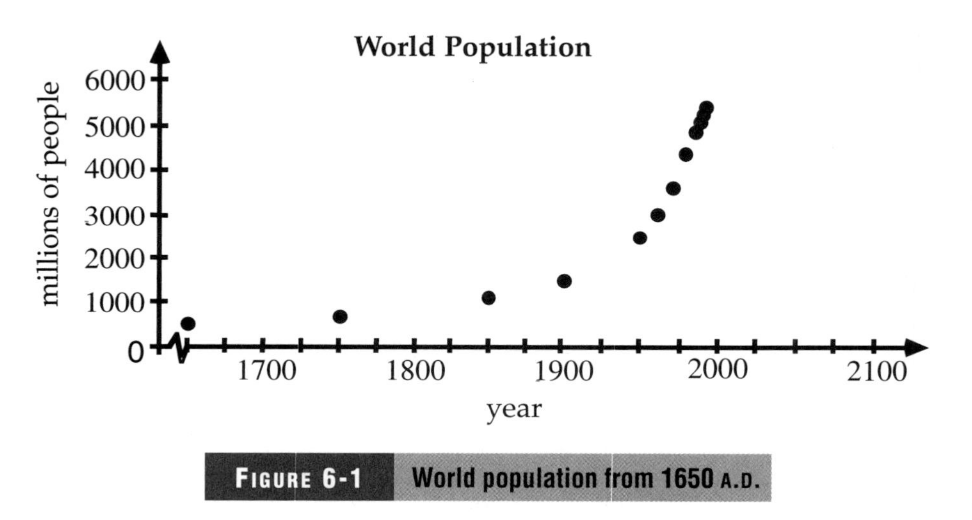

FIGURE 6-1 World population from 1650 A.D.

Discussion 1

a. Describe any pattern you see in the world's population since 1650.

b. Based on the pattern you find, predict what you think the world population will be in the year 2075.

c. A prediction is only as good as the information and assumptions on which it is based. The human population has not always grown as rapidly as it has in the past 40 years. Describe any current events that might alter how fast the human population will increase.

Exploration

Statistics like those shown in Figure **6-1,** along with an appropriate mathematical model, allow researchers to make forecasts about population trends. For example, scientists at the United Nations predict a world population of at least 8.2 billion by the year 2020.

Simulations are experiments that researchers often use to help predict real-world situations. They gather the results of the simulations and analyze them. Then they compare this data with known information about the actual population. If the results seem questionable, the simulation may be revised. This modeling process can be summarized by the following five steps:

- creating a model
- translating the model into mathematics
- using the mathematics
- relating the results to the real-world situation
- revising the model.

In the following exploration, you investigate this modeling process using a population of Skeeters.

a. Obtain a large, flat container with a lid, a sack of Skeeters, and several sheets of graph paper.

b. Before beginning the simulation, read Steps **1–7** below and predict the number of Skeeters in the box after 20 shakes.

1. Place two Skeeters in your container. This is the initial population.
2. After closing the lid, shake the container.
3. Open the lid and count the number of Skeeters with the marked side up.
4. Skeeters reproduce asexually (by themselves). Reproduction is triggered when the marked side of a Skeeter is exposed to light. Add one Skeeter to the container for each mark counted.
5. Record the total number of Skeeters now in the container. This is the end of one "shake."

   The end of each shake represents the end of one time period. The number of Skeeters present at the end of a shake is the total population at that time. (Remember that at shake 0, the number of Skeeters was 2.)
6. Design a method of recording and organizing your data.
7. Repeat Parts **2–5** for 15 shakes.

c. 1. Create a scatterplot to display the data you recorded. Represent the shake number on the x-axis and the total population on the y-axis. Select a scale for each axis that will allow you to make predictions for shake numbers through 20.

   2. Describe any patterns you see in your data.

d. 1. Use the pattern described in Part **c** to predict the number of Skeeters after shake 20.

   2. Is your box large enough to hold this population? Explain your response.

   3. Predict how many shakes it would take for the Skeeter population to reach 1000. Describe how you reached your prediction.

Discussion 2

a. Discuss any similarities or differences you observe between your scatterplot and those of your classmates.

b. How did the number of Skeeters in your population change during the exploration?

c. 1. Consider your scatterplot as describing the change in the population of Skeeters over time. Use this idea to explain the shape of the graph.

   2. How do the graphs obtained in the exploration compare to the linear graphs explored in previous modules?

d. 1. What other types of living creatures might show the same pattern of population growth as the Skeeters?

   2. What limitations might this simulation have in modeling a real-world population?

Genetics and environment can cause differences in appearance and behavior within any population. In this activity, you investigate some Skeeter populations with different growth characteristics.

Exploration

In this exploration, each color of Skeeter has its own growth characteristics and initial population. Table **6-1** on the next page shows a list of these characteristics for each color.

Table 6-1 ■ *Skeeter Growth Characteristics*

Color	Growth Characteristics	Initial Population
green	For every green Skeeter with or without a mark showing, add 2 green Skeeters.	1 green
yellow	For every yellow Skeeter with or without a mark showing, add 1 yellow Skeeter.	1 yellow
orange	For every orange Skeeter with a mark showing, add 1 orange Skeeter.	1 orange
red	For every red Skeeter with a mark showing, add 1 red Skeeter.	2 red
purple	For every purple Skeeter with a mark showing, add 1 purple Skeeter.	5 purple

a. Consider the information given in Table **6-1.**

1. Predict what will happen to the population of green Skeeters for the first 3 shakes.
2. Predict which population will be largest after 10 shakes.

b. Obtain a large, flat container with a lid, a sack of Skeeters of different colors, and a sheet of graph paper. Place the initial population of each color of Skeeters (indicated in Table **6-1**) in the box.

c. Place the lid on the container and shake it.

d. At the end of each shake, use the growth characteristics from Table **6-1** to add the appropriate number of Skeeters of each color.

e. Record the total number of Skeeters of each color at the end of each shake. (Record the initial population as the number at shake 0.)

f. Repeat Parts **c–e** for 10 shakes.

g. After 10 shakes, graph the data for each Skeeter population on the same coordinate system, using different colors to indicate the different populations.

Note: Save your data for the orange, red, and purple populations for Activities **2** and **3.**

Discussion

a. Describe the relationship between the numbers of yellow Skeeters at the end of two consecutive shakes.

b. 1. Describe the relationship between the number of yellow Skeeters at the end of a shake and the shake number.

2. Restate this relationship as a mathematical equation.

c. Does your equation from Part **b** describe the population of yellow Skeeters after any shake? Explain your response.

d. In the relations you graphed in Part **g** of the exploration, which values represent the domain and which values represent the range?

e. Recall that a **function** is a relation for which each element of the domain corresponds to exactly one element of the range. In other words, a set of ordered pairs (x,y) is a function if every value of x is paired with a value of y and every value of x occurs in only one ordered pair.

For which colors of Skeeters is the relationship between shake number and population a function?

f. A **vertical line test** can be used to determine when a graph does *not* represent a function. If it is possible to draw a vertical line that intersects a graph at more than one point, then this graph is not the graph of a function.

Which of the graphs below does not represent a function? Use the definition of a function to support your response.

1.

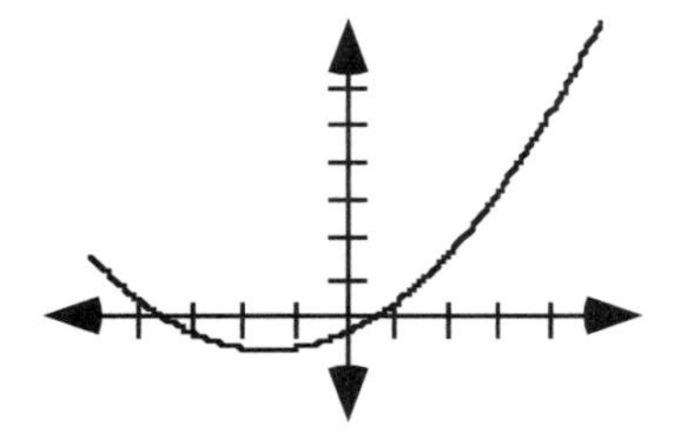

2.

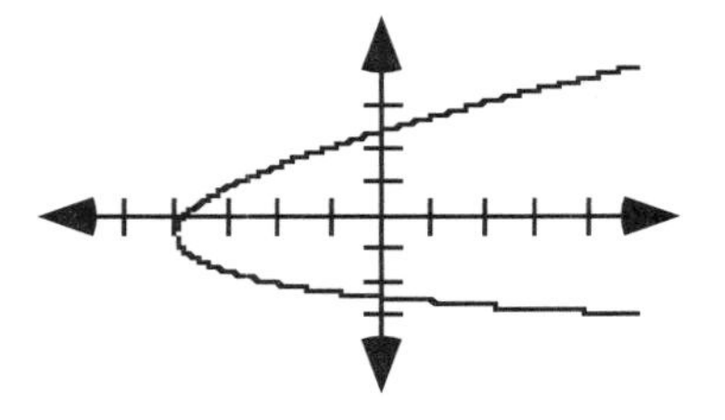

g. Do any of the graphs you created in Part **g** of the exploration fail the vertical line test?

mathematics note

Discussing several different functions at the same time can be confusing if they all contain the notation "$y =$." In **function notation,** a symbol or letter is used to name the function. This letter is followed by a set of parentheses containing the variable representing the domain, an equals sign (=), and the rule for the function.

For example, the function $y = 2x + 4$ can be written as $f(x) = 2x + 4$ (pronounced "f of x equals two x plus four"). Similarly, the function $y = -3x + 2$ can be written as $g(x) = -3x + 2$. In these examples, the letters f and g designate two different functions. The variable x inside the parentheses indicates that it represents the domain in both functions. Finally, $2x + 4$ and $-3x + 2$ are the rules for the functions.

To evaluate a function for a given number, use that number to replace the variable inside the parentheses. For example, consider the function $f(x) = 2x + 4$. The notation $f(-5)$, pronounced "f of negative five," indicates the value of function f when $x = -5$. Substituting for x in the rule of the function:

$$\begin{aligned} f(-5) &= 2(-5) + 4 \\ &= -10 + 4 \\ &= -6 \end{aligned}$$

Because $f(-5) = -6$, the ordered pair $(-5,-6)$ is a point on the graph of the function f.

h. Use the notation $g(s)$ to describe the population of green Skeeters after shake number s.

1. Given this notation, what does $g(4)$ mean?
2. How could you use function notation to describe the other populations of Skeeters in the exploration?

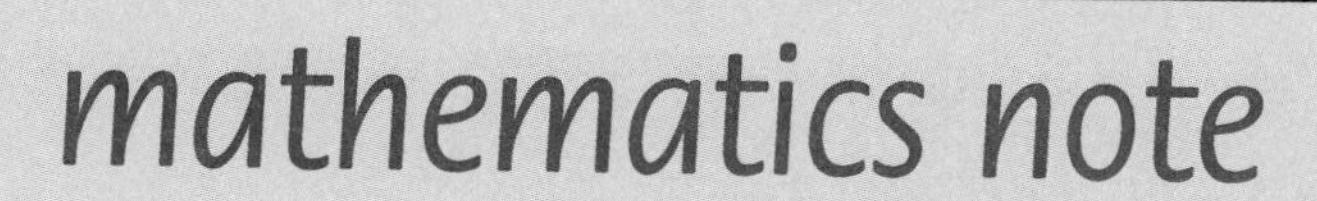

The **growth rate** of a population from one time period to the next is the percent increase or decrease in the population between the two time periods.

For example, Table **6-2** shows the population of wild horses on an island over three years.

TABLE 6-2 ■ *A Horse Population*

Year	Total Population
1992	15
1993	18
1994	24

The growth rate of the horse population from 1993 to 1994 is:

$$\frac{24-18}{18} \approx 0.33 = 33\% \text{ per year}$$

i. Is the growth rate constant from shake to shake for each population of Skeeters in the exploration? Explain your response.

Warm-Up

1. Determine the percent increase in each of the following populations:

   a. initial population = 250; current population = 325

   b. initial population = 25,000; current population = 40,000

2. Write each the following using exponential notation.

   a. $3 \bullet 3 \bullet 3 \bullet 3 \bullet 3$

   b. $7 \bullet 7 \bullet 7$

   c. $15 \bullet 15 \bullet 15 \bullet 15$

3. Write each of the following in expanded form.

   a. 5^2

   b. 2^5

   c. 11^3

4. Evaluate each of the following functions for the given value of x.

   a. $f(x) = 3 - 12x;\ x = 2$

   b. $h(x) = 2^x - 1;\ x = 3$

   c. $k(x) = 2x + 4;\ x = 7$

Assignment

1.1 a. Complete the following table for the yellow Skeeter population.

Shake Number	Total Population	Expanded Notation	Exponential Notation
0	1	$1 \bullet 1$	$1 \bullet 2^0$
1	2	$1 \bullet 2$	$1 \bullet 2^1$
2	4	$1 \bullet 2 \bullet 2$	$1 \bullet 2^2$
⋮	⋮	⋮	⋮
10			

b. Using function notation, write an equation that relates shake number to the total population after that shake.

c. Is the equation you wrote in Part **b** a function? Explain your response.

d. 1. Describe how to predict the total population of yellow Skeeters for shake numbers greater than 10.

2. Predict the total population of yellow Skeeters for shake 20.

e. 1. By what factor is the population of yellow Skeeters increased after each shake?

2. Explain how this factor relates to the equation you wrote in Part **b.**

f. What is the growth rate for the population of yellow Skeeters?

1.2 Create a table like the one in Problem **1.1** for your data for the green Skeeter population.

a. Use the table to determine how the shake number relates to the total population after that shake. Using function notation, write an equation for finding the population based on the shake number.

b. Predict the shake number at which the population of green Skeeters will be close to the population of yellow Skeeters at shake 24.

c. 1. By what factor is the population of green Skeeters increased after each shake?

2. Explain how this factor relates to the equation you wrote in Part **a.**

d. What is the growth rate for the green Skeeter population?

mathematics note

When the values for a variable depend on the outcome of another variable, that variable is **dependent.**

When the values for a variable do not depend on the outcome of another variable, that variable is **independent.**

In a savings account, for example, the amount of time for which money remains in the account determines the amount of interest earned. In this situation, time is the independent variable, while interest earned is the dependent variable.

When drawing a graph, the values for the independent variable are plotted along the horizontal axis. The values for the dependent variable are plotted along the vertical axis.

1.3 a. Compare the equations you wrote in Problems **1.1b** and **1.2a.** Describe any similarities or differences you observe.

b. Which quantity represents the dependent variable in these equations, the population or the shake number? Explain your response.

c. Rewrite each equation in terms of a dependent variable (y) and an independent variable (x).

1.4 Consider some Skeeters whose population growth can be modeled by the equation $y = 1 \bullet 5^x$, where y represents the total population after a shake and x represents the shake number.

a. Use this equation to predict the population after 10 shakes.

b. How does the population after each shake compare to the population before the shake?

* * * * *

1.5 In January of 1990, Maridee deposited $5000 in a savings account. At the end of each year, the interest earned was added to the account. The following table shows the account balance, after interest was added, during the five years from 1990 to 1994.

Year	Account Balance
1990	$5000.00
1991	$5250.00
1992	$5512.50
1993	$5788.13
1994	$6077.53

a. Create a scatterplot of the information in the table.

b. What is the growth rate in the account per year?

c. Use the growth rate determined in Part **b** to calculate the account balance at the end of 1995.

d. In what year will the account balance have doubled Maridee's original deposit?

1.6 One type of Skeeter produces 3 offspring after every shake, whether the marked side is showing or not.

a. Using an initial population of 1 of these Skeeters, create a table that shows the shake number and total population for the first 6 shakes.

b. Write an equation in the form $y = 1 \bullet b^x$ that models the growth in this population.

c. Determine the total population after 10 shakes.

d. Does this population have a constant growth rate? If so, calculate this growth rate. If not, determine the growth rates between consecutive shakes for the first 6 shakes.

ACTIVITY 2

In Activity **1** you looked at Skeeter populations that doubled or tripled after each shake. What happens if the ratio of consecutive populations is not an integer value?

Discussion 1

a. Recall the orange Skeeter population from Activity **1.** After each shake, only the Skeeters with the marked side showing produced offspring. If you shook a box containing 10 of these Skeeters, how many would you expect to land with the marked side up?

b. How does the probability of a Skeeter landing with the marked side up compare with the probability of a tossed coin landing heads up?

c. What growth rate would you expect to find between consecutive shakes of the orange Skeeter population?

d. One possible model for the population growth of green Skeeters is $g(s) = 1 \bullet b^s$, where $b = 1 + r$. In this model, r represents the growth rate expressed as a decimal. Explain why $b = 1 + r$.

Exploration

In this exploration, you determine a growth rate for the orange Skeeter population.

a. 1. Create a spreadsheet with headings like those in Table **6-3** below.

TABLE 6-3 ■ *Orange Skeeter Population and Growth Rate*

Shake	Expected Population	Actual Population	Actual Growth Rate (from Previous Shake)
0	1	1	
⋮	⋮	⋮	
10			

2. Use the growth rate determined in Part **c** of Discussion **1** to calculate the expected population after each shake. Record this in the appropriate column of the table.

3. Enter the actual data for the orange Skeeter population obtained in Activity **1** in the appropriate column of the spreadsheet.

4. Use the spreadsheet to calculate the actual growth rates between consecutive shakes. Record these values in the appropriate column.

b. On the same set of axes, create scatterplots of the expected data and the actual data for the orange Skeeter population.

c. 1. Use the growth rate from Part **c** of Discussion **1** to write an equation that describes the expected population after x shakes.

   2. Sketch a graph of the equation on the same set of axes as the scatterplots from Part **b.**

Discussion 2

a. In Part **b** of the exploration, how does the graph of the actual data compare with the graph of the expected data?

b. How well does the equation from Part **c** of the exploration model the actual data for the orange Skeeter population?

Warm-Up

1. For each annual growth rate below, determine the value of b in the corresponding equation of the form $y = 1 \bullet b^x$.

   a. 20%

   b. 50%

   c. 3%

   d. 100%

   e. 125%

   f. 10.5%

2. For each of the following values of b in an equation of the form $y = 1 \bullet b^x$, determine the growth rate per time period.

   a. 1.2

   b. 2.4

   c. 1.07

   d. 1 + 0.33

   e. 1.259

   f. 1.002

3. Given the initial values and annual growth rates below, determine the values for each of the next five years. Round all values to the nearest tenth.

   a. initial value = 10; growth rate = 20%

   b. initial value = 3000; growth rate = 5%

Assignment

2.1 Imagine that you have a container of 20 Skeeters. After shaking the container, you add one Skeeter for every Skeeter with its marked side up.

a. How many Skeeters would you expect to add at the end of the first shake? What would you expect the total population to be after the first shake?

b. How many Skeeters would you expect to add at the end of the second shake? What would you expect the total population to be after the second shake?

c. If you had p Skeeters before a shake, how many would you expect to add after the shake?

d. What is the growth rate for this population?

2.2 When Skeeters are shaken in a container, is the probability of a Skeeter landing marked side up always 1/2? Explain your response.

2.3 In 1990, the population of Tanzania was approximately 27,000,000 people. The expected growth rate is 3.5% per year.

a. Calculate the expected population in each of the 10 years after 1990.

b. Make a scatterplot of the expected population data from Part **a.**

c. How do you think the expected values for Tanzania's population will compare with the actual values? Explain your response.

2.4 Chauncy's parents have decided to offer him a weekly allowance. During the first year, he will receive $10 per week. In each of the following years, they have given him the choice of either a $7 raise or a 40% increase in his weekly allowance.

If Chauncy plans on living at home for the next 5 years, which proposed increase should he choose? Explain your response.

2.5 In each year between 1990 and 1995, Sue earned a gross salary of $30,000. In 1990, she paid $4338 in federal income taxes. In 1991, she paid $3905 in federal income taxes.

a. Calculate the growth rate in Sue's federal income taxes between 1990 and 1991.

b. Use this rate to predict the taxes Sue can expect to pay in 1995.

c. Describe some possible limitations in using this model to predict Sue's taxes.

ACTIVITY 3

How does the initial population size influence future Skeeter populations? In this activity, you use technology to model the growth of three Skeeter populations from Activity **1.**

Discussion 1

a. Compare your data for the orange, red, and purple Skeeter populations from Activity **1.** Explain any similarities or differences you see.

b. What effect, if any, does the initial population appear to have on the growth of each population?

Exploration

In this exploration, you observe how initial population can affect population growth.

a. Create a spreadsheet with headings like those in Table **6-4** below. Use initial populations of 1 orange Skeeter, 2 red Skeeters, and 5 purple Skeeters.

TABLE 6-4 ■ *Three Skeeter Populations*

Shake No.	Orange	Red	Purple
0	1	2	5
⋮	⋮	⋮	⋮

b. Using an expected growth rate of 0.5 Skeeters per shake, generate a table of values for each population for 20 shakes.

c. On the same set of axes, create a scatterplot of the expected data for each population for the first 5 shakes.

d. On another set of axes, create a scatterplot of the expected data for each population for 20 shakes.

Discussion 2

a. How do the growth rates you observed in the red, purple, and orange Skeeter populations in Activity **1** compare to the expected growth rate of 0.5?

b. Compare the population data you collected in Activity **1** with the expected data generated by the spreadsheet. What similarities or differences do you see?

c. 1. In Part **c** of the exploration, what similarities or differences do you see in the scatterplots for the three populations?

   2. Is it possible to determine the initial size of each population by looking at the graph?

d. Describe the mathematical operations used to calculate the population of purple Skeeters in your spreadsheet.

e. If a current population (p) of Skeeters has a growth rate of r, explain why the equation for the total population (T) after the next shake can be expressed as $T = p(1 + r)$.

f. 1. If the population before a given shake is $p(1 + r)$, what expression can be used to describe the total population after that shake?

   2. Describe a relationship between initial population (p), growth rate (r), shake number (n), and total population (T) after that shake number.

Warm-Up

1. Given the following equations in the form $T = p(1 + r)^n$, identify the initial population and the growth rate.

   a. $y = 4 \bullet 3^x$

   b. $y = 100(1.23)^x$

   c. $y = 1500(1.008)^x$

2. Given the following initial values and annual growth rates, write an exponential equation to describe the pattern of growth.

   a. initial value = 5; growth rate = 100%

   b. initial value = 4000; growth rate = 5.15%

   c. initial value = 25; growth rate = 40%

Assignment

3.1 How closely does the relationship found in Part **f** of Discussion **2** model the data collected in Activity **1** for the orange and red Skeeter populations? Explain your response.

3.2 One equation that can be used to determine the total Skeeter population (T) given an initial population p, a growth rate r, and a shake number n, is

$$T = p(1 + r)^n$$

This is one example of an **exponential equation.** The general form of an exponential equation is $y = a \bullet b^x$.

a. What would each variable in the general form of an exponential equation represent in terms of a Skeeter population?

b. What effect would a change in the initial population have on the equation?

c. Use appropriate technology to create a graph that shows the growth of a Skeeter population with an initial size of 4 and a growth rate of 150% per shake.

3.3 A constant growth rate of 0.5 per shake produces little change in population size from one shake to the next when the shake number is small, but results in greater increases in the size of each successive population after many shakes. Explain why this is so.

mathematics note

The exponential equation $y = a \bullet b^x$ can be used to describe a pattern of **exponential growth.** If this equation describes population growth, a represents the size of the initial population. The value of b is the sum of two percentages: 100 (representing the initial population) and r (representing the growth rate). The independent variable x represents a time period.

Considering a population of Skeeters, for example, the independent variable x represents the shake number at which the population is counted. The dependent variable y represents the total population. A population of Skeeters with an initial population of 6 and a growth rate of 0.5% per shake can be modeled by the equation $y = 6 \bullet 1.005^x$.

3.4 Two of your classmates have used a spreadsheet to model the growth of a population of Skeeters. The initial population was 7. After shake 8, the total population was 2,734,375. What growth rate did they use? *Hint:* Substitute the appropriate values into an equation of the form $y = a \bullet b^x$ to find b; then use this value to determine the growth rate.

3.5 a. The relation $y = 3 \bullet 2^x$ models the growth in a population of Skeeters. Describe the values of the domain and range in this setting.

b. Is this relation a function? Explain your response.

3.6 **a.** The two equations below represent two different populations of Skeeters. Graph both equations on the same set of axes. When will these populations be approximately the same size?

1. $y = 10 \bullet 1.5^x$

2. $y = 1 \bullet 2^x$

b. Find the size of each population when $x = 0$. What do these values represent?

3.7 The table below shows the population of Skeeters in a container after each of 5 shakes. Write an equation which could be used to describe this data. (Your equation may not describe the data exactly.)

Shake Number	Population Total
0	2
1	7
2	25
3	86
4	300
5	1050

* * * * *

3.8 The following table shows the growth in a savings account with an initial deposit of $4000.

Year	Account Balance
1990	$4000.00
1991	$4160.00
1992	$4326.40
1993	$4498.50
1994	$4679.40

a. Write an equation in the form $y = a \bullet b^x$ to describe this data.

b. Using your equation, what is the value of y when $x = 0$?

c. What is the value of x when the initial deposit of $4000 has doubled?

3.9 In 1987, Vincent Van Gogh's painting *Irises* was auctioned for $53.9 million. Assume that the painting's value grew exponentially since 1889. If the painting initially sold for $50, by what percentage did its value increase each year?

Research Project

Imagine your own population of creatures with a growth rate and initial population different from those used in the explorations.

a. Use a spreadsheet to simulate the growth in this population for at least 10 time periods. Display your simulated data in both a table and a graph.

b. Find an equation that models the growth in the population over time.

c. Write a story about your population. Include a description of the growth rate and explain the consequences this rate will have on the population over time.

In 1991, the world's human population was approximately 5.3 billion. This total was increasing by about 250,000 per day, or 3 people every second. At this rate, over 1 billion people will have been added to the Earth's population by the end of the decade.

As a citizen of Earth and the United States, you have some questions to consider when making future personal and political decisions. What is the growth rate of the world population? How does this rate compare with the growth rate of the U.S. population? Is a growth rate of zero desirable? If so, how can zero population growth be obtained?

Exploration

Table **6-5** shows the population of the United States at 10-year intervals from 1790 to 1990.

TABLE 6-5 ■ *U.S. Population from 1790 to 1990*

Year of Census	Number of People	Year of Census	Number of People	Year of Census	Number of People
1790	3,929,214	1860	31,443,321	1930	122,775,046
1800	5,308,483	1870	39,818,449	1940	131,669,275
1810	7,239,881	1880	50,155,783	1950	150,697,361
1820	9,638,453	1890	62,947,714	1960	179,323,175
1830	12,866,020	1900	75,994,575	1970	203,302,031
1840	17,069,453	1910	91,972,266	1980	226,545,805
1850	23,191,876	1920	105,710,620	1990	248,709,873

SOURCE: U.S. Bureau of the Census.

a. Identify any patterns you see in the data in Table **6-5.**

b. In the previous activities, you calculated growth rates for Skeeter populations between consecutive shakes. Use a similar technique to calculate the growth rates for the U.S. population for each 10-year period.

Discussion

a. What historical events might have affected U.S. population growth during the past 200 years?

b. How would you find a representative growth rate for the U.S. population for the 200-year period from 1790 to 1990?

c. If a population with a growth rate of 0 has a birth rate of 0.05 per year, what is the death rate?

d. Consider a population with a growth rate of –0.05 per year and an initial population of 65. What equation could you use to model this population?

e. How does a negative growth rate affect the total population over time?

Warm-Up

1. Jurek invested $10,000 in an account that promised 17% annual growth. If the company's predictions are true, what would the value of this investment be in 10 years?

2. In 2004, Marissa bought a new car for $14,000. In the past, the value of this car has decreased at an average rate of 21% per year. If this trend continues, what will her car be worth in 7 years?

Assignment

4.1 You can make predictions about the future by describing the patterns found in the U.S. population data and displaying these patterns in graphs or equations.

a. Predict what the U.S. population would have been in 1990 if the growth rate had remained unchanged since 1790. Compare this number to the actual population in 1990.

b. Describe how you could use either the data in Table **6-5** or an exponential equation to predict the U.S. population in the year 2040.

c. If the future growth rate remains the same as it was from 1980 to 1990, predict the U.S. population in the year 2040.

4.2 **a.** Select a growth rate that produces a decreasing population in each successive 10-year period.

b. Use this growth rate and the U.S. population in 1990 to predict the U.S. population in 2040.

c. What conditions might cause a population to decrease?

4.3 From 1920 to 1930, the U.S. population grew by approximately 16%.

a. Use this growth rate to estimate the U.S. population in 1940 and 1950.

b. Compare your estimates with the actual values for the U.S. population given in Table **6-5.**

4.4 The following table shows the predicted growth rates, per year, in the populations of three urban areas. Use this data to predict the population of each city in the year 2023. What do you notice about the predicted populations for these cities?

City	2003 Population	Annual Growth Rate
New York	18,300,000	0.66%
Shanghai	12,800,000	–0.12%
Lagos	10,100,000	4.51%

SOURCE: United Nations Department of Economic and Social Affairs.

4.5 How does a growth rate of 0 affect total population numbers over time?

4.6 In 1930, the U.S. national debt totaled $16,185,000,000. By 1940, it had risen to $42,968,000,000.

a. Calculate the percent increase in the national debt over the decade from 1930 to 1940.

b. What would the national debt have been in 1990 if the growth rate from 1930 to 1940 had remained unchanged?

c. Since 1930, there have been periods of increase and decrease in the growth rate of the national debt. The actual debt in 1990 was about $3,233,000,000,000.

1. In 1980, the national debt was $907,700,000,000. Calculate its growth rate from 1980 to 1990.

2. What would the national debt have been in 2000 if the growth rate from 1980 to 1990 had remained unchanged? How does this figure compare with the actual debt in 2000 of $5.7 trillion?

4.7 The enrollment at Eagle Canyon High School has been increasing steadily in the past few years. The present high school building is designed for a maximum of 1000 students. Within the next 5 years, the school board wants to build an addition that will increase the high school's capacity by 200 students.

a. Last year's enrollment at Eagle Canyon High was 947 students. This year's enrollment is 958 students. If this annual growth rate remains unchanged, will the new addition be needed within 5 years? Explain your response.

b. Assume that the growth rate in the student population remains unchanged. Even with the completion of the high school addition, will the school still have enough capacity for the next 20 years? Explain your response.

Summary Assessment

The table below contains data on the population, growth rate, land area, and population density for four nations. Use this information to complete Problems **1–4.**

Nation	2000 Population	Annual Growth Rate	Land Area (km^2)	Density (people/km^2)
Canada	31,278,000	1.0%	8,968,000	3.5
China	1,268,853,000	0.7%	9,327,000	136.0
Hungary	10,137,000	–0.3%	92,000	110.2
India	1,002,708,000	1.6%	2,972,000	337.4

SOURCE: U.S. Bureau of the Census.

1. For each nation listed in the table, write an exponential equation that describes its population growth.

2. Assuming that the given growth rates remain unchanged, predict the years in which the 2000 populations of Canada and Hungary will have doubled.

3. Although India has a smaller population than China, it is growing at a faster rate.

   a. Determine the year in which India's population will surpass that of China.

   b. What will India's population density be at that time?

4. If these four nations continue to grow at their current rates until 2040, which nation will show the greatest change in population density? Support your conclusion with figures and graphs.

Module Summary

* A **simulation** is an experiment conducted to investigate real-world situations.
* The **growth rate** of a population from one time period to the next is the percent increase or decrease in the population between the two time periods.
* When the values for a variable do not depend on the outcome of another variable, that variable is **independent.**
* When the values for a variable depend on the outcome of another variable, that variable is **dependent.**
* When drawing a graph, the values for the independent variable are plotted along the horizontal axis. The values for the dependent variable are plotted along the vertical axis.
* The exponential equation $y = a \bullet b^x$ can be used to describe a pattern of **exponential growth.** If this equation describes population growth, a represents the size of the initial population. The value of b is the sum of two percentages: 100 (representing the initial population) and r (representing the growth rate). The independent variable x represents a time period.

Oil: Black Gold

module 7

Introduction

Large oil spills consistently make international headlines. During the past three decades, Brazil, France, Great Britain, Kuwait, Russia, and Spain all have experienced damaging spills. The worst incident in North America occurred in 1989, when the tanker *Exxon Valdez* dumped about 258,000 barrels of oil into Alaska's Prince William Sound.

The barrel is the international standard for measuring crude oil. Because 1 barrel of oil equals 42 U.S. gallons, the *Exxon Valdez* spilled about 10,800,000 gallons.

Discussion 1

a. Describe the number of gallons mentioned above in more familiar terms. For example, how many times would this much oil fill up your classroom?

b. How is the environment affected when oil is spilled into a body of water?

c. What methods are used to clean up oil spills?

Exploration

What happens when crude oil hits water? What shape does the spill make? How large an area will the spill cover? In the following exploration, you simulate the effects of an oil spill on water.

a. Pour water into a shallow container to a depth of approximately 2 cm.

b. Use a medicine dropper to add one drop of oil to the water. Observe how the oil and water interact.

c. Place a second drop of oil on the center of the first drop and note the changes that occur in the oil slick.

d. Quickly add several more drops of oil to the center of the existing slick. Record the number of drops added and note any changes that occur.

Discussion 2

a. In Part **b** of the exploration, how is the volume of oil in the drop related to the volume of oil in the slick?

b. Describe the geometric properties of the oil slick after the additional drops of oil were added.

c. How thick do you think the oil slick is?

d. How could you estimate the area covered by the surface of the oil slick?

e. When an oil spill occurs in the real world, what natural factors might affect the shape of the slick?

To reduce oil's harmful effects on the environment, clean-up efforts typically begin as soon as possible after a spill. Clean-up crews need to know both the area of the surface covered by the spill and the volume of oil, to help plan their work. Because precise answers are seldom available, they use working approximations. To make such approximations, the edges of oil slicks can be modeled using **simple closed curves.**

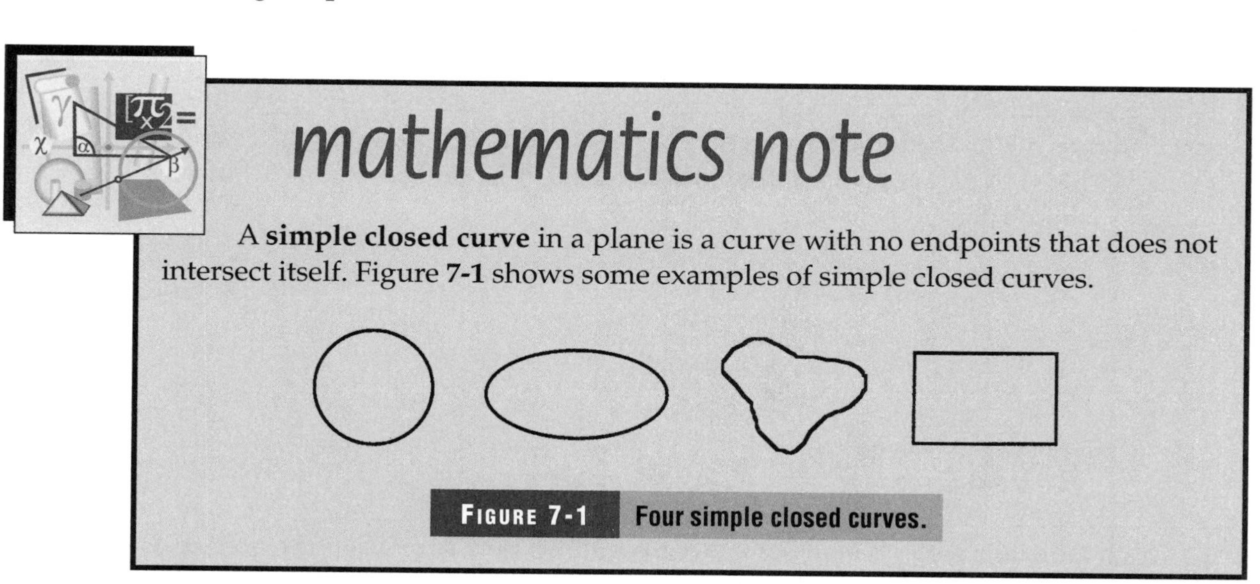

mathematics note

A **simple closed curve** in a plane is a curve with no endpoints that does not intersect itself. Figure **7-1** shows some examples of simple closed curves.

FIGURE 7-1 Four simple closed curves.

Exploration

Figure **7-2** shows the shapes of two oil slicks. In the following exploration, you investigate two different methods for estimating the area and volume of these slicks.

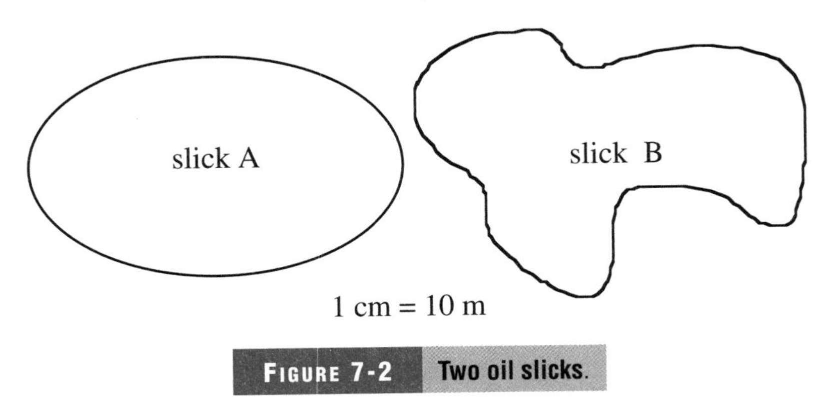

FIGURE 7-2 Two oil slicks.

a. In the module "What Will We Do When the Well Runs Dry," you estimated the area of irregular shapes by counting squares on a sheet of graph paper.

1. Use this method and a centimeter grid to estimate the area of each slick in Figure **7-2.**
2. The oil in each slick is 1 mm deep. Use the formula for the volume of a cylinder to determine the volume of each slick.

mathematics note

A **cylinder** is a three-dimensional solid with bases that are congruent, simple closed curves (nonpolygons) in parallel planes. For example, Figure **7-3** shows three different cylinders.

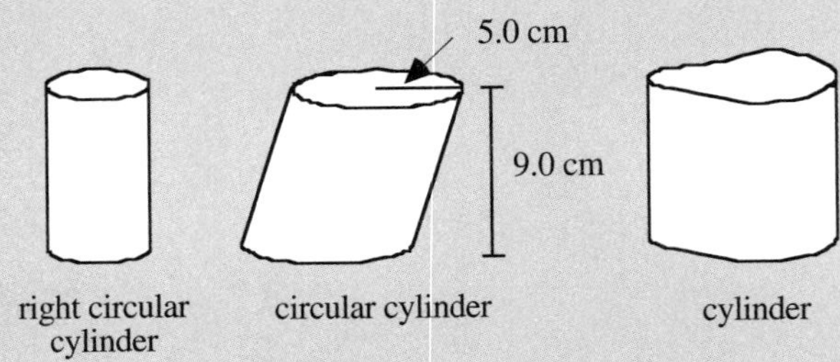

FIGURE 7-3 Three cylinders.

The volume (V) of a cylinder can be found by multiplying the area of its base (B) by its height (h): $V = B \bullet h$.

For example, to find the volume of the circular cylinder in Figure **7-3,** first you must calculate the area of the base. Because the base is a circle with a radius of 5.0 cm, its area is $\pi(r^2) = \pi(5\text{ cm})^2 \approx 79\text{ cm}^2$. Because the height of the cylinder is 9.0 cm, its volume is $79\text{ cm}^2(9\text{ cm}) \approx 710\text{ cm}^3$.

b. Another method for estimating the area of irregular shapes uses the formula for the area of a circle with a radius r, $A = \pi r^2$. Complete Steps **1–5** below for both slicks in Figure **7-2.**

1. Locate a point at the approximate center of the slick.
2. Measure the distance from the center to several random points on the edge of the slick.
3. Find the mean of the distances from Step **2.** This mean is the approximate radius of a circle with comparable area.
4. Use the mean radius found in Step **3** and the formula for the area of a circle to estimate the area of the slick.
5. Assuming that the oil is 1 mm deep, determine the volume of the slick.

Discussion

a. When using a grid to estimate area, why do you divide the number of partially covered squares by 2?

b. How could you modify the grid used in Part **a** of the exploration to obtain more accurate estimates of area?

c. How might an environmental engineer find the area covered by the surface of an oil spill?

d. 1. Compare the two estimates you obtained for the volume of each slick.
   2. If you were in charge of cleaning up slick B, which estimate would you use?

Warm-Up

1. Find the area of each of the following figures and describe how you determined your responses.

a.

3 cm
3 cm
3 cm
2.1 cm
3 cm
3 cm

b.

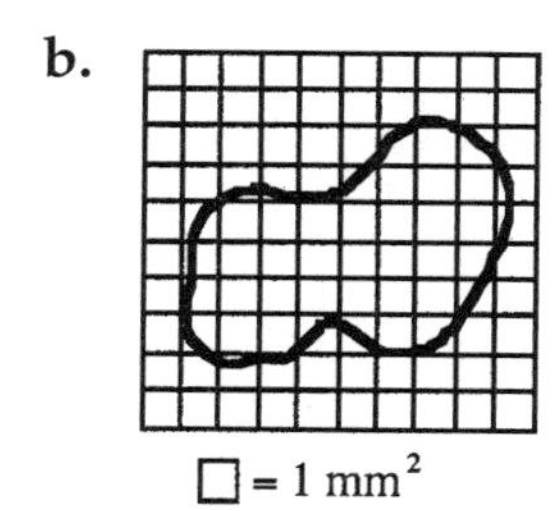

c.

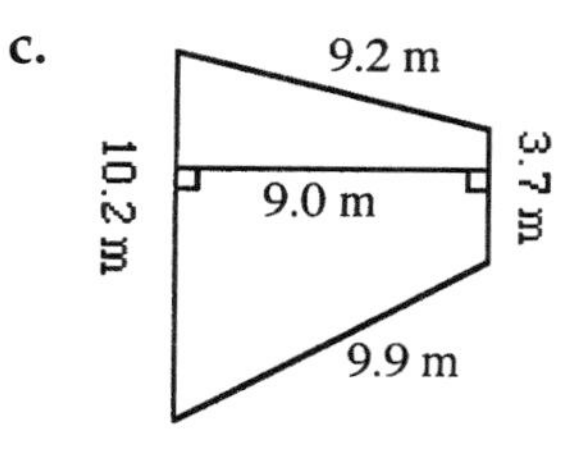

2. The formula for the volume of a prism or a cylinder is $V = B \bullet h$, where V is the volume, B is the area of the base, and h is the height.

Write an equation for the volume of each figure below, including the correct formula for the area of the base. Use your equations to calculate the volume of each figure.

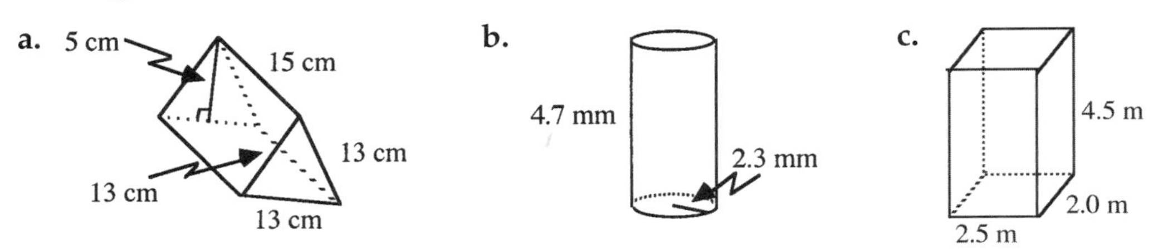

Assignment

1.1 a. Determine the volume of each fuel tank below in cubic centimeters.

1. This truck fuel tank is a rectangular prism.

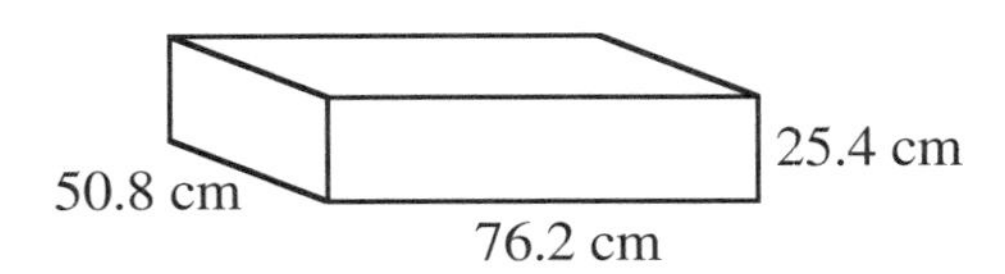

2. This boat fuel tank is a triangular prism in which the bases are right triangles.

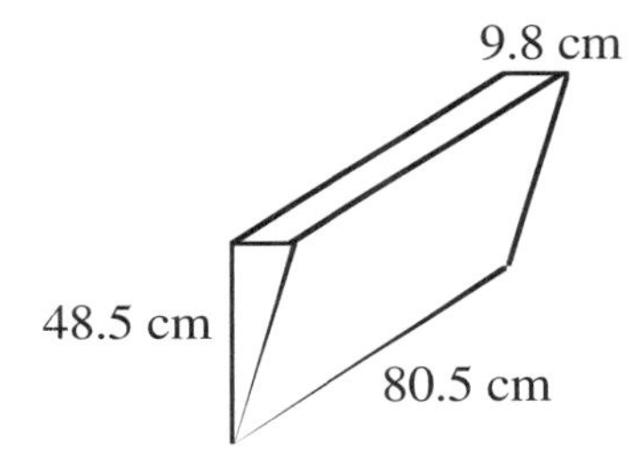

b. How many liters of fuel will each tank hold?
Note: 1 cm^3 = 1 mL; 1 m^3 = 1000 L.

1.2 Paper usually is purchased in reams. One ream contains 500 sheets of paper and is about 5.2 cm thick. Considering this information, find the volume of one sheet of letter-size paper in cubic centimeters. **Note:** The dimensions of a sheet of letter-size paper are approximately 21.5 cm by 27.9 cm.

1.3 The tank on the oil truck in the figure below is a circular cylinder. Determine the volume of the tank.

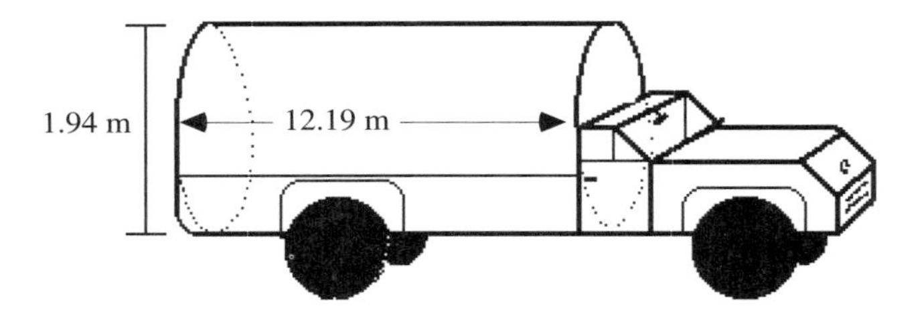

1.4 Imagine that some highly refined oil is spilled into a calm body of water. Under these conditions, the oil can spread to a very thin film, approximately $2.5 \bullet 10^{-3}$ cm thick.

a. What type of three-dimensional figure could be used to describe the oil slick?

b. The mean radius of the slick is 405 m. Determine the volume of oil in the spill in liters.

1.5 **a.** Estimate the area that would be covered by a spill of 1 barrel of highly refined oil in a calm body of water. (There are approximately 3.8 L in 1 gal.) Describe how you determined your estimate.

b. Do you think that an actual spill of 1 barrel of oil will spread as much as you estimated in Part **a**? Why or why not?

1.6 The following diagram shows an aerial view of an oil slick. The grid superimposed on the photograph has squares that measure 1 km on each side.

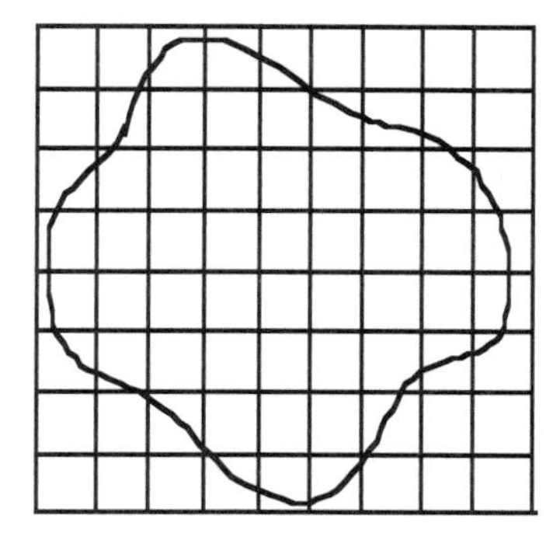

a. Estimate the area covered by the slick.

b. Determine the volume of oil involved in the spill if the slick is 0.05 cm thick. Record your answer in barrels. (There are 42 gal in 1 bbl.)

1.7 In December, 1989, an explosion on an Iranian supertanker spilled 19 million gallons of crude oil into the Atlantic Ocean. The oil slick covered an area of about 260 km^2.

a. Approximately how thick was this oil slick?

b. How does the thickness of this spill compare to the thickness of a spill of highly refined oil?

* * * * *

1.8 The federal government assures wheat farmers of a certain base price per bushel if they farm a limited acreage. To determine if a farmer is in compliance, regulators take an aerial photograph of the farm. The diagram below shows an aerial view of a wheat field with a pond. This farm has been allotted a maximum of 200 acres of wheat. (One acre is approximately 4047 m^2.) Is this farmer in compliance?

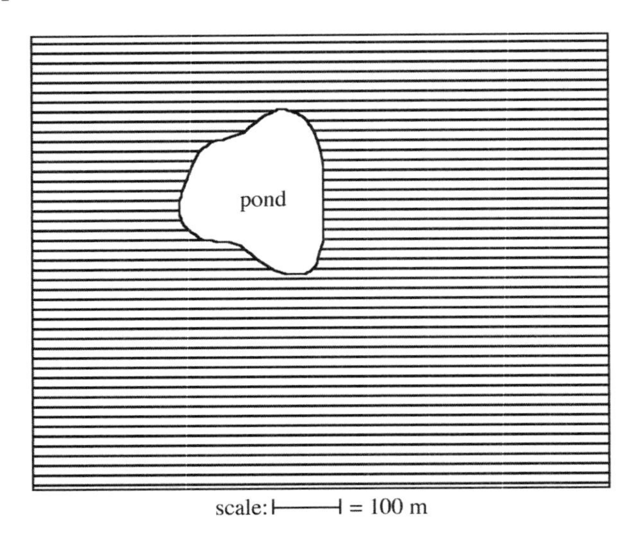

1.9 Use an ordinary soft-drink can to complete Parts **a–c** below.

a. Measure the height and diameter of the can.

b. Use these measurements to find the volume of the can in cubic centimeters.

c. Convert the volume of the can in cubic centimeters to milliliters. How does this value compare to the volume printed on the can?

A **simulation** of a real-world event involves creating a similar, but more simplified, model. In the introduction, for example, you simulated an oil spill on the ocean using a few drops of oil in a pan of water. In this activity, you simulate oil spills on land by placing drops of oil on sheets of paper.

Exploration

In this exploration, you simulate spills involving eight different volumes of oil. **Note:** Save your data, observations, and calculations for the assignment in this activity.

a. Obtain a small amount of oil, a medicine dropper, a ruler, eight sheets of absorbent paper, and some paper towels.

b. Spread the eight sheets of absorbent paper on a flat, nonabsorbent surface. Arrange the sheets so that they do not touch each other. Number the sheets from 1 through 8 and place a pencil dot in the middle of each sheet. Be careful not to fold or wrinkle the paper.

c. Carefully place 8 drops of oil on the pencil dot on sheet 8. Make the size of each drop as consistent as possible.

   Continue creating oil spills of different volumes by placing 7 drops on sheet 7, 6 drops on sheet 6, and so on.

d. Without disturbing the sheets of paper, observe each spill and record your observations. Describe the general relationship between the volume of oil (number of drops) and the shape and area of the spill.

e. Determine the mean radius of each spill to the nearest 0.1 cm. Start with sheet 1 and continue in numerical order to sheet 8.

f. 1. Determine the area covered by each spill and record these values in Table **7-1** below.

TABLE 7-1 ■ *Volume and Area of Oil Spills*

Volume (drops)	Area (cm^2)
0	0
1	
2	
⋮	
8	

   2. Create a scatterplot of the data in Table **7-1.** Represent the area covered by the spill on the y-axis and the volume of oil in drops on the x-axis.

   3. Determine the equation of a line that reasonably approximates the data. The line should have the same y-intercept as the scatterplot.

g. Use your equation to predict the area of an oil spill with each of the following volumes:

   1. 0.04 drops
   2. 0.5 drops
   3. 2.5 drops
   4. 25 drops ($\approx$ 1 mL)
   5. 25,000 drops ($\approx$ 1 L)

h. For each spill in Table **7-1,** calculate and record the ratio of the area covered to the volume (number of drops).

i. Dispose of the oil-soaked paper as directed by your teacher.

Discussion

a. What observations did you make concerning the spread of the oil, the shape of the spill, and the area covered by the spill?

b. What problems did you encounter in measuring the area covered by the oil spills?

c. 1. How does the precision of your measurement of the mean radius affect the accuracy of the calculated area?

   2. What implications does your response have for measuring actual oil spills?

d. 1. Describe the area you predicted for an oil spill of 1 L (approximately 25,000 drops) in Part **g** of the exploration.

   2. Do you think that this prediction is realistic? Explain your response.

e. Is it reasonable to assume that 0 drops of oil produce an oil spill with a surface area of 0 cm^2? Explain your response.

f. 1. Describe any pattern you observed in the ratios of surface area to volume determined in Part **h** of the exploration.

   2. What method might you use to find a single number m to represent all these ratios?

   3. If this value of m were used to write an equation $y = mx$, what would each variable represent in terms of the oil spills?

   4. How does this equation compare to the one you found in Part **f** of the exploration?

   5. Could this equation be used to accurately predict the area of an oil spill of 500 bbl on the ground? If not, how could you change the model to improve the prediction?

mathematics note

One quantity is **directly proportional** to another when the ratio of the two quantities is constant (the same). The constant is the **constant of proportionality** and the ratio is a **direct proportion.**

A direct proportion can be described by a linear equation of the form $y = mx$, where m is the constant of proportionality. The graph of a direct proportion always contains the origin because $y = 0$ whenever $x = 0$.

For example, in the direct proportion $y = 2x$, the constant of proportionality is 2. A graph of $y = 2x$ is shown in Figure **7-4.**

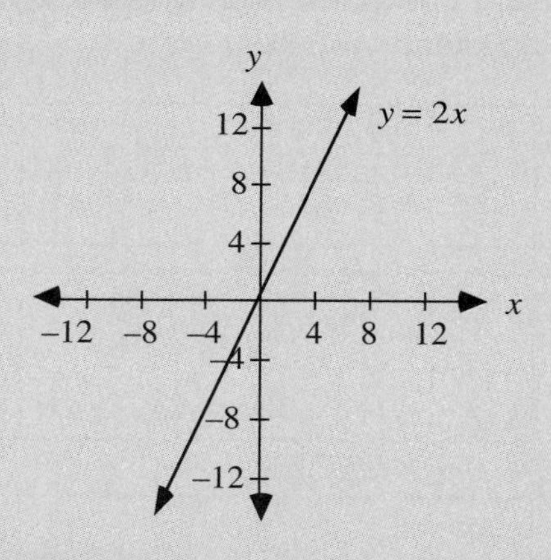

FIGURE 7-4 **Graph of a direct proportion.**

g. Given the direct proportion $y = mx$, describe how the values of y change as:

1. the values of x increase when $m > 0$
2. the values of x increase when $m < 0$

h. Are an oil spill's area and volume directly proportional? Explain your response.

i. If you know any point with coordinates (p,q) on the graph of a direct proportion, what is the slope of the line?

Warm-Up

1. Determine which of the following graphs, if any, depict direct proportions.

a.

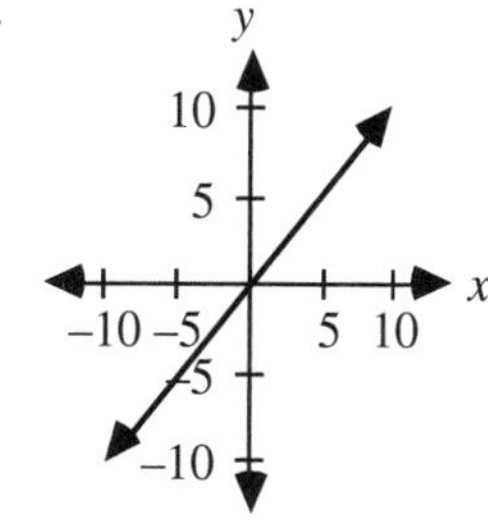

b.

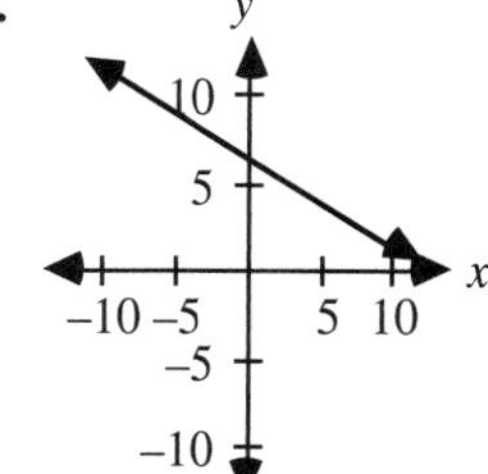

c.

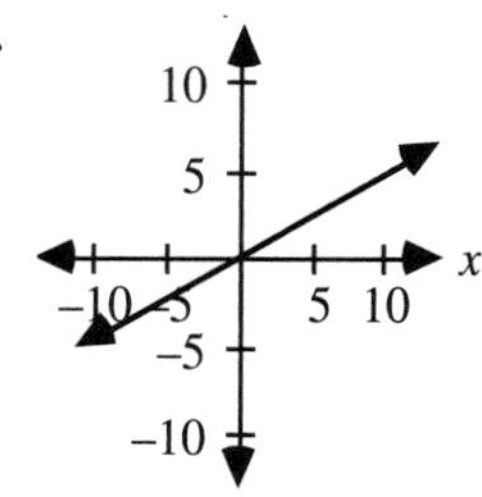

2. Determine which of the following equations, if any, are direct proportions. If an equation represents a direct proportion, identify the constant of proportion.

a. $y = 0.75x$

b. $y = 4x - 7$

c. $y = 10x$

d. $y = -(3/2)x$

e. $y = x^2$

f. $y = 2/x$

Assignment

2.1 Determine if x and y are directly proportional in each of the following relationships. Defend your responses.

a.

x	1	3	4	6	25
y	3	9	12	18	75

b.

x	1	3	4	6	25
y	8	14	17	23	80

c.

x	0	3	4	5	7
y	0	10	17	26	50

2.2 Which of the scatterplots below, if any, appear to represent direct proportions? Defend your responses.

a.

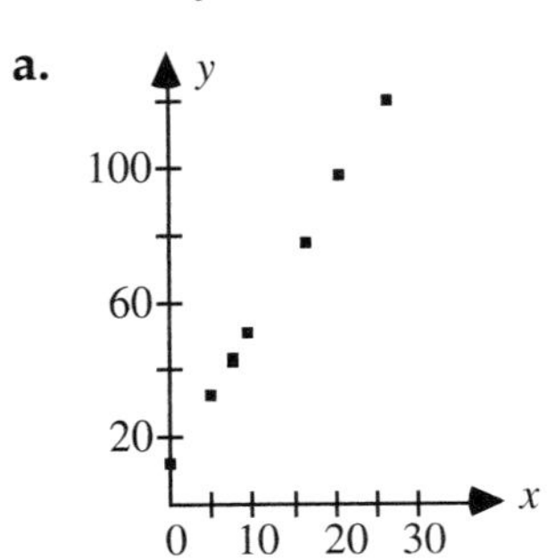

b.

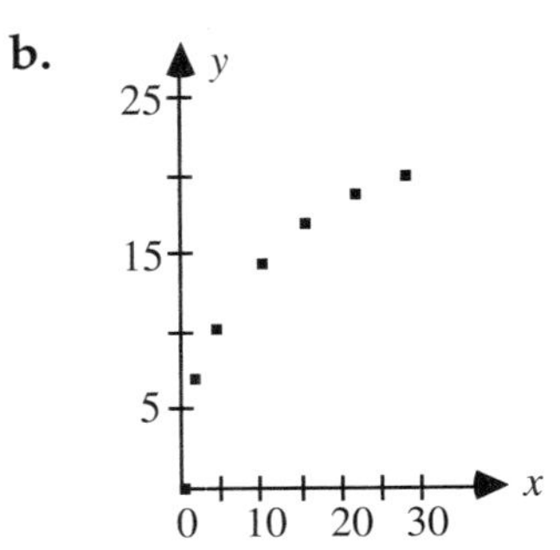

c.

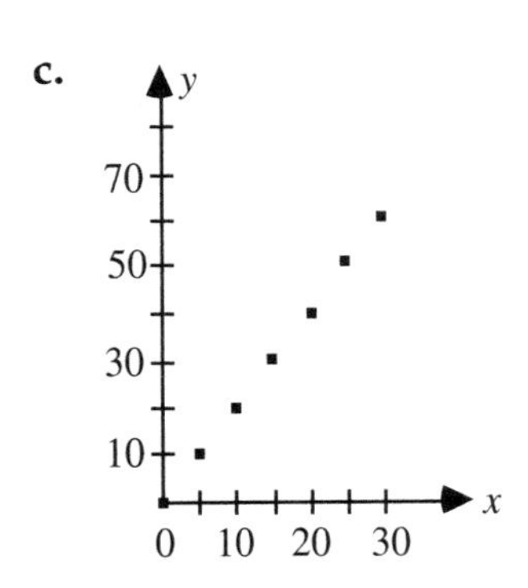

d.

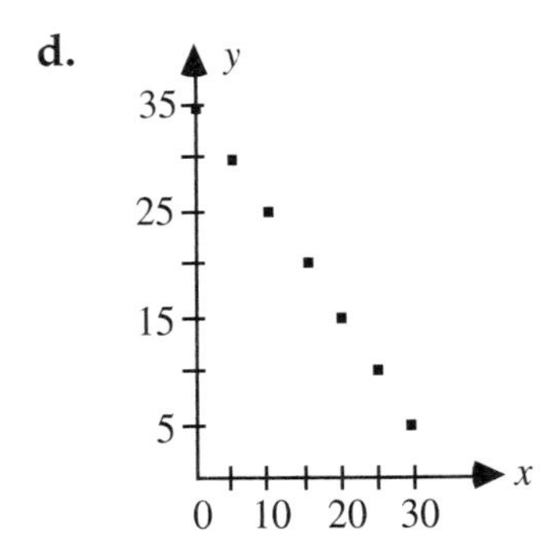

2.3 **a.** Graph each of the following equations of direct proportions on the same coordinate system, with $0 \le x \le 10$. Compare the graphs.

1. $y = 0.5x$

2. $y = 5x$

3. $y = 1x$

4. $y = -0.25x$

5. $y = 1.75x$

6. $y = -3.5x$

b. In your own words, describe the characteristics of the graph of a direct proportion.

2.4 Use your data from the exploration to answer the following questions.

a. Is the mean radius of an oil spill directly proportional to the volume of the spill?

b. Is the square of the mean radius directly proportional to the volume?

2.5 When oil is spilled on a sheet of absorbent paper, the spill can be modeled by a cylinder. In this situation, the base of the cylinder is the shape of the spill, while the height of the cylinder is the thickness of the paper.

The volume of a cylinder is determined by multiplying the area of the base by the height. Is the volume of the spill directly proportional to the area covered by the spill? Explain your response.

2.6 In a circle, the circumference (C) is directly proportional to the diameter (d). The constant of proportionality is π.

a. Write an equation for this direct proportion.

b. Is the relationship for each of the following a direct proportion? If so, write an equation for the proportion and identify the constant of proportionality. If not, explain why not.

1. the circumference of a circle and its radius
2. the area of a circle and its radius.

2.7 The relationship between temperature measured in degrees Fahrenheit (F) and temperature measured in degrees Celsius (C) is:

$$C = \frac{5}{9}F - \frac{160}{9}$$

Explain why this relationship is not a direct proportion.

2.8 Hailstones are formed when raindrops are caught in updrafts and carried into high clouds containing very cold air. The radius of a hailstone is directly proportional to the amount of time it remains in the high cloud.

a. After remaining in a high cloud for 10 sec, a hailstone has a radius of about 1.3 cm. What was the radius of the hailstone after 1 sec?

b. Write an equation for this direct proportion.

c. How long would a hailstone have to remain in high clouds to reach a radius greater than 2.5 cm?

2.9 In 1980, per capita personal income in the United States was $9948. Ten years later, per capita income rose to $18,699.

a. What was the total increase in per capita personal income from 1980 to 1990?

b. Assume that the yearly increases in per capita income and the number of years after 1980 are directly proportional.

1. What was the yearly increase in per capita personal income between 1980 and 1990?

2. Write an equation for the direct proportion between yearly increases in per capita income and number of years after 1980.

c. 1. Predict the per capita personal income in 1994.

2. Write an equation that could be used to model the per capita income for any year after 1980.

3. Does this equation define a direct proportion? Explain your response.

d. The actual per capita personal income in 1994 was $21,846. What limitations might the model in Part **c** have for predicting per capita personal income?

As soon as a quantity of oil is spilled, it starts to spread. If not contained, the resulting slick can cover a very large area. As the oil continues to spread, the depth of the slick decreases. In the following exploration, you investigate the relationship between the depth of a spill and the area it covers.

Exploration

When liquid is poured into a cylindrical container, the surface of the liquid takes the same shape as the base of the container. In this exploration, you use a fixed amount of water to represent the volume of an oil spill. The spread of the spill is simulated by pouring the water into several containers with different base areas. **Note:** Save your work, including the spreadsheet, for use in the assignment.

a. Obtain a cylindrical container from your teacher. Determine and record its base area (B) in square centimeters.

b. Pour 200 mL of water into the container. Measure and record the height (h) of the water in centimeters.

c. Calculate $B \bullet h$, where B is the base area and h is the height of the water in the container. Label the product with the appropriate units and record the result.

d. 1. Collect the class data for the different containers.

   2. Enter the data in a spreadsheet.

   3. Sort the data so that the base areas appear in ascending order (from least to greatest).

e. Create a scatterplot of the height of the water versus the base area.

Discussion

a. 1. What should be true of each value for $B \bullet h$ calculated in Part **c** of the exploration?

   2. Do the class values support this conclusion? Explain your response.

b. Describe the graph obtained in Part **e** of the exploration.

c. Consider a right circular cylinder and a right triangular prism with the same base areas. Each contains an equal volume of water. Does the height of the water depend on the shapes of the bases?

d. 1. In the exploration, what happened to the height of the water as it was poured into containers with larger base areas?

   2. Is the height directly proportional to the area of the base? Explain your response.

e. Do you think that examining the heights of liquid in a series of containers with increasing base areas provides a good model of the spread of an oil spill? Explain your response.

Warm-Up

1. Identify each of the following data sets as directly proportional, inversely proportional, or neither.

a.

x	3	–10	–2	2.5	20
y	1.67	–0.5	–2.5	0.2	0.25

b.

x	–3	6	15	–21	12
y	–2	4	10	–14	8

c.

x	8	–12	–2	–3	4
y	–1/2	–4/3	–1	–7/3	0

d.

x	6	12	4	–3	24
y	2	1	3	–4	0.5

2. Identify each of the following situations as involving a direct proportion, an inverse proportion, or neither.

   a. the number of children at a party and the average amount each will receive from a piñata full of treats

   b. the number of people at a barbecue and the kilograms of hamburger needed

   c. the number of miles hiked and the number of calories expended

   d. the number of people in a family and the number of slices each receives from one pizza shared equally

   e. the number of raffle tickets sold and the probability of winning the grand prize.

Assignment

3.1 In the exploration, you poured 200 mL of water into containers with different base areas.

a. Let B represent the base area of a container and h represent the height of water in the container. Write an equation that describes the relationship of B and h to 200 mL.

b. Solve this equation for h.

c. Graph the equation on the same set of axes as the scatterplot from Part **e** of the exploration.

d. Which appears to be the better model of the experiment in the exploration—the scatterplot or the graph of the equation? Defend your choice.

e. Why can there be no negative values for h?

3.2 **a.** Solve the equation you wrote in Problem **3.1a** for B.

b. **1.** Predict the area covered by an oil spill of 200 mL if it spreads to a thickness of $2.5 \bullet 10^{-3}$ cm.

2. If the spill is circular, what is its diameter?

3.3 Consider a spill of 100 bbl of highly refined oil on a calm body of water.

a. Write an equation that models this spill in terms of B, h, and 100 bbl.

b. How many cubic centimeters of oil are there in 100 bbl? (There are approximately 160 L in 1 bbl; 1 cm^3 contains 1 mL.)

c. Rewrite your equation in Part **a** by replacing 100 bbl with its equivalent in cubic centimeters.

d. Determine the area (in square kilometers) covered by a 100-bbl spill that spreads to a thickness of $2.5 \bullet 10^{-3}$ cm.

e. If the spill is circular, what is its diameter?

3.4 **a.** Solve the following equation for y: $20 = x \bullet y$.

b. Choose at least five different values for x. Find the corresponding y-values and organize these results in a table.

c. As the values of x increase, what happens to the corresponding values of y? Is this consistent with what you observed in the exploration? Explain your response.

mathematics note

One quantity is **inversely proportional** to another when the product of the two quantities is constant. An inverse proportion can be described by an equation of the form $xy = k$, where k is the **constant of proportionality.** The equation of an inverse proportion can also be written in the form $y = k/x$.

For example, the inverse proportion $xy = 2$ can be written as $y = 2/x$. The graph of $y = 2/x$ is shown in Figure **7-5.**

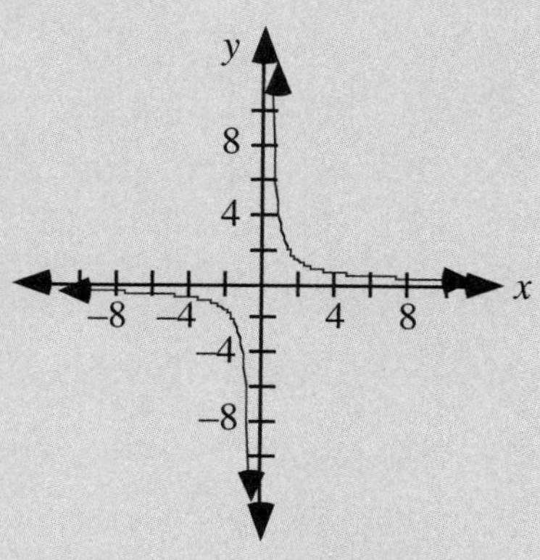

FIGURE 7-5 **Graph of an inverse proportion.**

3.5 **a.** Solve each of the following inverse proportions for y in terms of x and identify the constants of proportionality.

1. $x \bullet y = 20$ | **2.** $x \bullet y = 10$

3. $y \bullet x = 5$ | **4.** $0.5 = y \bullet x$

b. Using a graphing utility, graph the equations from Part **a** on the same set of axes, where $-10 \leq x \leq 10$. What appears to be true about each of the graphs?

c. **1.** As the x-values approach 0, what happens to the corresponding y-values?

2. As the x-values increase from 100 to 1000 to 10,000, what happens to the corresponding y-values?

3. As the x-values decrease from –100 to –1000 to –10,000, what happens to the corresponding y-values?

d. How does the constant of proportionality affect the graph?

e. What does the constant of proportionality represent in the equation you wrote in Problem **3.1**?

* * * * *

3.6 **a.** Compare the shapes of the graphs of a direct proportion and an inverse proportion.

b. Compare the equations of a direct proportion and an inverse proportion.

3.7 Consider the set of ordered pairs shown in the following table.

x	y
1	100
2	50
4	25
5	20
10	10
20	5
25	4

a. Create a scatterplot of this data.

b. As the values of x become large, what happens to the values of y?

c. As the values of x become small, what happens to the values of y?

d. Is the relationship between x and y a direct proportion, an inverse proportion, or neither? Justify your conclusion.

e. Write an equation that describes this relationship and identify the constant of proportionality, if one exists.

f. Describe a real-world situation that might generate these ordered pairs.

3.8 At 0°C, 32.0 g of oxygen gas occupies a volume of 22.4 L with a pressure of 1.0 atmosphere (atm). As the volume is decreased at constant temperature, the pressure changes as shown in the following table.

Volume (L)	Pressure (atm)
22.4	1.00
17.1	1.31
11.2	2.00
5.60	4.00
2.24	10.0

a. Create a scatterplot of the data.

b. At constant temperature, are pressure and volume directly proportional or inversely proportional? Explain your response.

c. 1. Write an equation that describes the relationship and identify the constant of proportionality.

2. Graph this equation on the same set of axes as the scatterplot from Part **a.**

d. Predict the pressure on 32.0 g of oxygen gas when the volume is 20.5 L.

3.9 Wavelength and frequency are two characteristics of waves. **Wavelength** is the distance between two consecutive peaks or troughs in a wave. **Frequency** is the number of wavelengths that pass a given point in a certain amount of time.

The standard unit of frequency is the **hertz (Hz).** One hertz is equal to 1 cycle per second. For example, the diagram below shows a wave with a frequency of 4 cycles per second, or 4 Hz.

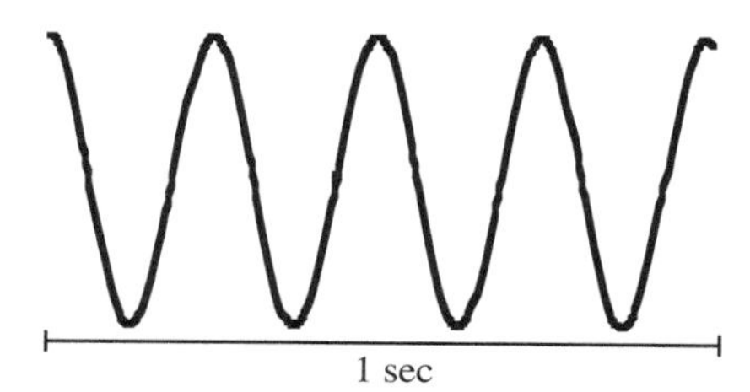

The table below shows the wavelengths and frequencies of some different forms of electromagnetic radiation.

Electromagnetic Radiation	Wavelength (m)	Frequency (Hz)
gamma rays	$1.0 \bullet 10^{-12}$	$3.0 \bullet 10^{20}$
X rays	$1.0 \bullet 10^{-10}$	$3.0 \bullet 10^{18}$
red light	$7.0 \bullet 10^{-7}$	$4.29 \bullet 10^{14}$
microwaves	$1.0 \bullet 10^{-2}$	$3.0 \bullet 10^{10}$
radio waves	$1.0 \bullet 10^{2}$	$3.0 \bullet 10^{6}$

a. Is the relationship between wavelength and frequency a direct proportion or an inverse proportion? Explain your response.

b. Write an equation that describes this relationship.

c. Identify the constant of proportionality.

d. Violet light has a wavelength of about $4.0 \bullet 10^{-7}$ m. Use your equation from Part **b** to determine the frequency of violet light.

Summary Assessment

1. The diagram below shows the shape of an oil slick that spread to a thickness of $2.5 \bullet 10^{-3}$ cm.

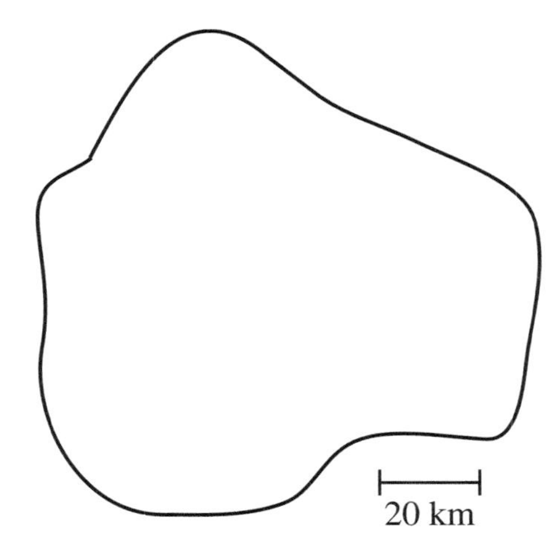

Estimate the volume of oil in the spill in gallons.

2. a. Assuming that the spilled oil spreads to a thickness of $2.5 \bullet 10^{-3}$, complete the following table.

Area of Slick (km^2)	Volume of Spill (gal)
5000	
7500	
10,000	
25,000	

b. Determine the type of relationship formed by the data collected in the table. Create a graph that displays this relationship.

c. Find an equation that models the graph from Part **b.**

d. Use this equation to predict the number of gallons of oil that would create a slick of 71,000 km^2.

3. Assuming constant pressure, the time required to fill an oil tank is inversely proportional to the square of the diameter of the hose used to fill it. The table below shows the diameters of four hoses and the corresponding times to fill the tank.

Diameter (cm)	Square of Diameter	Time (min)
2		36
3		16
4		9
6		4

a. Complete the column for the squares of the diameters.

b. Create a scatterplot of the time versus the square of the diameter.

c. Find an equation that represents this inverse proportion.

d. Predict how long it would take to fill the tank using a hose with a diameter of 10 cm.

e. Predict the diameter of a pipe that could fill the tank in 30 min.

Module Summary

- ✷ A **simple closed curve** in a plane is a curve with no endpoints that does not intersect itself.
- ✷ A **cylinder** is a three-dimensional solid with bases that are congruent simple closed curves (non-polygons) in parallel planes.
- ✷ The volume (V) of a cylinder can be found by multiplying the area of its base (B) by its height (h): $V = B \bullet h$.
- ✷ One quantity is **directly proportional** to another when the ratio of the two quantities is constant (the same). The constant is the **constant of proportionality** and the ratio is a **direct proportion.**
- ✷ A direct proportion can be described by an equation of the form $y = mx$, where m is the constant of proportionality. The graph of a direct proportion always contains the origin because $y = 0$ whenever $x = 0$.
- ✷ One quantity is **inversely proportional** to another when the product of the two quantities is constant.
- ✷ An inverse proportion can be described by an equation of the form $xy = k$, where k is the **constant of proportionality.** The equation of an inverse proportion can also be written in the form $y = k/x$.

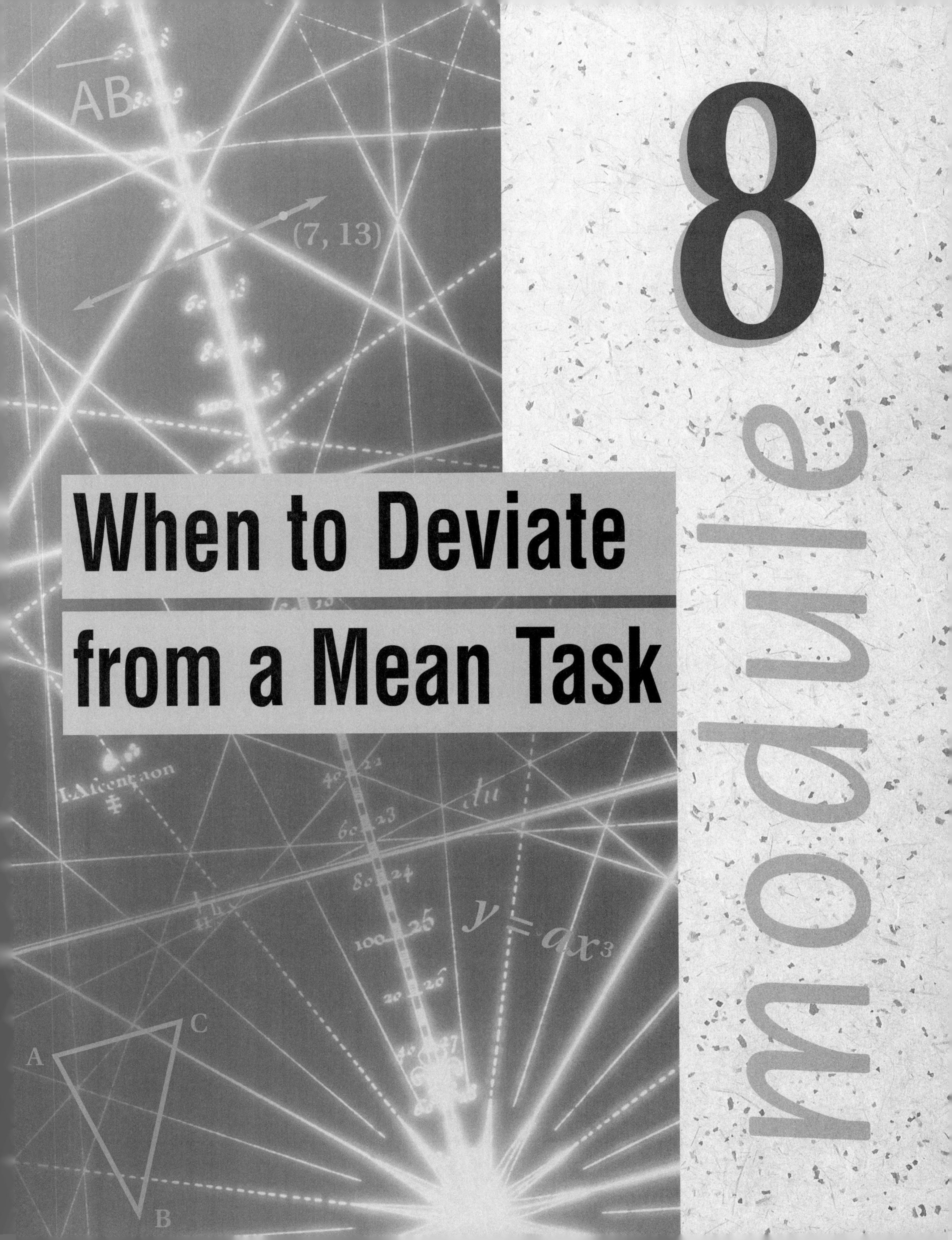
8
module
When to Deviate from a Mean Task

Introduction

At Two Eagle High School, the senior class is responsible for writing and editing the annual yearbook. This year's seniors want to include stories about events such as the recycling drive and the Academic Bowl. Using statistics reported for each story, the seniors claim their class is the best in the school. The other classes, however, are unhappy with this assessment. They want to do their own analysis of the data. In this module, you develop some statistical methods for responding to the seniors' claim.

ACTIVITY 1

Statistics are used by all sorts of people and in all forms of communication. We use statistics to explain points of view, promote special interests, and compare specific quantities. We can represent a statistical summary of data in many different ways. Two of the most commonly used methods for displaying statistics are **histograms** (a type of bar graph) and **pie charts.**

mathematics note

Histograms display information using rectangles or bars. The bars must be of uniform width and the scales must have uniform intervals.

For example, Figure **8-1** shows a histogram of the number of movies attended by Two Eagle students in September. The horizontal axis shows the number of movies attended, while the vertical axis shows the number of students in each category.

September Movie Attendance

number of students: 0, 5, 10, 15, 20, 25
number of movies attended: 1, 2, 3, 4, 5, 6

FIGURE 8-1

Histogram of September movie attendance.

Exploration

The seniors on the Two Eagle yearbook staff want to include the first semester honor roll in their annual publication. They chose the graph shown in Figure **8-2** to display their statistics.

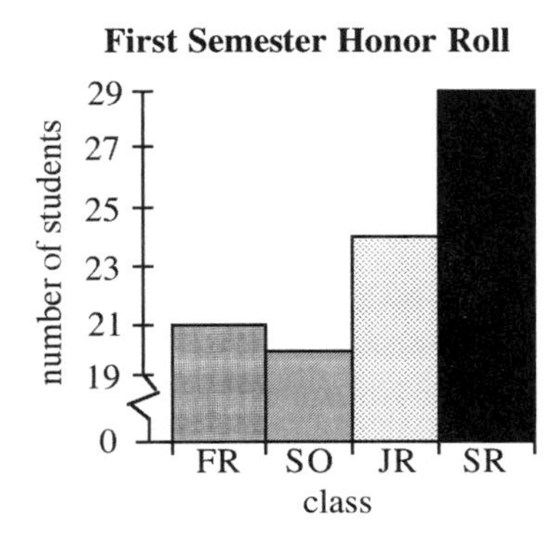

FIGURE 8-2 A histogram of the first semester honor roll.

Notice the break in the vertical axis. In this case, the break indicates that the numbers from 0 to 19 are not shown on the graph.

In some cases, the type of information shown in Figure **8-2** can be interpreted more easily when displayed in a different form. One option is a **frequency table.**

mathematics note

A **frequency table** consists of two columns. One column contains a data item; the other displays the number of observed occurrences of that item. The number of occurrences of any particular data item is its **frequency.**

For example, the histogram in Figure **8-1** was generated from the frequency table shown in Figure **8-3.** This table summarizes the results of a survey of 80 students.

Number of Movies	Frequency
1	10
2	15
3	9
4	7
5	22
6	17
Total	80

FIGURE 8-3
Frequency table for September movie attendance.

a. Use the data presented in Figure **8-2** to create the corresponding frequency table.

b. Use your frequency table from Part **a** to create a histogram with a vertical axis that begins at 0 and ends at 30, without a break. Compare this new graph with the original in Figure **8-2. Note:** Save your frequency table and histogram for use later in this module.

c. Two Eagle High has a total of 104 freshmen, 81 sophomores, 110 juniors, and 128 seniors. Create another histogram to show the percentage of honor-roll students in each class. Compare this histogram with the one shown in Figure **8-2.**

Discussion

a. How accurately does the graph in Figure **8-2** portray the number of students from each class on the honor roll?

b. Compare your graphs from Parts **b** and **c** of the exploration. Which graph do you prefer? Explain your response.

c. How could the statistics encountered in the exploration be used to favor a particular class?

mathematics note

Pie charts (or circle graphs) consist of circular regions divided into sectors, each representing a percentage of the whole. For example, the pie chart in Figure **8-4** illustrates the same data as the histogram in Figure **8-1.**

FIGURE 8-4 **Pie chart of September movie attendance.**

As with the corresponding histogram, you can generate the pie chart in Figure **8-4** using a frequency table. Determine the percentages by dividing each frequency by the total. Then, to determine the measure of the central angle that should represent each frequency, multiply these percentages by 360°.

For example, 10 students attended 1 movie in September. This represents 10/80 or 12.5% of the total. The measure of the central angle for the corresponding sector of the circle is $0.125 \bullet 360° = 45°$.

d. The sum of the percentages in the pie chart in Figure **8-4** is 100%. How could you round each percentage to the nearest whole number, while maintaining a sum of 100%?

Warm-Up

1. The students in Mrs. Davis' math class rolled a die a total of 94 times with the following results: 13 ones, 16 twos, 18 threes, 12 fours, 20 fives, and 15 sixes.
   - **a.** Create a frequency table to organize the data.
   - **b.** Draw a histogram for the given information.
   - **c.** Find the degrees of the central angle of each sector if this information were graphed in a pie chart.

Assignment

1.1 **a.** Use the frequency table from Part **a** of the exploration to construct a pie chart.

b. Compare the pie chart to the histogram in Figure **8-2.** What advantages or disadvantages do you observe with the pie chart?

c. If the number of students in the sophomore class doubled, while the number of sophomores on the honor roll remained the same, would you need to adjust your pie chart? Explain your response.

d. Upon seeing your pie chart, one student commented, "The seniors had the largest percentage of their class on the honor roll." Explain why this is a misinterpretation of the pie chart.

1.2 To display additional information on the same graph, a histogram can be "stacked." Both histograms below were created using information from the same survey.

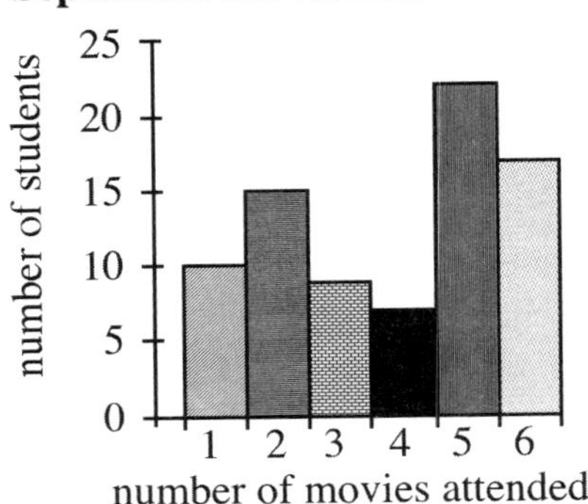

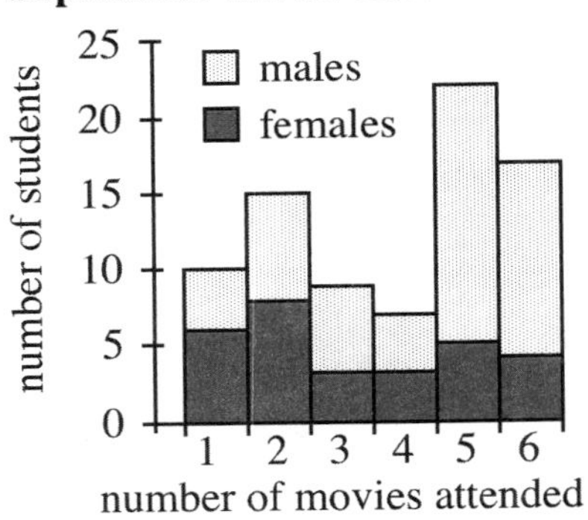

a. Use the stacked histogram on the right to make an interpretation of the data that was not possible with the histogram on the left.

b. Explain why it might be difficult to use the stacked histogram to compare the numbers of male students in each attendance category.

1.3 Your frequency table from Part **a** of the exploration describes the number of students from each class on the first semester honor roll. Two Eagle High has a total of 104 freshmen, 81 sophomores, 110 juniors, and 128 seniors.

a. Create a stacked histogram that displays both these sets of information.

b. Using your stacked histogram, can you identify the class with the largest number of students on the first semester honor roll? Explain your response.

c. Using your stacked histogram, can you identify the class with the greatest percentage of students on the first semester honor roll? Explain your response.

1.4 The following graph summarizes the results of Two Eagle High's recycling drive. The yearbook staff plans to use this graph to show that the seniors collected more aluminum than any other class.

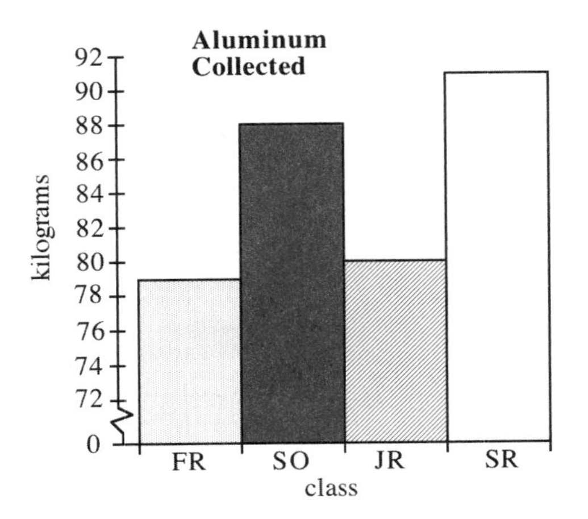

a. How could you change the histogram to represent the freshman class more positively?

b. Two Eagle High has a total of 104 freshmen, 81 sophomores, 110 juniors, and 128 seniors. Using this information, create a graph which shows that a class other than the seniors was most effective in collecting aluminum for the recycling drive.

1.5 The numbers of males and females inducted in the Two Eagle High School Honor Society are displayed in the table below.

Class	Gender	No. of Applicants	No. Inducted
Junior	male	20	12
	female	10	5
Senior	male	20	6
	female	40	16

a. Using the data in this table, create a graph to support each of the following statements.

1. The females at Two Eagle High are better students than the males.
2. The males at Two Eagle High are better students than the females.
3. The honor society's selection process favored seniors.
4. The honor society's selection process favored juniors.

b. Do you think it is possible to use accurate statistics to support an inaccurate or deceptive position? Explain your response.

* * * * *

1.6 The following table shows the land area and 2003 population for Alaska, Texas, California, and Montana.

State	Land Area (km^2)	2003 Population
Alaska	1,477,267	648,818
California	403,970	35,484,453
Montana	376,991	917,621
Texas	678,358	22,118,509

a. 1. Create a pie chart of the information on land area.

2. Use your chart to compare the areas of each of the following pairs of states: Alaska and Texas; Alaska and California; Alaska and Montana.

b. 1. Create a pie chart of the information on population.

2. Use this chart to compare the populations of each of the following pairs of states: California and Texas; California and Alaska; California and Montana.

1.7 The following table shows the land area and 2003 population of the five most densely populated states.

State	Land Area (km^2)	2003 Population
Connecticut	12,550	3,483,372
Maryland	25,316	5,508,909
Massachusetts	20,300	6,433,422
New Jersey	19,215	8,638,396
Rhode Island	2,706	1,076,164

a. Jody claims that Rhode Island has the most people per square kilometer because it has the smallest area. Is her claim correct? Explain your response.

b. Use a histogram to compare the population densities of the five states.

1.8 Use each of the following types of graphs to emphasize a characteristic of your state.

a. a pie chart

b. a histogram.

Research Project

Design and write a survey on a topic of interest to your school. The survey should consist of no more than 10 carefully worded questions.

Give the survey to 30 people in your school.

After completing Activities **1–4** of this module, analyze the collected data using appropriate graphs and statistical measurements.

Prepare an oral presentation that describes the conclusions you drew from the results of the survey.

When researchers report statistical information, they often represent the elements of an entire data set with a single number. For example, instead of listing the size of each class in your school, you might give the school's mean class size. In this case, the mean (or average) class size is a single statistic "representing" all class sizes. Statistics such as the mean, median, and mode are **measures of central tendency.**

Exploration

The Two Eagle High Physical Education Department administers a fitness test before allowing students to participate in sports. This test includes a check of the student's resting and active pulse rates. In this exploration, you collect and analyze data on pulse rates for three levels of activity.

a. After sitting quietly for a period of five minutes, measure and record your pulse rate (beats per minute).

b. Exercise for one minute. Immediately after exercising, measure and record your pulse rate again.

c. Rest from your exercise for two minutes. Measure and record your pulse rate one more time.

d. Organize the class data in a table. **Note:** Save this table for use in the assignment.

e. For each level of activity, determine a representative pulse rate for the class using a measure of central tendency.

Discussion

a. What were the representative pulse rates for your class? How did you choose these numbers?

b. How did changing the level of activity affect the representative pulse rate?

c. In discussing an individual's pulse rate, what additional information might be important?

d. Do you think that your class statistics are representative of the entire student body?

Warm-Up

1. Find the mean of each of the following sets of numbers.

   a. 7, 3, 5, 5, 4, 6

   b. 23, 53, 45, 17

   c. 9.3, 2.6, 4.4, 8.1, 5.9

2. Find the median of each set of numbers below.

   a. 4, 7, 9, 2, 2, 3, 5, 1

   b. 13.1, 15.2, 14.6, 13.35, 15.5, 14.16, 14.32, 15.07, 13.05

   c. 35, 72, 69, 44, 29, 14, 16, 83, 67, 88

3. Find the mode of each of the following sets.

   a. 1, 5, 3, 2, 3, 4, 5, 6, 5

   b. 68, 84, 75, 84, 95, 76, 75, 82, 97

   c. 4.3, 5.7, 6.2, 4.7, 5.5, 6.7, 5.2, 6.5

Assignment

2.1 The following table shows the number of siblings reported by nine students at Two Eagle High School.

Student	Number of Siblings
A	1
B	0
C	2
D	2
E	0
F	3
G	2
H	6
I	1

a. Which measure of central tendency best represents the number of siblings per student? Justify your choice.

b. Create a frequency table of this data. For example, because students B and E each have 0 siblings, the frequency for 0 siblings is 2.

c. Use your frequency table to create the corresponding histogram. Represent the number of siblings on the horizontal axis and the frequency on the vertical axis.

2.2 Often we use measures of central tendency to describe an entire set of data. But in situations involving small data sets, measures of central tendency can be misleading.

a. Identify four people in your community with different occupations. Make a table that displays each person's occupation and estimated annual income. Determine the mean, median, and mode of the income data.

b. Add the occupation and estimated annual income of a professional athlete to your table. Determine the mean, median, and mode of the income data for this new group.

c. Does the mean income you calculated in Part **a** accurately represent the incomes of the original group? Explain your response.

d. Does the mean income you calculated in Part **b** accurately represent the incomes of the new group? Explain your response.

e. Which of the three measures of central tendency—mean, median, or mode—is most affected by data values very different from the majority of values? Which of the three measures of central tendency is affected the least?

2.3 Describe a set of data in which the mode does not exist.

2.4 Describe some possible pitfalls associated with using a measure of central tendency to describe a set of data.

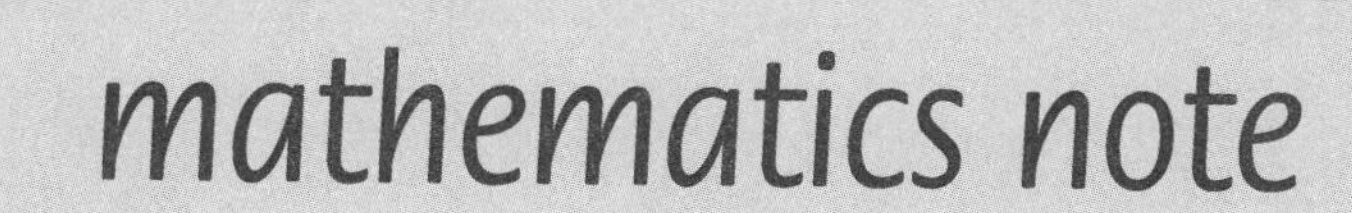

A **stem-and-leaf** plot displays the values in a data set. To simplify interpretation, data is usually ordered and a legend is included.

For example, the stem-and-leaf plot in Figure **8-5** displays the number of hours worked by the Two Eagle yearbook staff during the month of September.

Stem	Leaves	
0	1257	
1	4688	
2	03357	
3	788999	
4	1145	
5		
6	7	1|4 represents 14 hr

FIGURE 8-5 Hours worked by Two Eagle yearbook staff.

In the row that reads 2 | 03357, the stem is 2. The numbers 0, 3, 3, 5, and 7 are leaves. This row represents the data points 20, 23, 23, 25, and 27 hr. The stem 5 has no leaves. This indicates that none of the staff worked from 50 hr to 59 hr.

A **back-to-back stem-and-leaf plot** can be used to compare two sets of data. The stems are placed in the center column of the plot. One set of leaves is placed to the left of the stems, the other set to the right.

For example, the back-to-back stem-and-leaf plot in Figure **8-6** displays the same information on work hours as Figure **8-5.** It also shows how those hours were distributed between the boys and the girls.

Girls		Boys
52	0	17
84	1	68
53	2	037
997	3	889
5	4	114
	5	
7	6	

4|1|6 represents 16 hr for boys and 14 hr for girls

FIGURE 8-6 **Hours worked by girls and boys on the yearbook staff.**

2.5 The **range** of a data set is the difference between the greatest data value and the least data value. The range provides one indication of how widely the data varies.

a. Determine the range of the data in Figure **8-5.**

b. Can the range of a set of data be negative? Explain your response.

2.6 The heights in centimeters of 10 students at Two Eagle High are listed below. The heights of females are underlined.

153, 157, 163, 165, 166, 169, 170, 173, 176, 185

a. Determine the mean, median, and mode of the data.

b. Construct a stem-and-leaf plot of the data, using the first two digits of the heights as the stems and the last digits as the leaves.

c. Find the range of heights.

d. Create a histogram of the data using the following intervals for heights in centimeters: [150, 159], [160, 169], [170, 179], and [180, 189].

e. Separate the data into two categories: heights of female students and heights of male students. Use the data to make a back-to-back stem-and-leaf plot.

f. Use the back-to-back stem-and-leaf plot to create a stacked histogram.

2.7 Advertisers often omit important information in their sales pitches. One advertisement in the Two Eagle yearbook claims that "after more than a million miles of testing, our automobiles had a repair-free record."

a. Does the "repair-free" statistic alone convince you that the cars are reliable? Describe one way in which a "million miles of testing" could fail to prove reliability.

b. To convince you that the cars are reliable, which measure of central tendency should the advertisement mention?

2.8 **a.** Based on the pulse-rate data you collected in the exploration, create an advertisement about the physical fitness of America's youth. Make any claim you can support.

b. What are some of the weaknesses of your claim?

* * * * *

2.9 **a.** Use measures of central tendency to compare the New England states with the Mountain states.

	State	Land Area (km^2)	1990 Population
New England States	Connecticut	12,550	3,287,116
	Maine	79,939	1,227,928
	Massachusetts	20,300	6,016,425
	New Hampshire	23,231	1,109,252
	Rhode Island	2,706	1,003,464
	Vermont	23,956	562,758
Mountain States	Arizona	296,400	3,665,228
	Colorado	268,660	3,294,394
	Idaho	214,235	1,006,749
	Montana	376,991	799,065
	Nevada	284,397	1,201,833
	New Mexico	314,334	1,515,069
	Utah	212,816	1,722,850
	Wyoming	251,501	453,588

b. Would you rather live in the New England states or the Mountain states? Use the statistics from Part **a** to support your choice.

2.10 **a.** Create a back-to-back stem-and-leaf plot to represent the land areas of the states in the following two regions. (You might want to round these values before creating your stem-and-leaf plot.)

	State	Land Area (km^2)
Region 1	Alabama	131,443
	Florida	139,852
	Georgia	150,010
	Mississippi	121,506
	North Carolina	126,180
	South Carolina	77,988
	Tennessee	106,759
Region 2	Illinois	143,987
	Indiana	92,904
	Iowa	144,716
	Michigan	147,136
	Ohio	106,067
	Wisconsin	140,673

b. Compare the land areas for the two regions.

To help identify potential athletes, the Athletic Department would like a profile of all Two Eagle High students. Larger hands give basketball or volleyball players an advantage, so the coaches of those two teams are especially interested in student hand spans. A hand span is the distance from the end of the thumb to the end of the little finger when the two are stretched as far apart as possible.

Exploration

The hand spans, in centimeters, of 22 sophomores at Two Eagle High School are listed below (hand spans of females are underlined): 15.4, 23.4, 19.9, 14.8, 17.6, 19.3, 20.7, 22.3, 20.0, 16.4, 18.1, 19.6, 21.9, 24.1, 17.5, 23.9, 25.2, 18.5, 24.1, 17.6, 15.8, 23.4.

a. 1. Order the hand-span data from least to greatest.

   2. Determine the median of the entire set of data.

   3. Determine the median of the "upper half" of the data. This number is the **upper quartile.**

   4. Determine the median of the "lower half" of the data. This number is the **lower quartile.**

   5. Calculate the difference between the upper and lower quartiles. This difference is the **interquartile range.**

   6. Data values that are more than 1.5 times the interquartile range above the upper quartile or 1.5 times the interquartile range below the lower quartile are **outliers.** Identify the outliers, if any, in the hand-span data.

mathematics note

A **box-and-whisker plot** (or box plot) is a way to represent a set of data graphically. A box plot displays the median, lower quartile, and upper quartile of a data set, along with any outliers. It may be constructed either horizontally or vertically.

A box-and-whisker plot can be created using the following steps.

- Order the data from least to greatest.
- Draw a scale that covers the range of data.
- Draw a rectangular box that stretches from the lower quartile to the upper quartile. (The width of the box is not significant.)
- Place a bar inside the box to mark the median.
- Find the interquartile range.
- Determine if there are any outliers.
- Mark any outliers with asterisks.
- Draw the **whiskers** (segments that connect each end of the box to the farthest data values which are *not* outliers).

For example, the following data set describes the number of minutes spent doing mathematics homework by 30 Two Eagle sophomores: 0, 4, 5, 9, 9, 9, 10, 16, 16, 18, 18, 18, 18, 19, 21, 21, 21, 21, 22, 22, 22, 23, 24, 26, 26, 27, 29, 29, 39, 45.

For this data set, the lower quartile (LQ) is 16, the median (M) is 21, the upper quartile (UQ) is 24, and the interquartile range is $24 - 16 = 8$. The outliers are values less than $16 - (1.5)8 = 4$, or greater than $24 + (1.5)8 = 36$. A box plot for this data is shown in Figure **8-7**.

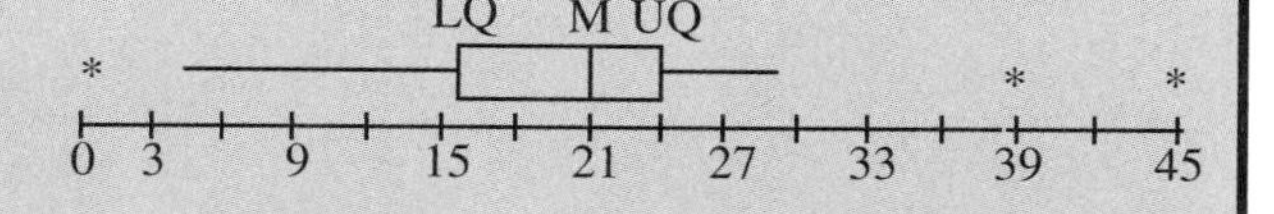

Figure 8-7 Box-and-whisker plot.

b. Create three different box-and-whisker plots of the hand-span data. One should display the data for all 22 students, one should display just the boys' hand spans, and one should display just the girls' hand spans. Compare the three plots. **Note:** Save these plots for use in the assignment.

c. Measure and record the span of your dominant hand in centimeters.

d. Add your hand-span measurement to the hand spans of all 22 students. Create a box-and-whisker plot for this new data set. Compare this plot to the plot for all 22 students from Part **b.**

e. Add your hand-span measurement to either the boys' or the girls' data. Create a box-and-whisker plot for this new set of data. Compare this plot to the corresponding plot from Part **b.**

Discussion

a. What would have more impact on a box-and-whisker plot—adding a data value within the interquartile range, or adding an outlier? Explain your response.

b. What advantages are there to using the median instead of the mean when describing a data set?

c. Is the mean of a data set readily identifiable in a box-and-whisker plot? Explain your response.

d. What are some of the advantages and disadvantages of using a box-and-whisker plot to illustrate data?

e. A box-and-whisker plot naturally leads to a so-called "five-point analysis" of a data set. What do you think these five points are?

Warm-Up

1. Find the range of each set below.

   a. 37.6, 55.3, 42.8, 61.1, 28.6, 84.9, 69.2

   b. 15, 42, 27, 13, 41, 35, 38, 55, 14

   c. 1.1, 1.5, 1.42, 1.06, 1.54, 1.32, 1.83, 1.8, 1.7, 1.73, 1.54

2. Find the median, lower quartile, upper quartile, and the interquartile range of each of the following sets of numbers.

   a. 23, 56, 76, 41, 54, 22, 72, 55, 46, 76

   b. 3.5, 2.2, 4.9, 3.6, 2.8, 4.5, 3.7, 3.9, 4.6

3. a. A data set has a lower quartile value of 11 and an upper quartile value of 18. An outlier must be less than what value or greater than what value?

   b. A data set has a lower quartile value of 27.5 and an upper quartile value of 44.3. An outlier must be less than what value or greater than what value?

Assignment

3.1 Use the box-and-whisker plots from Part **b** of the exploration to help answer the following questions about box-and-whisker plots in general. Explain your response for each one.

   a. Are the lengths of the whiskers related to the interquartile range?

   b. How would adding an outlier to the data affect the plot?

   c. How would adding a data point within the interquartile range affect the plot?

3.2 Using as many statistical measures as you can, describe how your hand span compares to each of the following:

   a. the hand spans of all 22 Two Eagle sophomores

   b. the hand spans of the sophomore girls

   c. the hand spans of the sophomore boys.

3.3 The world's tallest man, Robert Wadlow, had a hand span of about 37 cm. If this value were added to the data set in the exploration, would it be considered an outlier?

3.4 The following graph shows box plots for the number of sit-ups performed by three different classes at Two Eagle High.

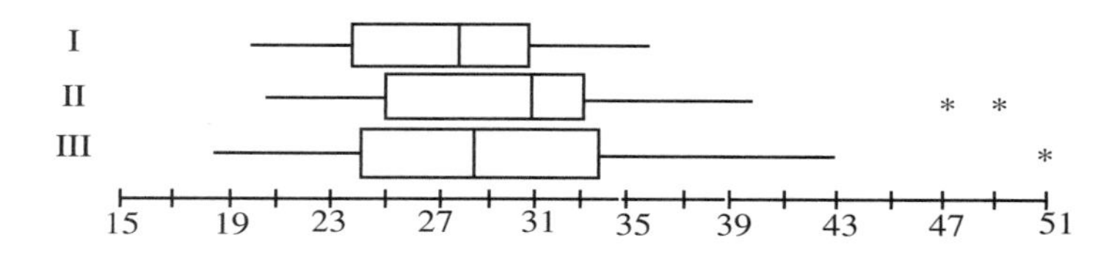

   a. Which class had the person who did the most sit-ups?

   b. For which class did the number of sit-ups vary the least?

   c. Which class had the greatest upper quartile?

   d. In which class did the bottom 25% perform the most sit-ups?

   e. Which class has the greatest number of students?

3.5 Create a set of data with at least 16 items in which the mean and the median have the same value and there is at least one outlier. Explain the process you used to create the data set. Make a box plot of your data.

* * * * *

3.6 A survey conducted at two different universities, A and B, produced the following box plots.

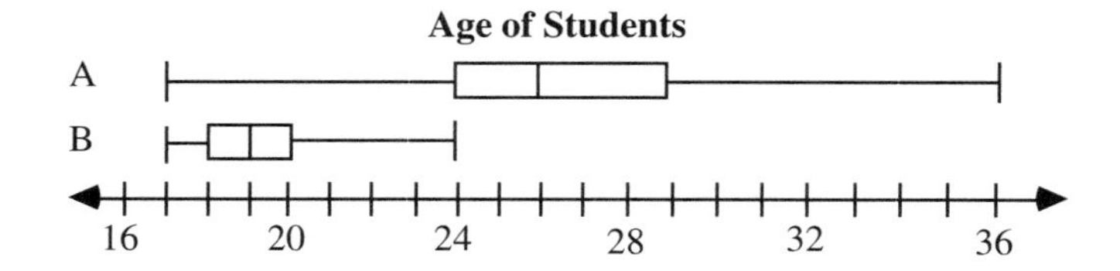

a. Use the information in the plots to compare the students at university A to the students at university B.

b. Describe some information which might have been determined from the data but is not shown in the box plots.

3.7 **a.** Create a box plot for each of the following sets of data.

1. {5,5,5,5,5,30,30,30,30,30,70,70,70,70,70,95,95,95,95,95}

2. {5,6,7,28,37,41,50,61,68,76,89,92,95}

b. Compare the two plots.

c. Explain why a five-point analysis using box plots sometimes can be misleading.

d. Identify a type of graph that would better show the differences in the two data sets. Create the corresponding graphs.

Measures of central tendency are not always useful when comparing data sets. If the mean, median, and a mode of a data set are the same, or relatively close, other statistical measures are needed to provide a better picture of the data.

Exploration 1

Every year, Two Eagle High sponsors a competition between classes called the Academic Bowl. The rules for the contest are listed below.

- Each class may enter only one team.
- Each team must consist of four students from one class.
- Each match is scored on a 100-point scale.
- Team scores are determined by averaging the scores of the four team members.
- Team members may work independently or cooperatively.
- Team members may change after any match.

The teams meet five times during the year, with the overall winner advancing to a state competition. Based on the information in Table **8-1,** the seniors believe that they should be declared the winners.

TABLE 8-1 ■ *Results of the Academic Bowl*

	Freshmen	Sophomores	Juniors	Seniors
Match 1	100	74	82	99
Match 2	60	90	72	66
Match 3	77	85	88	85
Match 4	94	82	89	100
Match 5	85	85	85	66

You have been selected as a judge for this year's contest. How will you choose a winner?

a. Enter the data from Table **8-1** in a spreadsheet. Record the scores for each team in its own column. **Note:** Save this spreadsheet for use in Exploration **2.**

b. Create a histogram for each team's scores. To simplify comparisons, all four histograms should be the same size and should have the same scales.

c. Use your histograms along with the measures of central tendency (mean, median, and mode) to determine the winner of the Academic Bowl.

d. Describe the process you used to choose a winner.

Discussion 1

a. Which class did you select as the winner? What criteria did you use?

b. Using the histograms you created in Part **b** of Exploration **1,** compare the range in scores for each class.

c. Would the difference in the range of scores for each class provide a reasonable criterion for selecting a winner? Explain your response.

d. Which of the rules for the competition might affect the range of scores? Explain your response.

Exploration 2

In Exploration **1,** you found that measures of central tendency alone might not provide enough information to select a winner for the Academic Bowl. Along with the mean, median, or mode, the variation among scores might be used to help determine a winner.

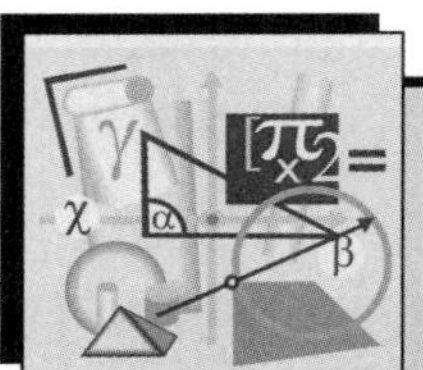

mathematics note

There are several methods for measuring variation in a set of data. One of these measures, **mean absolute deviation,** describes the average distance from the mean for the numbers in a data set.

The numbers in a data set with n items may be represented by symbols, such as $x_1, x_2, x_3, \ldots, x_n$. These symbols are **subscripted variables,** and the natural numbers $(1, 2, 3, \ldots, n)$ are the **subscripts.** The symbol x_1 (read "x sub one") represents the first number in the data set, the symbol x_2 (read "x sub two") represents the second number in the data set, and so on. In a data set with n items, the symbol x_n (read "x sub n"), represents the last number in the set.

For a set of data with n items represented by $x_1, x_2, \ldots, x_n$, the mean absolute deviation is given by:

$$\frac{|x_1 - \mu| + |x_2 - \mu| + \cdots + |x_n - \mu|}{\;}$$

where the notation $|\;|$ represents absolute value and μ, the lowercase Greek letter *mu,* is the mean of the data.

For example, consider the five match scores for the seniors in the Academic Bowl. The mean (μ) of these scores is 83.2. The distance from the mean for each score—in other words, the absolute value of the difference between the score and the mean—is shown in Figure **8-8.** The mean absolute deviation of the scores is the mean of these distances: $68.8/5 \approx 13.8$.

Score	Distance from Mean
99	15.8
66	17.2
85	1.8
100	16.8
66	17.2
Total	68.6

FIGURE 8-8
Distance from mean of the seniors' scores.

a. Use the data in Table **8-1** to determine the mean absolute deviation for each team's scores.

b. Create a set of scores using any five values from 50 to 100. Experiment with these values to obtain a set of scores with a mean absolute deviation of 0. Record your data set.

c. Create another set of scores with any five values from 50 to 100. Experiment with these to obtain a set of scores with a mean absolute deviation as great as possible. Record your data set.

Discussion 2

a. Why is absolute value used in the calculation of mean absolute deviation?

b. Mean absolute deviation is defined as the average distance from the mean for the numbers in a data set. How does the formula given in the mathematics note illustrate this definition?

c. Figure **8-9** below shows a histogram of the number of parking tickets issued by a traffic officer in five days. The horizontal line indicates the mean number of tickets per day. How is the distance from the top of each bar to the line related to mean absolute deviation?

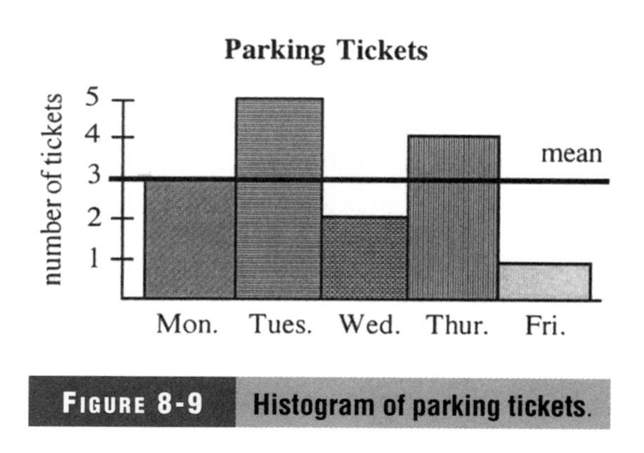

FIGURE 8-9 **Histogram of parking tickets.**

d. How do the histograms from Exploration **1** reflect the fact that the mean absolute deviations for the teams are different?

e. How would considering the mean absolute deviation of each team's scores affect your choice for the winner of the Academic Bowl?

f. How might mean absolute deviation and measures of central tendency be used to predict a team's score in a sixth match?

g. Which team is least likely to score 95 in a sixth match? Explain your response.

Warm-Up

1. Evaluate each of the following expressions.

   a. $|5|$ **b.** $|-6|$

   c. $|3 - 7|$ **d.** $5|-2|$

   e. $|-4 \bullet -7|$ **f.** $|-35| \bullet |20|$

2. Evaluate each of the following using the given condition, if any.

   a. $|a|$, if $a > 0$ **b.** $|y|$, if $y < 0$

   c. $|x + y|$, if $x + y > 0$ **d.** $|a - b|$, if $a - b < 0$

   e. $-4|-2y|$, if $-2y < 0$ **f.** $|x^2 + y^2|$

3. Calculate the mean absolute deviation for each set of numbers.

   a. 87, 94, 72, 65, 97, 77

   b. 34.6, 54.6, 42.8, 51.5, 60.9, 22.7, 43.9

Assignment

4.1 The following graphs display the scores for each member of the junior and sophomore teams in the fifth match of the Academic Bowl.

The members of the junior team scored 85, 85, 75, and 95, while all the members of the sophomore team scored 85.

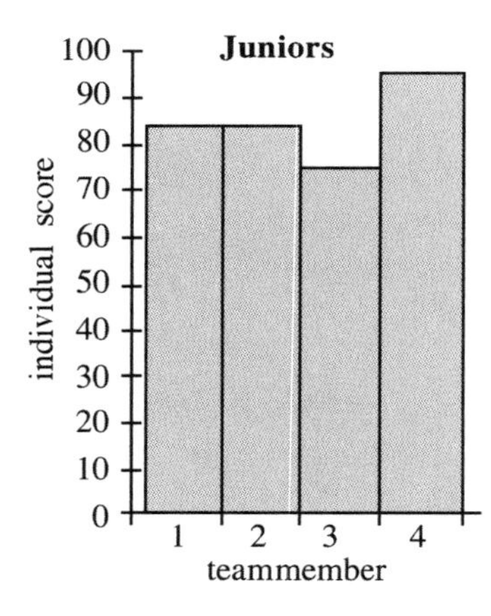

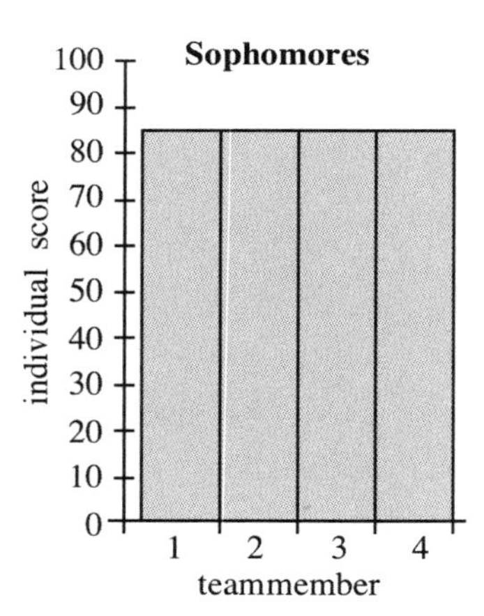

a. Can you differentiate between these two data sets using measures of central tendency alone? Explain your response.

b. Use the juniors' scores to describe how two unequal scores can have equivalent measures of deviation from the mean.

c. If team member 4 on the junior team scored 90 instead of 95, and team member 3 scored 80 instead of 75, how would this affect the mean absolute deviation? Explain why this occurs.

d. How would the mean absolute deviation be affected if a fifth member of the junior team scored 85? Explain your response.

4.2 The individual scores for the seniors in the fifth match of the Academic Bowl were 65, 99, 45, and 55. For the freshmen, the individual scores were 77, 93, 77, and 93.

a. Use this information, along with that given in Problem **4.1,** to determine the mean absolute deviation for the scores of each team in the fifth match.

b. Why can the mean absolute deviation for the sophomores' scores be determined without any calculations?

c. According to the rules for the Academic Bowl, team members may work independently or cooperatively. Describe the method that you think each team might have used. Explain your reasoning.

4.3 The two histograms below display the results of an academic bowl at a neighboring school. Each graph shows both the team scores and their distances from the mean for five matches.

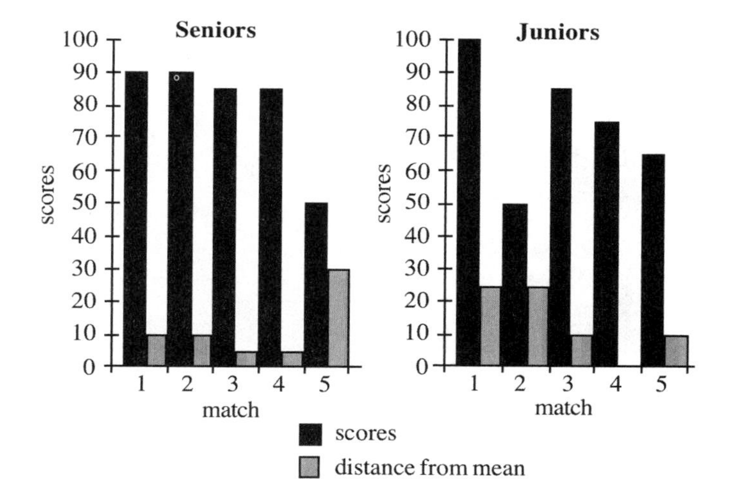

a. Identify the scores that deviate more than "an average amount" from the mean.

b. What statistical measure did you use to determine "an average amount" in Part **a**?

c. What is the significance of the missing bar in the fourth match for the juniors?

4.4 As described in the mathematics note, the mean of the Two Eagle seniors' five match scores is 83.2, with a mean absolute deviation of 13.8. The scores within 1 mean absolute deviation of the mean are contained in the interval [69.4, 97].

a. Describe how the interval [69.4, 97] was determined.

b. When is a data point 0 mean absolute deviations from the mean?

c. Determine the interval that contains scores within 2 mean absolute deviations of the mean. (*Hint:* Make sure that the extreme values in this interval make sense.)

4.5 The scores for the senior team in Problem **4.3** were 90, 89, 87, 86, and 51. The scores for the junior team were 100, 50, 85, 75, and 65.

a. Calculate the mean absolute deviation for each team's scores.

b. How does the mean absolute deviation describe the variation in scores for each team?

c. For each team, identify all scores more than 1 mean absolute deviation from the mean.

4.6 The winning team in the Academic Bowl advances to the state competition. In the past, teams that score at least 80 points typically place among the top three at state. Select a winning team from Two Eagle High and justify your choice.

* * * * *

4.7 The table below shows some statistics for two basketball players at Two Eagle High. Rita is the leading scorer for the girls' team and Bernard is the leading scorer for the boys' team.

Player	Rita	Bernard
Average Points per Game	25	25
Mean Absolute Deviation (in Points per Game)	5	15
Points Scored in Last Game	35	35

a. Which player is the more consistent scorer? Explain your response.

b. For each player, identify the range of values that are within 1 mean absolute deviation of the mean.

c. Which player's performance in the last game is more impressive? Explain your response.

d. Both the boys' and girls' teams score an average of 60 points per game, with the same mean absolute deviation. Compare the range of the average scoring of Rita's teammates to that of Bernard's teammates.

4.8 At the end of the cross country season, the coach presents an award to the most improved runner. This award goes to the athlete whose time in the sixth race of the season is most extraordinary when compared with the mean time of the previous five races. The table below shows the times in each race for the top three candidates. Which runner should receive the award? Justify your choice.

	Runner 1	Runner 2	Runner 3
Race 1	25 min, 30 sec	20 min, 10 sec	22 min, 15 sec
Race 2	23 min, 45 sec	19 min, 50 sec	25 min, 20 sec
Race 3	24 min, 15 sec	21 min, 30 sec	20 min, 15 sec
Race 4	22 min, 5 sec	19 min, 45 sec	24 min, 25 sec
Race 5	21 min, 10 sec	18 min, 40 sec	20 min, 10 sec
Race 6	21 min, 5 sec	19 min, 20 sec	21 min, 45 sec

Mean absolute deviation can help you interpret a set of data when considered along with measures of central tendency. Another measure of the spread in a data set is **standard deviation.** Mean absolute deviation and standard deviation are usually close in value. However, standard deviation is preferred by statisticians because of its mathematical properties.

mathematics note

Standard deviation is a common measure of the spread in a data set. To calculate it, first square the individual distance from the mean (the deviation) for each piece of data. Then find the mean of these squared deviations. The standard deviation is equal to the non-negative square root of the mean of the squared deviations.

Standard deviation is often represented by the symbol σ (the lowercase Greek letter *sigma*). For a population with n members represented by $x_1, x_2, \ldots, x_n$, where μ is the mean, the standard deviation is given by the formula below:

$$\sigma = \sqrt{\frac{(x_1 - \mu)^2 + (x_2 - \mu)^2 + \cdots + (x_n - \mu)^2}{n}}$$

For example, consider the scores for the freshman team in the fifth match of the Academic Bowl. The mean score (μ) is 85.25. The sum of the squared deviations may be calculated by using a spreadsheet, as shown in Figure **8-10.**

Score (x_n)	($x_n - \mu$)	$(x_n - \mu)^2$
85	−0.25	0.06
74	−11.25	126.56
92	6.75	44.56
90	4.75	22.56
	Total	194.74

FIGURE 8-10 **Determining standard deviation.**

The mean of the sum of the squared deviations is $194.74/4 \approx 48.69$. The standard deviation is $\sqrt{48.69} \approx 6.98$.

Discussion

a. How are the formulas for standard deviation and mean absolute deviation similar? How are they different?

b. How is the difference between the mean and each data point kept positive in the formula for standard deviation?

c. What is the purpose of taking the square root of the mean squared deviation?

d. Why is it important to consider only the non-negative square root?

Warm-Up

1. Simplify each of the following radical expressions.

   a. $\sqrt{25}$ b. $\sqrt{3/4}$ c. $\sqrt{-5}$

   d. $\sqrt{\dfrac{3+5+8}{7}}$ e. $\sqrt{\dfrac{(3-7)^2}{8}}$ f. $\sqrt{\dfrac{(8-10)^2+(12-10)^2}{2}}$

2. Is the following equation true: $\sqrt{3^2 + 4^2} = 3 + 4$? Justify your response.

3. Calculate the standard deviation of each of the following sets of numbers.

   a. 3, 5, 8, 2, 4, 7, 1, 8, 6, 6

   b. 45, 47, 41, 42, 48, 43

   c. 19.2, 83.6, 34.5, 74.3, 99.4, 23.3, 52.4, 48.3

Assignment

5.1 In the five matches of Two Eagle's Academic Bowl, the senior team scored 99, 66, 85, 100, and 66. Calculate the mean and the standard deviation for these scores.

5.2 Many calculators have built-in functions to compute the mean and standard deviation for a set of data.

Enter the Academic Bowl scores for the juniors (82, 72, 88, 89, and 85), the sophomores (74, 90, 85, 82, and 85), and the freshmen (100, 60, 77, 94, and 85) into your calculator.

   a. Use a calculator function to find the mean for each team's scores. One symbol commonly used to represent the mean is $\overline{x}$. What notation does your calculator use?

   b. Use a calculator function to find the standard deviation for each team's scores. One common notation for standard deviation is σ. What notation does your calculator use?

5.3 The past 12 drama performances at Two Eagle High attracted the following audiences: 220, 210, 180, 170, 120, 60, 40, 80, 110, 150, 200, and 260. This data is displayed in the line plot below. The mean for the 12 performances is identified by the middle arrow. The other two arrows indicate values 1 standard deviation from the mean.

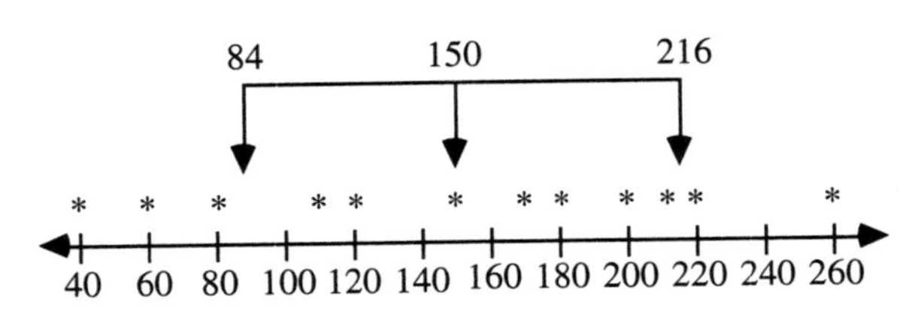

a. How many performances were attended by an audience more than 1 standard deviation from the mean?

b. In this data set, are there any audiences more than 2 standard deviations from the mean? Explain your response.

* * * * *

5.4 The following table shows the mass in kilograms for the players on a high school football team.

54	85	78	67	75
75	76	75	80	85
62	90	88	79	68
55	95	65	85	92
62	83	72	90	88

a. Find the mean mass for the players on the team.

b. Calculate the standard deviation for the mass of the players.

c. What percentage of the players have a mass more than 1 standard deviation from the mean?

d. Are there any players whose masses are more than 2 standard deviations from the mean? If so, identify their masses.

5.5 The interval [230, 450] represents values within 1 standard deviation of the mean for a data set.

a. Determine the mean of the data set.

b. Determine the interval that represents values within 2 standard deviations of the mean.

c. Determine the interval that represents values within 3 standard deviations of the mean.

Summary Assessment

At Two Eagle High, the biology teacher has two classes: third period and fifth period. Both classes take the same tests. On previous tests, the average score in each class has been very close.

On the most recent test, the third-period class received the following scores: 52, 60, 66, 71, 72, 73, 75, 76, 77, 77, 78, 80, 82, 84, 85, 88, 89, and 90.

On the same test, the fifth-period class received these scores: 76, 77, 78, 79, 80, 80, 82, 83, 84, 85, 85, 88, 90, 90, 90, 92, 92, 96, 96, and 99.

1. Create a back-to-back stem-and-leaf plot of this data.

2. Determine the mean test score for each class.

3. Create a box plot of the data for each class and write a summary of your observations.

4. a. Determine the standard deviation for the test scores from each class.

   b. What percentage of the scores in each class are within 1 standard deviation of the mean?

Module Summary

- **Histograms** display information using rectangles or bars. The bars must be of uniform width and the scales must have uniform intervals.
- **Pie charts** (or circle graphs) consist of circular regions divided into sectors that each represent a percentage of the whole.
- A **frequency table** consists of two columns. One column contains a data item; the other displays the number of observed occurrences of that item. The number of occurrences of any particular data item is its **frequency.**
- The **mean, median,** and **mode** are **measures of central tendency.** They are often described as "representative" of the numbers in a data set.
- A **stem-and-leaf plot** displays the values in a data set. To simplify interpretation, data is usually ordered and a legend is included. A **back-to-back stem-and-leaf plot** may be used to compare two sets of data.
- The **range** is a measure of spread found by subtracting the least data value from the greatest data value.
- The **lower quartile** is the median of the lower half of the data points. The **upper quartile** is the median of the upper half of the data points.
- The **interquartile range** is the difference between the upper quartile and the lower quartile.
- **Outliers** are extreme data values more than 1.5 times the interquartile range above the upper quartile or below the lower quartile.
- A **box-and-whisker plot** (or box plot) displays the median, lower quartile, upper quartile, and outliers (if any) of a data set. The **whiskers** are segments that connect each end of the box to the farthest values which are not outliers.
- The numbers in a data set with n items may be represented by symbols, such as $x_1, x_2, x_3, \ldots, x_n$. These symbols are **subscripted variables,** and the natural numbers $(1, 2, 3, \ldots, n)$ are the **subscripts.** The symbol x_1 (read "x sub one") represents the first number in the data set, the symbol x_2 (read "x sub two") represents the second number in the data set, and so on. In a data set with n items, the symbol x_n (read "x sub n"), represents the last number in the set.
- **Mean absolute deviation** is a measure of spread that describes the average distance from the mean for the numbers in a data set. For a set of data with n items represented by $x_1, x_2, \ldots, x_n$, the mean absolute deviation is given by:

$$\frac{|x_1 - \mu| + |x_2 - \mu| + \cdots + |x_n - \mu|}{}$$

where the notation $|\,|$ represents absolute value and μ is the mean of the data.

✷ **Standard deviation** is another measure of spread. For a population with n members represented by $x_1, x_2, \ldots, x_n$, where μ represents the mean, the standard deviation is given by:

$$\sigma = \sqrt{\frac{(x_1 - \mu)^2 + (x_2 - \mu)^2 + \cdots + (x_n - \mu)^2}{n}}$$

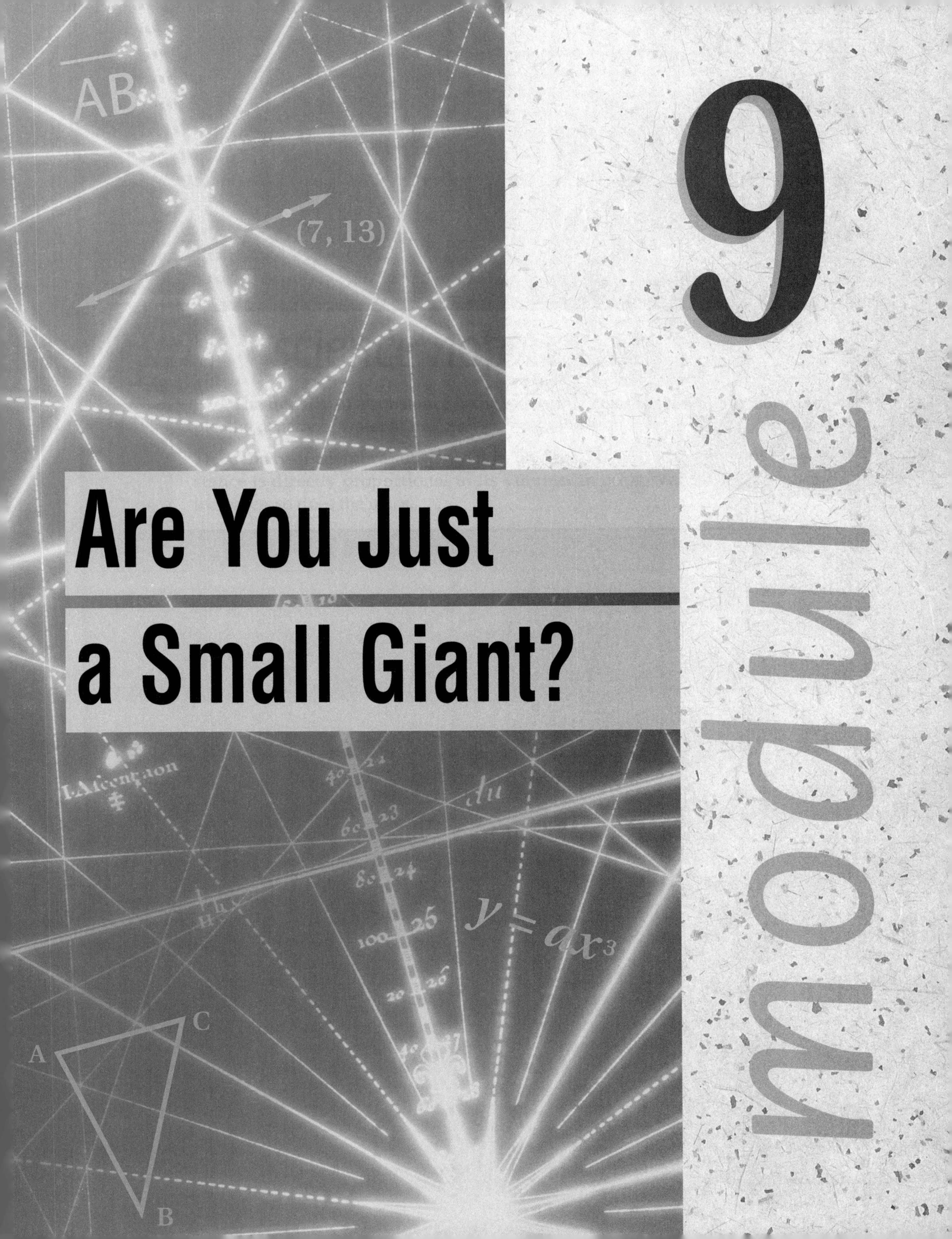

Module 9

Are You Just a Small Giant?

Introduction

Robert Wadlow (1918–1940) was the world's tallest human, according to *The Guinness Book of World Records.* Wadlow's measurements at the time of his death are listed in Table **9-1.**

Table 9-1 ■ *Robert Wadlow's Measurements at Death*

Height	272 cm
Weight	1950 N
Mass	199 kg
Shoe Length	47 cm
Hand Length	32 cm
Arm Span	289 cm
Ring Size	25

How does your size and shape compare with Wadlow's? If Robert Wadlow were alive today, would the two of you look similar? The answer to this question depends on the definition of *similar.*

mathematics note

Two ratios, a/b ($b \neq 0$) and c/d ($d \neq 0$), are **proportional,** or **in proportion,** if:

$$\frac{a}{b} = \frac{c}{d}$$

When two such ratios are proportional, it is also true that a/c and b/d are proportional, where $c \neq 0$ and $d \neq 0$.

In mathematics, two objects are **similar** if they have the same shape and the ratios of corresponding lengths are proportional. The ratio of corresponding sides is the **scale factor.**

For example, Figure **9-1** shows two similar triangles, *ABC* and *DEF*.

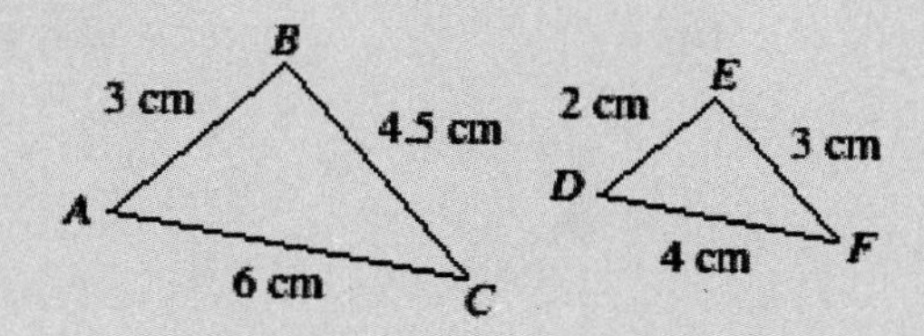

FIGURE 9-1 **Two similar triangles.**

Because *ABC* and *DEF* are similar, the ratios of corresponding sides are proportional and equal to the scale factor. In this case, the scale factor is 1.5.

$$\frac{AB}{DE} = \frac{BC}{EF} = \frac{AC}{DF} = 1.5$$

When two triangles are similar, the measures of the corresponding angles also are equal.

Discussion

a. When a photograph is enlarged, is the new image similar to the original? Explain your response.

b. Explain why a photographic image of a person is not similar to the actual person.

c. 1. How are scale factors used in scale drawings?

   2. Do scale drawings always produce similar figures?

d. Describe the equation that results when the following proportion is solved for y.

$$\frac{y}{x} = \frac{a}{b}$$

e. In the module "Oil: Black Gold," you learned that a direct proportion can be described by a linear equation of the form $y = mx$, where m is the constant of proportionality.

   Does the equation you described in Part **d** represent a direct proportion? If so, identify the constant of proportionality. If not, explain why not.

f. Describe some other examples of similar objects.

ACTIVITY 1

Are Robert Wadlow's dimensions proportional to those of other people? In this activity, you compare Wadlow's measurements at the time of his death with the measurements of other humans.

Exploration

In this exploration, you use proportions to investigate similarity in scale drawings. You also use proportions to determine if two people are similar.

Figure **9-2** shows a scale drawing of Robert Wadlow and his father.

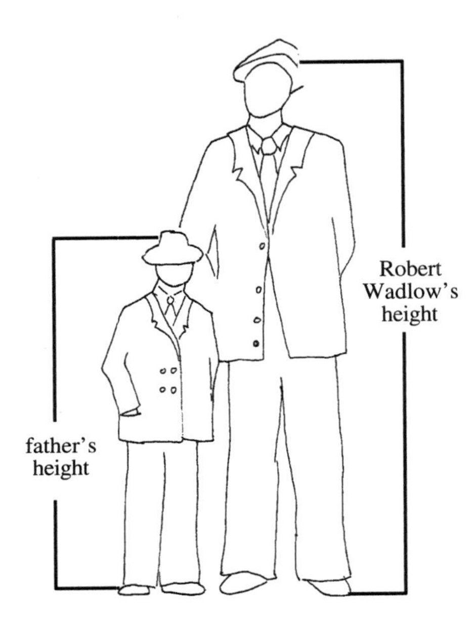

FIGURE 9-2 **Scale drawing of Robert Wadlow and his father.**

a. Obtain a second scale drawing of Robert Wadlow and his father from your teacher.

   1. Measure Robert Wadlow's height, in centimeters, in both drawings.

   2. Determine the ratio of the height from Figure **9-2** to the height from the template.

b. 1. Measure the height, in centimeters, of Wadlow's father in both drawings.

   2. Determine the ratio of the height from Figure **9-2** to the height from the template.

c. 1. Do your results in Parts **a** and **b** indicate that the measurements in the two drawings are proportional?

   2. Are the two drawings similar? Explain your response.

d. Provide additional evidence for (or against) your response to Part **c1** by taking a third measurement on each drawing and determining the ratio of the measurements.

e. 1. Write the ratio of Wadlow's actual height to the height of his image in Figure **9-2.**

   2. Use this ratio and the height of Wadlow's father in Figure **9-2** to write a proportion that can be used to determine the father's actual height.

   3. Determine the father's actual height.

f. Repeat Part **e** using the scale drawing on the template.

g. Compare the height you determined in Part **f** with the height you determined in Part **e3.**

h. 1. Measure your height and shoe length in centimeters.

   2. Use these measurements to determine if you are similar to Robert Wadlow at the time of his death.

i. 1. Use your height and shoe length and the shoe length of a classmate to predict the height of that classmate.

   2. Compare the predicted height with your classmate's actual height.

   3. What do your results indicate about the two of you?

Discussion

a. Can you use your measurements from Part **h** of the exploration to make predictions about the measurements of other people? Explain your response.

b. If two polygons are similar, their corresponding sides are proportional. What is the relationship between their corresponding angles?

c. In the equation below, why can't b and d be equal to 0?

$$\frac{a}{b} = \frac{c}{d}$$

d. Use the terms *proportional, similar,* and *scale factor* to describe how a photocopier preserves similarity while enlarging or reducing.

Warm-Up

1. Solve each of the following proportions for x.

   a. $\frac{3}{8} = \frac{x}{56}$

   b. $\frac{4}{7} = \frac{47}{x}$

   c. $\frac{x}{9} = \frac{13}{79}$

   d. $\frac{1}{x} = \frac{22}{37}$

2. Which of the following equation(s) do not have the same solution as the one below?

$$\frac{14}{x} = \frac{84}{45}$$

   a. $\frac{14}{x} = \frac{45}{84}$

   b. $\frac{84}{14} = \frac{45}{x}$

   c. $\frac{x}{45} = \frac{14}{84}$

Assignment

1.1 Use Robert Wadlow's shoe length and height to estimate each of the following:

   a. the height of a similar person with a shoe length of 40 cm

   b. the shoe length of a similar person with a height of 165 cm.

1.2 a. A family of five all have proportional shoe lengths and heights. The shoe length and height, in centimeters, of one member of the family can be written as the ordered pair (21,126). Use these dimensions to complete the ordered pairs for the rest of the family.

   1. brother: (12,____)

   2. mother: (24, ____)

   3. sister: (____, 108)

   4. father: (____, 216)

   b. In the following table, the ratios of corresponding lengths are expressed in the form "row:column." Use the ordered pairs from Part **a** to complete a copy of the table, expressing ratios in terms of whole numbers.

Family Member	father	mother	brother	sister
father	1:1	3:2		
mother				
brother			1:1	2:3
sister				

1.3 A person similar to you has a thumb length of 6.5 cm. Use your thumb length and height to estimate this person's height.

1.4 A newborn baby is 46 cm long, with a head circumference of 33 cm. Are you similar to this baby? Explain your response.

1.5 During a criminal investigation, a detective photographed the print of a suspect's shoe next to the outline of a penny, as shown below.

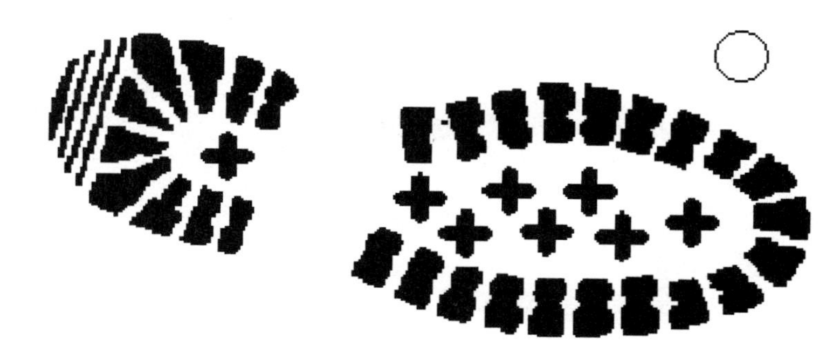

a. Use this photograph to determine the length of the footprint.

b. Predict the suspect's height if the suspect is similar to Robert Wadlow.

c. What other useful predictions might the detective make from this footprint?

1.6 A basketball player's height is 2.5 m. Assuming that the player's shape is similar to yours and that height is proportional to wrist circumference, determine the circumference of the player's wrist.

1.7 **a.** Theo can keyboard 2000 words in 50 min. He has 90 min available to enter a 3500-word essay in the computer. Will he be able to finish in time?

b. Theo requires 3 min per 1000 words to proofread a document. How much time will it take for him to proofread his essay?

c. Will Theo need more than 90 min to finish his essay if he also plans to proofread it? Explain your response.

1.8 The speed of an object caught in a whirlpool is inversely proportional to its distance from the whirlpool's center. If an object's speed is 7.8 cm/sec at a distance of 900 cm from the center, what is its speed at a distance of 10 cm from the center?

In Activity **1**, you used scale factors to predict lengths in similar figures. In this activity, scale factors will be used to predict areas of similar figures.

Exploration

All squares are similar. How is the scale factor for two squares related to their areas? To answer this question, complete Parts **a–e.**

a. Table **9-2** lists the side lengths of nine different squares. Draw each of these squares on a sheet of centimeter graph paper.

TABLE 9-2 ■ *Side Lengths of Squares*

Square	Side Length (cm)
A	1.0
B	2.0
C	3.0
D	4.0
E	5.0
F	6.0
G	1.5
H	2.5
I	1.2

b. How do you think scale factors might be used to predict the areas of these squares?

c. Complete Table **9-3** using the formula for the area of a square.

TABLE 9-3 ■ *Side Lengths and Areas of Squares*

Square	Side Length (cm)	Area (cm^2)
A	1	
B	2	
C	3	
D	4	
E	5	
F	6	
G	1.5	
H	2.5	
I	1.2	
J	z	
K	y	

d. Use the information in Table **9-3** to complete Table **9-4,** using whole numbers to express each ratio.

Table 9-4 ■ *Scale Factors and Ratios of Areas of Squares*

Squares	Ratio of Side Lengths (Scale Factor)	Ratio of Areas
A to B		
E to A		
B to D		
E to C		
I to A		
G to A		
J to F		
J to K		

mathematics note

To raise a fraction to a power n, where n is a non-negative integer, both the numerator and the denominator may be raised to the indicated power. In general,

$$\left(\frac{a}{b}\right)^n = \frac{a^n}{b^n}$$

where $b \neq 0$.

For example, the fraction 3/4 can be raised to the third power as follows:

$$\left(\frac{3}{4}\right)^3 = \frac{3^3}{4^3} = \frac{27}{64}$$

e. Use the information in Table **9-4** to describe the relationship between the scale factor for two squares and the ratio of their areas.

f. Predict whether the relationship between scale factor and area for squares is also true for similar triangles.

g. To test your prediction in Part **f,** complete Steps **1–4** below.

1. Using a geometry utility, construct a triangle ABC.

2. Connect the midpoints of the sides of triangle *ABC* to form triangle *IGH*. Your construction should now resemble the one shown in Figure **9-3.**

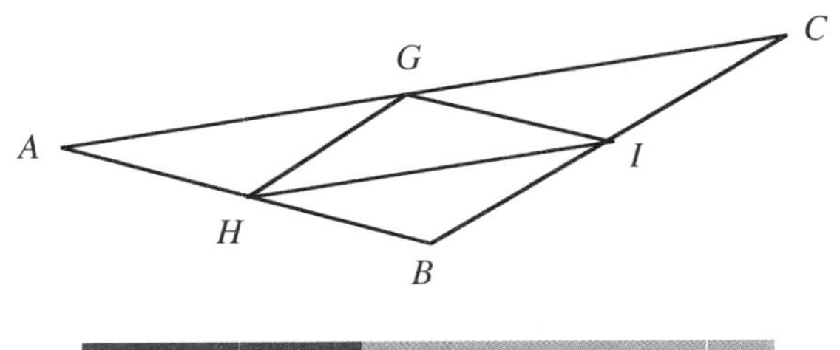

FIGURE 9-3 Triangles ***ABC*** and ***IGH***.

3. Using the lengths of corresponding sides and the measures of corresponding angles, prove that triangles *ABC* and *IGH* are similar.
4. Determine the relationship between the scale factor of the two triangles and the ratio of their areas.

Discussion

a. Why are all squares similar?

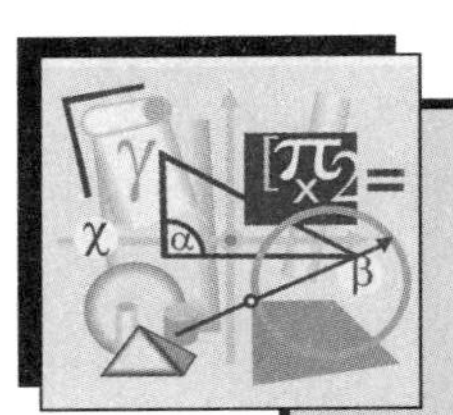

mathematics note

A **square root** of a non-negative number a is a number s such that $s^2 = a$.

For example, because $5^2 = 25$, the number 5 is a square root of 25. Because $(-5)^2 = 25$, the number -5 is also a square root of 25.

The positive square root of a number is its **principal square root.** The principal square root of a is usually denoted by $\sqrt{a}$, although it may also be written as $\sqrt[2]{a}$. For example, $\sqrt[2]{25} = \sqrt{25} = 5$.

In general, an nth root of a non-negative number a is a number s such that $s^n = a$. The non-negative nth root of a is denoted as $\sqrt[n]{a}$.

The nth root of a fraction can be found by taking the nth root of the numerator and dividing it by the nth root of the denominator. In general,

$$\sqrt[n]{\frac{a}{b}} = \frac{\sqrt[n]{a}}{\sqrt[n]{b}}$$

where $b \neq 0$.

For example, the principal square root of 9/16 can be found as follows:

$$\sqrt[2]{\frac{9}{16}} = \sqrt{\frac{9}{16}} = \frac{\sqrt{9}}{\sqrt{16}} = \frac{3}{4}$$

b. When the side length of a square is doubled, what happens to the area of the square?

c. When the side lengths of a triangle are tripled, what happens to the area of the triangle?

d. If the area of a square is a cm^2, what is the side length of the square?

e. Consider two squares, one with an area of 49 cm^2 and another with an area of 1 cm^2. What is the scale factor for these squares?

f. In Table **9-4,** you recorded the ratio of the area of square J to the area of square K. What is the square root of this ratio?

g. Given the area of square A and the ratio of the side length of square A to the side length of square B, how could you determine the area of square B?

h. Do you think that the relationship between scale factor and the ratio of areas discovered in the exploration is true for all similar figures? Explain your response.

mathematics note

The ratio of the areas of two similar objects is the square of the ratio of the lengths of corresponding sides (the scale factor).

For example, if the scale factor for two similar objects is 4/5, the ratio of their areas is:

$$\left(\frac{4}{5}\right)^2 = \frac{4^2}{5^2} = \frac{16}{25}$$

Warm-Up

1. Calculate a real-number value for each square root below. Round non-integer values to the nearest hundredth.

   a. $\sqrt{121}$

   b. $\sqrt{56}$

   c. $\sqrt{-32}$

   d. $\sqrt{1}$

   e. $\sqrt{0}$

   f. $\sqrt{81/64}$

2. Polygons A, B, C, D, E, F, G, and H are all similar polygons. Use this information to complete the following table.

Polygons	Ratio of Side Lengths	Ratio of Areas
A and B	1:6	
C and D		9/16
E and F	$m:n$	
G and H		s/t

3. If the lengths of the sides of a square are tripled, by what factor is the perimeter increased? By what factor is the area increased?

4. If the area of a regular hexagon is quadrupled, by what amount are the lengths of the sides increased?

5. The areas of two similar parallelograms are 75 cm^2 and 52 cm^2, respectively. What is the scale factor of their lengths?

Assignment

2.1 A figure is enlarged until its area is 225 times the area of the original figure. By what number was each length in the original figure multiplied?

2.2 A circle with a radius of 3 cm is enlarged by a scale factor of 10. How many times the area of the original circle is the area of the larger circle?

2.3 The sides of a rectangle with an area of 80 m^2 are enlarged by a scale factor of 3. Find the area of the larger rectangle.

2.4 Zino's Pizzeria charges $11.30 for a pizza with a diameter of 30 cm and $18.95 for a pizza with a diameter of 41 cm.

a. The two pizzas are similar. Determine the scale factor when comparing the larger pizza to the smaller one.

b. Find the ratio of their areas.

c. Use the ratio of the areas and the price of the smaller pizza to determine a corresponding price for the larger pizza.

d. Decide which pizza is the better buy and explain your reasoning.

2.5 A professional basketball player 215 cm tall has a footprint with an area of 468 cm^2. This basketball player and Nelson have similar bodies. If the area of Nelson's footprint is 325 cm^2, how tall is Nelson?

2.6 The size of a television screen typically is reported in terms of the length of its diagonal. For example, if a store advertises a 50-cm screen, this means that the length of the screen's diagonal is 50 cm.

a. What is the ratio of the area of a 63-cm screen to the area of a 33-cm screen?

b. What is the length of the diagonal for a screen with twice the area of a 33-cm screen?

2.7 a. Determine the area of a right triangle with sides that measure 3 cm, 4 cm, and 5 cm.

b. Use your answer to Part **a** to predict the area of a right triangle with sides that measure 18 cm, 24 cm, and 30 cm.

c. Verify your prediction using the formula for the area of a triangle.

* * * * *

2.8 Andreas and Jonalynn installed new carpeting in two of their bedrooms. The floors in both rooms are rectangles. The smaller of the two rooms is 3.2 m wide and 4.1 m long. The ratio of the widths of the two rooms is 1.2, while the ratio of the lengths is 1.6.

a. Find the length and width of the larger room.

b. Can the ratios of the widths and the lengths of the two rooms be used to determine the ratio of the areas? Explain your response.

c. Find the areas of both rooms.

d. What is the ratio of the areas of the two rooms? Does this ratio verify your response to Part **b**? Why or why not?

2.9 Damion's Turf Service charges $50.00 to clean a section of artificial turf 10 yd wide and 20 yd long. Excluding the end zones, a football field is 50 yd wide and 100 yd long. How much should the company charge to clean a football field? Explain your response.

2.10 The figure below shows four rectangles and their dimensions in centimeters.

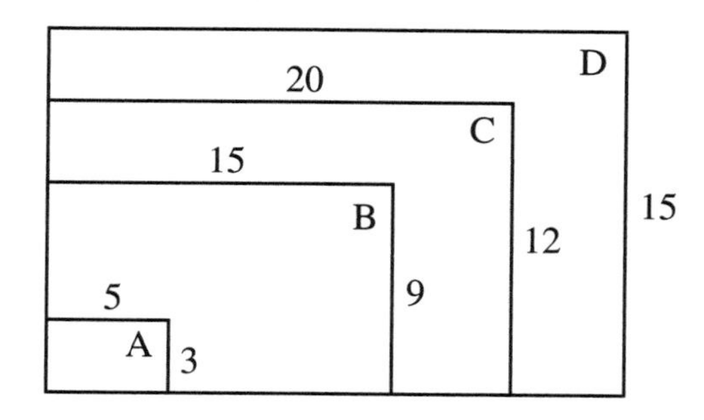

a. Compare the perimeters and areas of these rectangles.

b. Identify the rectangles that are similar and explain how you determined your response.

ACTIVITY 3

In previous activities, you used scale factors to predict lengths and areas for similar figures. In this activity, scale factors are used to predict volumes of similar objects.

Exploration

a. 1. Using a set of unit cubes, create a cube with an edge length of 2 units. Determine the volume of this cube and record it in the appropriate cell of Table **9-5.**

TABLE 9-5 ■ *Edge Length and Volume of Cubes*

Cube	Edge Length	Volume
A	1	1
B	2	
C		27
N	n	

2. Determine the edge length of a cube with a volume of 27 units^3 and record it in the appropriate cell of Table **9-5.**

3. Determine the volume of a cube with an edge length of n and record it in the appropriate cell of Table **9-5.**

b. 1. Use the information in Table **9-5** to complete Table **9-6.**

TABLE 9-6 ■ *Ratios of Edge Lengths and Volumes*

Cubes	Ratio of Edge Lengths (scale factor)	Ratio of Volumes
B to A	2/1	
B to C	2/3	
C to A		27/1
	a/b	

2. Describe the relationship between the ratio of the edge lengths (scale factor) for two cubes and the ratio of their volumes.

mathematics note

A **cube root** of a number a is a number b such that $b^3 = a$. Because $2^3 = 8$, for example, 2 is the cube root of 8.

The cube root of a is denoted by $\sqrt[3]{a}$. For example, $\sqrt[3]{-8} = -2$ and

$$\sqrt[3]{\frac{64}{125}} = \frac{\sqrt[3]{64}}{\sqrt[3]{125}} = \frac{4}{5}$$

Discussion

a. 1. What is the ratio of volumes for two cubes with volumes of 125 cm^3 and 8 cm^3?

   2. What is the ratio of the edge lengths for these cubes?

b. In general, what is the relationship between the scale factor and the ratio of volumes for two cubes?

c. If a cube is enlarged until its volume is 64 times the original volume, by what scale factor has each edge length been multiplied?

d. If the volume of a cube is d cm^3, what is the length of one edge?

e. Do you think that the relationship you described in Part **b** is true for all similar figures? Explain your response.

mathematics note

If the scale factor of two similar figures is a/b, then the ratio of their volumes is:

$$\left(\frac{a}{b}\right)^3 = \frac{a^3}{b^3}$$

For example, Figure **9-4** shows two cubes with edge lengths of 2 cm and 3 cm, respectively.

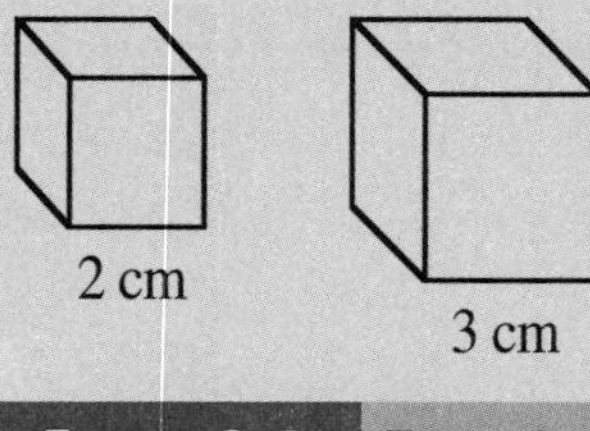

FIGURE 9-4 Two cubes.

Because the ratio of the edge lengths (scale factor) is $2/3$, the ratio of the volumes is:

$$\left(\frac{2}{3}\right)^3 = \frac{2^3}{3^3} = \frac{8}{27}$$

f. Consider two similar pyramids. The smaller has a volume of 18 cm^3. The sides of the larger pyramid are 3 times as long as the smaller pyramid's.

Describe how you could determine the volume of the larger pyramid.

Warm-Up

1. Calculate a real-number value for each cube root below. Round non-integer values to the nearest hundredth.

a. $\sqrt[3]{343}$ **b.** $\sqrt[3]{-1728}$ **c.** $\sqrt[3]{592.704}$ **d.** $\sqrt[3]{-4913}$

2. Complete the following table.

Scale Factor	Ratio of Areas	Ratio of Volumes
$3/5$		
	25:4	
		$m^3 : n^3$
	s^2/t^2	
	u/v	

Assignment

3.1 Consider two spheres: the smaller has a volume of 1 m^3, the larger has a volume of 343 m^3. What is the scale factor for these spheres?

3.2 Two eggs are similar in shape. One egg is twice as long as the other. What is the ratio of their volumes?

science note

The **density** of a substance is the ratio of its mass to its volume. For example, the density of water is 1 g/cm^3.

The density of any pure substance is a constant. Therefore, the mass of the substance is directly proportional to its volume. In other words, as the volume increases, so does the mass.

3.3 A steel sphere with a diameter of 4 cm has a volume of 33.5 cm^3. Its mass is 261 g.

a. What is the density of the sphere?

b. What is the density of a steel sphere with a diameter of 6 cm?

c. What is the scale factor between the 6-cm sphere and the 4-cm sphere?

d. What is the ratio of the volume of the 6-cm sphere to the volume of the 4-cm sphere?

e. How does the ratio of their volumes compare to:

1. the ratio of their masses?
2. the scale factor?

3.4 The two similar fish shown below are drawn to scale. The smaller fish is 25 cm long and has a mass of 0.75 kg. Assuming that the densities of the two fish are the same, use scale factor to estimate the length and mass of the larger fish.

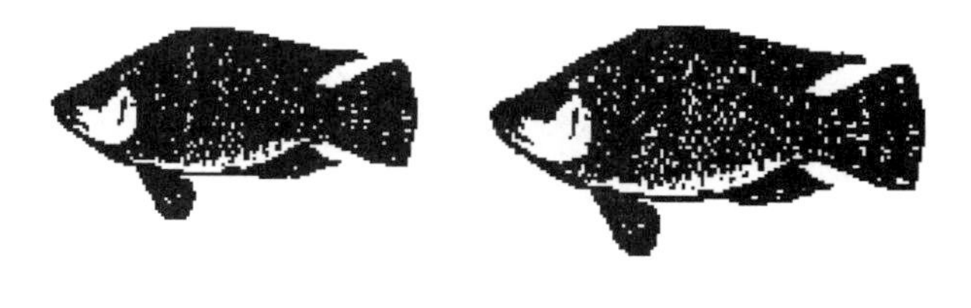

* * * * *

3.5 A baker's favorite pie recipe calls for 6 cups of apples to make a 9-inch pie. How many cups of apples should he use to make a similar 8-inch pie?

3.6 The circumference of one egg is three times the circumference of another egg. If the two eggs are similar, what is the ratio of the mass of the larger egg to the mass of the smaller egg?

In Activity **2,** you discovered that when a square's side length is doubled, its area is quadrupled. In this activity, you examine the relationship between length and area from a graphical point of view.

Exploration

The area of a square is related to the length of its sides. The area of a shoe print is related to the length of the shoe. How are these two relationships similar? How are they different?

a. Figure **9-5** shows a scale drawing of a child's shoe print. Each square in the drawing represents an area of 1 cm^2. Use this drawing to estimate the actual length and area of the shoe print.

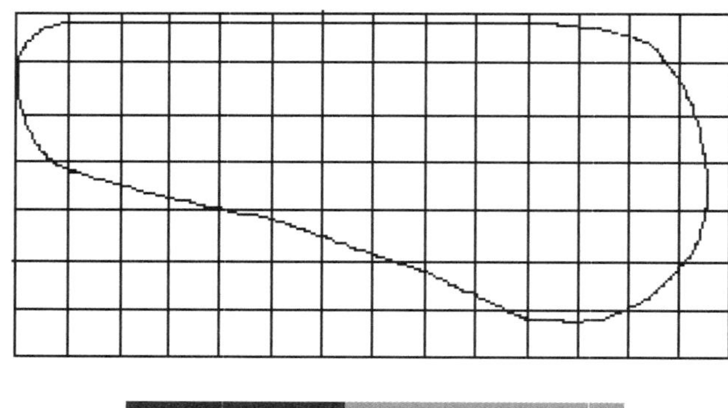

FIGURE 9-5 A child's shoe print.

b. Draw your own shoe print on centimeter graph paper. Measure its length and estimate its area.

c. 1. Collect and organize this information for the entire class. To this data set, add the child's data from Part **a** along with a shoe length of 0 cm and the corresponding area.

   2. Create a scatterplot of the class data. Let y represent area and x represent shoe length.

d. 1. Graph the formula for the area of a square on the same coordinate system as the scatterplot in Part **c.** Let y represent area and x represent side length.

2. Describe any similarities or differences you observe in the two graphs.

mathematics note

An equation of the form $y = ax^b$ is a **power equation.**

For example, the formula for the area of a square, $y = x^2$, is a power equation in which $a = 1$ and $b = 2$.

e. Find an equation of the form $y = ax^2$ that models the scatterplot in Part **c** by varying the value of a until the graph of the equation reasonably approximates the data points.

f. One way to determine if another power equation fits the data better than your equation from Part **e** is to compare the residuals.

1. Enter the class data in a spreadsheet with the following headings:

Length (x)	Area (y)	Predicted Area	Absolute Value of Residual

2. Use your model from Part **e** to determine the predicted area for each value of x.

3. Determine the absolute value of each residual.

4. Find the sum of the absolute values of the residuals.

g. Vary the value of a in your model of the form $y = ax^2$ to determine the equation that minimizes the sum of the absolute values of the residuals. Record this equation.

h. 1. Graph your equation from Part **g** on the same coordinate system as the scatterplot from Part **c** and print a copy of the resulting graph.

2. Mark the point on the scatterplot that represents your shoe length and area.

3. Mark the point on the curve that represents the ordered pair (x, y), where x is your shoe length and y is the predicted area. Connect this point to the point in Step **2.**

Discussion

a. Describe the general relationship between shoe length and the area of a shoe print.

b. Compare your equation in Part **g**, along with its corresponding sum of the absolute values of the residuals, with those obtained by others in the class.

c. How well does your equation model the data for your own shoe length and area?

d. How does the value of a affect the graph of the equation $y = ax^2$?

e. If the lengths of two similar shoe prints have a scale factor of 3, what is the ratio of their areas?

Warm-Up

1. Complete the following table of values for each equation below. Then sketch a graph of each equation.

x	–2	–1	0	1	2
y					

a. $y = 1.3x^2$ **b.** $y = 0.83x^3$

2. For each equation in Problem **1**, determine the value of x (to the nearest hundredth) when $y = 87.93$.

Assignment

4.1 In the exploration, you graphed equations of the form $y = ax^b$ where $b = 2$ and both the domain and range were limited to positive numbers. To observe how different values of a and b affect the graph of $y = ax^b$, use a graphing utility to complete Parts **a–c** below.

Sketch each set of graphs on a sheet of paper, using the same pair of axes for each set, and including the appropriate labels.

a. Graph at least three examples of each of the following. Let the domain be the set of real numbers from –10 to 10. Include one value for a where $|a| < 1$.

1. $y = ax^2$ where a is positive **2.** $y = ax^2$ where a is negative

b. Repeat Part **a** for $y = ax^3$.

c. Repeat Part **a** for $y = ax^b$ where b is greater than 3.

d. Describe how the values of a and b appear to affect the graph of $y = ax^b$.

4.2 Each of the following graphs was generated by an equation of the form $y = ax^b$. For each one, determine two equations with different values of b that produce graphs with roughly the same general shape.

a.

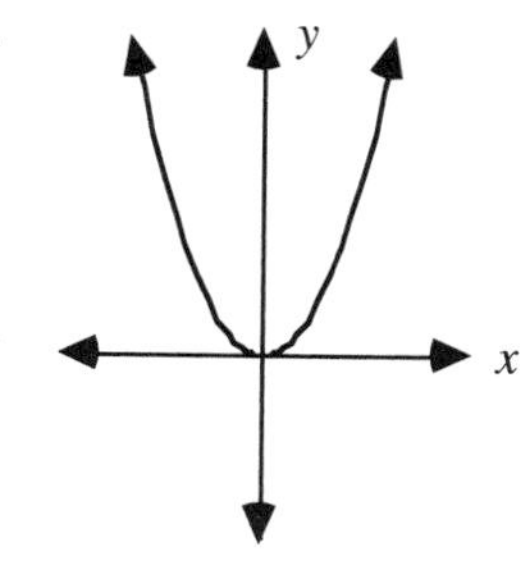

b.

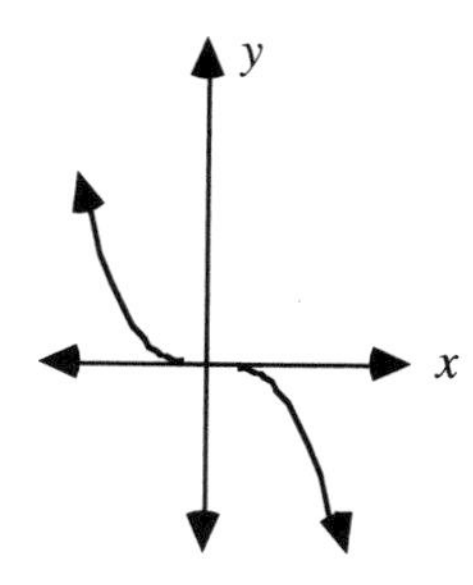

c.

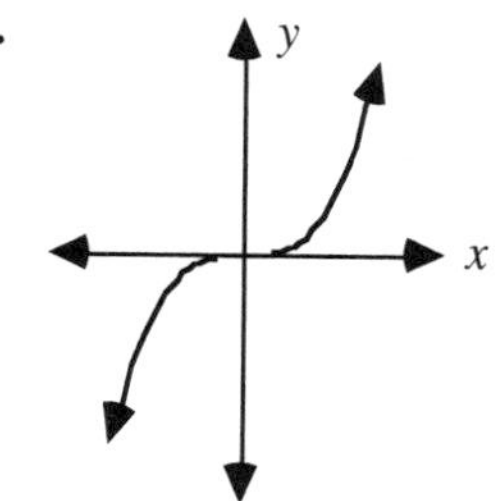

d.

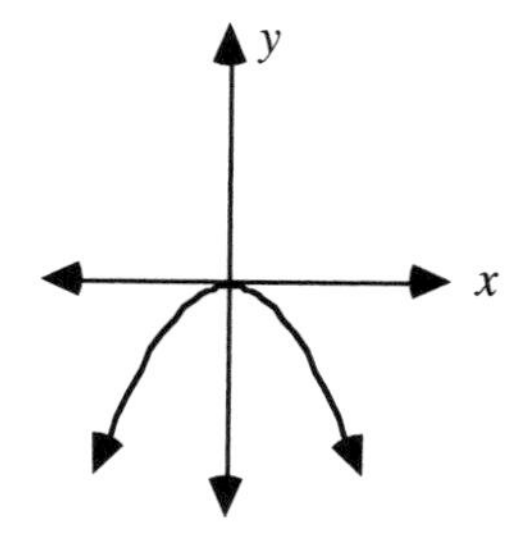

4.3 Assuming that Robert Wadlow is similar to you, estimate the area of his shoe print.

4.4 Neva is 170 cm tall. Estimate her shoe length and the area of her shoe print if she is similar to you.

4.5 The table below shows some data on the length and mass of bird eggs.

Type of Egg	Length (cm)	Mass (g)
hummingbird	1.3	0.5
black swift	2.5	3.5
dove	3.18	6.41
partridge	3.0	8.7
Arctic tern	4.2	18
grebe	4.3	19.7
Louisiana egret	4.5	27.5
very small chicken	5.2	44.8
mallard duck	6.17	80
very large chicken	6.5	85
great black-backed gull	7.62	111
Canada goose	8.9	197
condor	11.0	270
ostrich	17.0	1400

a. Make a scatterplot of this data. Let y represent mass in grams and x represent length in centimeters.

b. Find an equation of the form $y = ax^3$ that models the data.

c. Which type of egg fits the curve least well? Explain your response.

d. The egg of a bald eagle is 7.3 cm long. Use your equation to predict the mass of this egg.

e. Write a paragraph summarizing the relationship between the length and mass of bird eggs.

* * * * *

4.6 The table below shows the data collected as an object fell through the air.

Time (sec)	Distance (m)	Time (sec)	Distance (m)
0.00	0.000	0.35	0.539
0.05	0.000	0.40	0.717
0.10	0.017	0.45	0.920
0.15	0.072	0.50	1.144
0.20	0.152	0.55	1.393
0.25	0.256	0.60	1.668
0.30	0.387	0.65	1.889

a. Create a scatterplot of this data. Let y represent distance in meters and x represent time in seconds.

b. Use the process described in Parts **e–g** of the exploration to find an equation that models the data.

c. Graph this equation on the same coordinate system as in Part **a.**

d. Use your model to predict how far the object will fall in 2 sec.

The soles of your feet place a certain amount of pressure on the ground when you stand upright. In this activity, you explore the differences in pressure created by wearing shoes with flat soles, shoes with small heels, or no shoes at all.

science note

The kilogram is a unit of mass, even though it is often referred to as a metric unit of weight. Weight is a force determined by gravity. One metric unit of force is the **newton (N).** On the surface of the earth, the weight of an object in newtons is its mass in kilograms multiplied by 9.8 m/sec^2 (the acceleration due to gravity).

For example, the weight in newtons of a 70-kg person can be calculated as follows:

$$70 \text{ kg} \bullet \frac{9.8 \text{ m}}{\text{sec}^2} = \frac{686 \text{ kg} \bullet \text{m}}{\text{sec}^2} = 686 \text{ N}$$

Exploration

a. 1. Place your shoeless foot on a sheet of centimeter graph paper and trace around it. Use the tracing to estimate the area of your footprint without shoes.

2. Estimate the area of your shoe print when wearing shoes with flat soles. Assume that the bottom of your shoe makes complete contact with the ground.

3. Estimate the area of your shoe print when wearing a shoe with small heels.

b. Compare the three areas determined in Part **a.**

c. Determine your weight in newtons.

d. Find the pressure, in newtons per square centimeter, that your feet place on the ground in each of the following situations. *Hint:* Because your weight is distributed over both feet, divide this weight by the area of two footprints.

1. while not wearing shoes
2. while wearing shoes with flat soles
3. while wearing shoes with small heels

e. Compare the three pressures determined in Part **d.**

Discussion

a. When designing shoes for specific purposes, manufacturers often consider the amount of pressure that the foot places on the ground. For example, the sole on a running shoe typically has a greater area than the sole on a casual shoe.

Describe the purposes of some different types of shoes and the approximate area of the sole for each type.

b. Why do you think that high heels (and other shoes with small heel areas) are banned in some buildings?

c. Why does the frame of a bed with a mattress and box spring differ from the frame of a waterbed?

Warm-Up

1. Convert each of the following weights to mass in kilograms.

   a. 98 lb   b. 125 lb   c. 143 lb

2. Determine the weight in newtons of each of the following masses.

   a. 3.4 kg   b. 11.3 kg   c. 546 g

Assignment

5.1 Walking involves the smooth transfer of weight from one foot to the other. At the beginning of each step, about half your weight rests on the heel of the forward shoe.

a. Arlis wears shoes with a heel area of 0.75 cm^2 each. Sketch the print of one heel.

b. Arlis weighs 500 N. Estimate the pressure that the heel of her forward shoe places on the ground at the beginning of each step.

5.2 The diagram below shows the shape and dimensions of a typical snowshoe. Use this diagram to explain why snowshoes make it easier to stand or walk on snow.

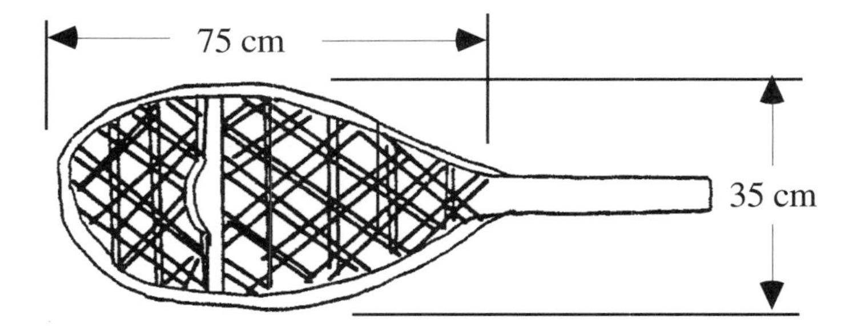

5.3 Assume that you and Robert Wadlow are similar. The area of Wadlow's shoe print is approximately 663 cm^2. Determine the pressure he places on the ground when standing upright. How does this amount differ from the pressure you place on the ground?

* * * * *

5.4 The diagram below shows a block of lead in the shape of a rectangular prism. The density of lead is 11.34 g/cm^3.

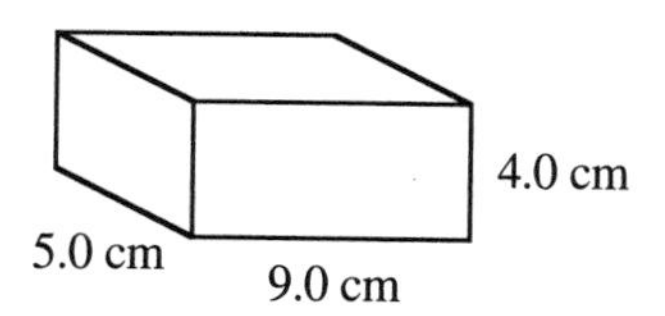

a. Calculate the pressure, in newtons per square centimeter, that the block exerts on the floor.

b. Suppose that the lead block is balanced on top of a wooden cube with an edge length of 2.5 cm. Assuming that the cube adds no significant mass to this situation, determine the pressure that the combination of block and cube exerts on the floor.

c. Explain any differences you observe in the pressures calculated in Parts **a** and **b.**

5.5 When placed upright on its base, a cylinder exerts a pressure of 0.50 N/cm^2 on the floor. The radius of the base is 35 cm. What is the mass of the cylinder?

5.6 Gravity on the planet Mars is about 1/3 the gravity on Earth. How much pressure would you place on the Martian surface when standing upright?

ACTIVITY 6

The **femur,** or thigh bone, extends from the hip to the knee. In humans, two femurs (one in each leg) support the weight of the body. A horse, however, has four related bones to bear its weight. Figure **9-6** shows scale drawings of both a human femur and the femur of a horse.

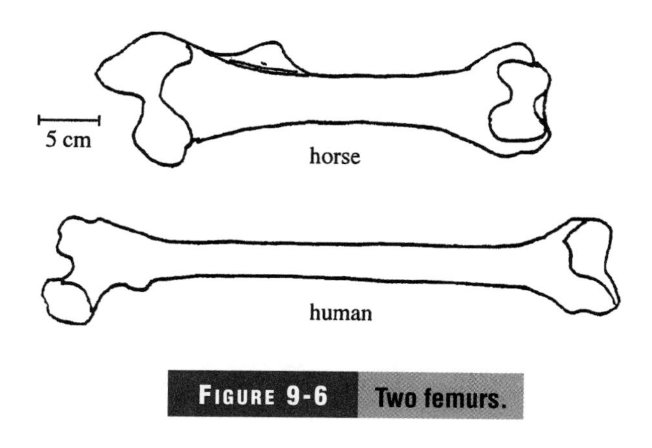

FIGURE 9-6 Two femurs.

How much weight can these bones support without breaking? In this activity, you build two model femurs and use them to investigate one limit to biological growth.

Exploration

a. Use paper cylinders to model each femur in Figure **9-6.** The diameter of each cylinder should equal the smallest diameter of each bone.

   Write the corresponding length, diameter, and circumference on each model. Compare the two models for similarity and record your observations.

b. Figure **9-7** shows that a **cross section** is the surface found by slicing an object perpendicular to its length.

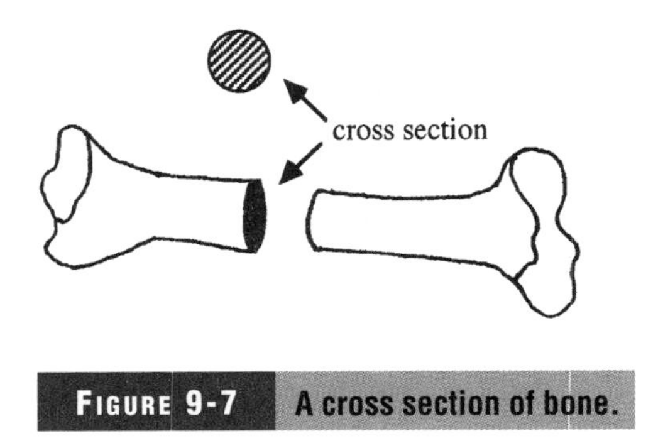

FIGURE 9-7 A cross section of bone.

   1. Using centimeter graph paper, draw an accurate cross section of each femur. Estimate the area of each cross section in square centimeters.
   2. Calculate the cross-sectional area of each femur and compare these values with your estimates.
   3. Write the calculated cross-sectional area on each model.
   4. The cross-sectional area of a bone is a good indicator of its relative strength. Compare the strength of the femurs shown in Figure **9-6.**

c. The person whose femur appears in Figure **9-6** was 180 cm tall and weighed 600 N. Imagine a similar person who is twice as tall (a giant).

   1. Use a strip of paper to make a cross-sectional model of the giant's femur, as shown in Figure **9-8.**

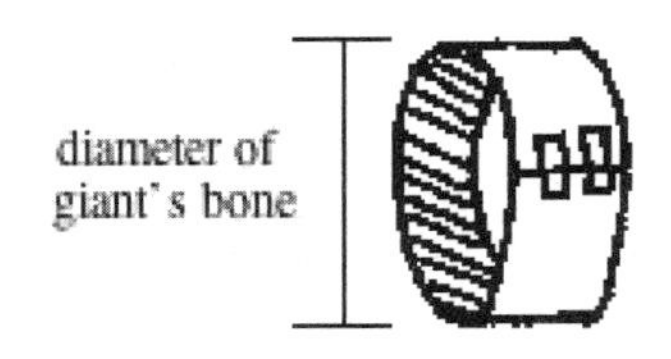

FIGURE 9-8 Paper model of cross section of bone.

2. Write the diameter, circumference, and cross-sectional area on your model.

3. Would the giant's bone have to support the same weight per square unit as the bone of the person who weighed 600 N? Explain your response.

4. Write a paragraph describing the femurs of the 600-N human and the giant, including the dimensions of the bones and the pressures on the cross-sectional areas.

5. The relationship between volume and area creates a tension on bone structure that affects the biological growth of animals. How might this tension affect the giant?

d. A vertical compression test measures how much pressure a bone can withstand before crushing. In one test, a human femur withstood a pressure of approximately 1200 N/cm^2.

Considering the results of this test, do you think that there is a limit on the size of humans? Explain your response.

e. To investigate this question further, create a spreadsheet with columns as in Table **9-7.** Complete the spreadsheet using the data from Parts **a** and **b** of this exploration.

TABLE 9-7 ■ *Scale Factor and Human Body Structure*

Scale Factor	Body Height (cm)	Femur Diameter (cm)	Cross-sectional Area of Femur (cm^2)	Body Weight (N)	Pressure on Femur (N/cm^2)
1	180			600	
2					
3					
⋮					
30					

f. Considering the information in your spreadsheet, do you think that there is a limit on the size of humans? Explain your response.

g. Use the data in your spreadsheet to create the following:

1. a scatterplot of femur diameter versus scale factor

2. a scatterplot of the cross-sectional area of a femur versus scale factor

3. a scatterplot of body weight versus scale factor.

h. 1. Predict the shape of a scatterplot of pressure on the femur versus scale factor.

2. Create a scatterplot of pressure on the femur versus scale factor. How does the shape of the graph compare with your prediction?

Discussion

a. What did you discover about the femurs of humans and horses?

b. Is it possible for a human to grow taller than Robert Wadlow? Explain your response.

c. Compare the three graphs you created in Part **g** of the exploration.

d. Describe the relationship between pressure on the femur and scale factor.

Warm-Up

1. Calculate the area of a circle with each of the following dimensions.

   a. $d = 4.7$ cm

   b. $r = 8\frac{3}{4}$ in.

   c. $d = 56.9$ m

2. A block of steel in the shape of a rectangular prism has a base 2 m by 3 m and a height of 5 m. A cubic meter of steel has a mass of about 8000 kg. Use this information to complete Parts **a–c**.

   a. Determine the mass of the block and the pressure (in N/m^2) it exerts on the ground.

   b. If the dimensions of the block were doubled, what would its volume be? What pressure would it exert on the ground?

   c. In general, what happens to the volume, mass, and pressure exerted on the ground as the dimensions of the block change by a given scale factor?

Assignment

6.1 The person whose femur is shown in Figure **9-6** weighed 600 N and was 180 cm tall. Assuming that your body is similar, use your height to estimate the pressure on your femur in newtons per square centimeter.

6.2 Assume that a human femur can withstand a pressure of approximately 1200 N/cm^2. Use your response to Problem **6.1** to determine the maximum weight that your femur can support. *Hint:* First, find the cross-sectional area of your femur.

6.3 Describe some other factors that might limit the maximum height of humans.

* * * * *

6.4 The mean height of male gorillas is approximately 1.8 m. Their mean mass is about 200 kg.

a. Determine the mean weight, in newtons, of male gorillas.

b. A gorilla's femur can support a maximum of 10 times the mean body weight. What is this maximum weight?

c. In one version of the story, the gorilla King Kong was supposed to be about 9.8 m tall. Is it possible for a gorilla like King Kong to exist? Explain your response.

6.5 The femur of a Tyrannosaurus in a Montana museum is 103 cm long and has a diameter of 25 cm. Scientists estimate that this dinosaur weighed between 35,000 N and 62,000 N. Which bone is subject to greater pressure: the femur of this Tyrannosaurus or the femur of a 600-N person? Explain your response.

Summary Assessment

Do you think that human siblings are similar? Use the data in the following table (or collect data from your own family) to support your response.

Sibling	Length of Foot (cm)	Circumference of Foot (cm)	Area of Footprint (cm^2)	Body Weight (N)
A	15.0	35	61	93
B	19.5	45	101	208
C	23.0	54	149	340
D	30.0	70	251	756

In justifying your position, include examples of each of the following:

- proportionality
- scale factors
- linear equations of the form $y = ax$
- power equations of the forms $y = ax^2$ and $y = ax^3$
- square roots
- cube roots.

Your report should also include predictions made using scale factors, graphs, and equations, and should use residuals to determine how well an equation models a data set.

Module Summary

- Two ratios, a/b ($b \neq 0$) and c/d ($d \neq 0$), are **proportional,** or **in proportion,** if

$$\frac{a}{b} = \frac{c}{d}$$

When two such ratios are proportional, it is also true that

$$\frac{a}{c} = \frac{b}{d}$$

where $c \neq 0$ and $d \neq 0$.

- Two objects are **similar** if they have the same shape and the ratios of corresponding lengths are proportional. The ratio of corresponding sides is the **scale factor.**
- To raise a fraction to a power n, where n is a non-negative integer, both the numerator and the denominator may be raised to the indicated power. In general,

$$\left(\frac{a}{b}\right)^n = \frac{a^n}{b^n}$$

where $b \neq 0$.

- A **square root** of a non-negative number a is a number s such that $s^2 = a$.
- The positive square root of a number is its **principal square root.** The principal square root of a is usually denoted by $\sqrt{a}$, although it may also be written as $\sqrt[2]{a}$.
- A **cube root** of a number a is a number b such that $b^3 = a$. The cube root of a is denoted by $\sqrt[3]{a}$.
- In general, the nth root of a non-negative number a is a number s such that $s^n = a$. The non-negative nth root of a is denoted as $\sqrt[n]{a}$.
- The nth root of a fraction can be found by taking the nth root of the numerator and dividing it by the nth root of the denominator. In general,

$$\sqrt[n]{\frac{a}{b}} = \frac{\sqrt[n]{a}}{}$$

where $b \neq 0$.

- An equation of the form $y = ax^b$ is a **power equation.**
- The ratio of the areas of two similar objects is the square of the ratio of the lengths of corresponding sides (the scale factor).

* If the scale factor of two similar figures is a/b, then the ratio of their areas is:

$$\left(\frac{a}{b}\right)^2 = \frac{a^2}{b^2}$$

while the ratio of their volumes is:

$$\left(\frac{a}{b}\right)^3 = \frac{a^3}{b^3}$$

* The **density** of a substance is the ratio of its mass to its volume.
* One metric unit of force is the **newton (N).** The weight of an object in newtons is its mass in kilograms multiplied by 9.8 m/sec^2 (the acceleration due to gravity).

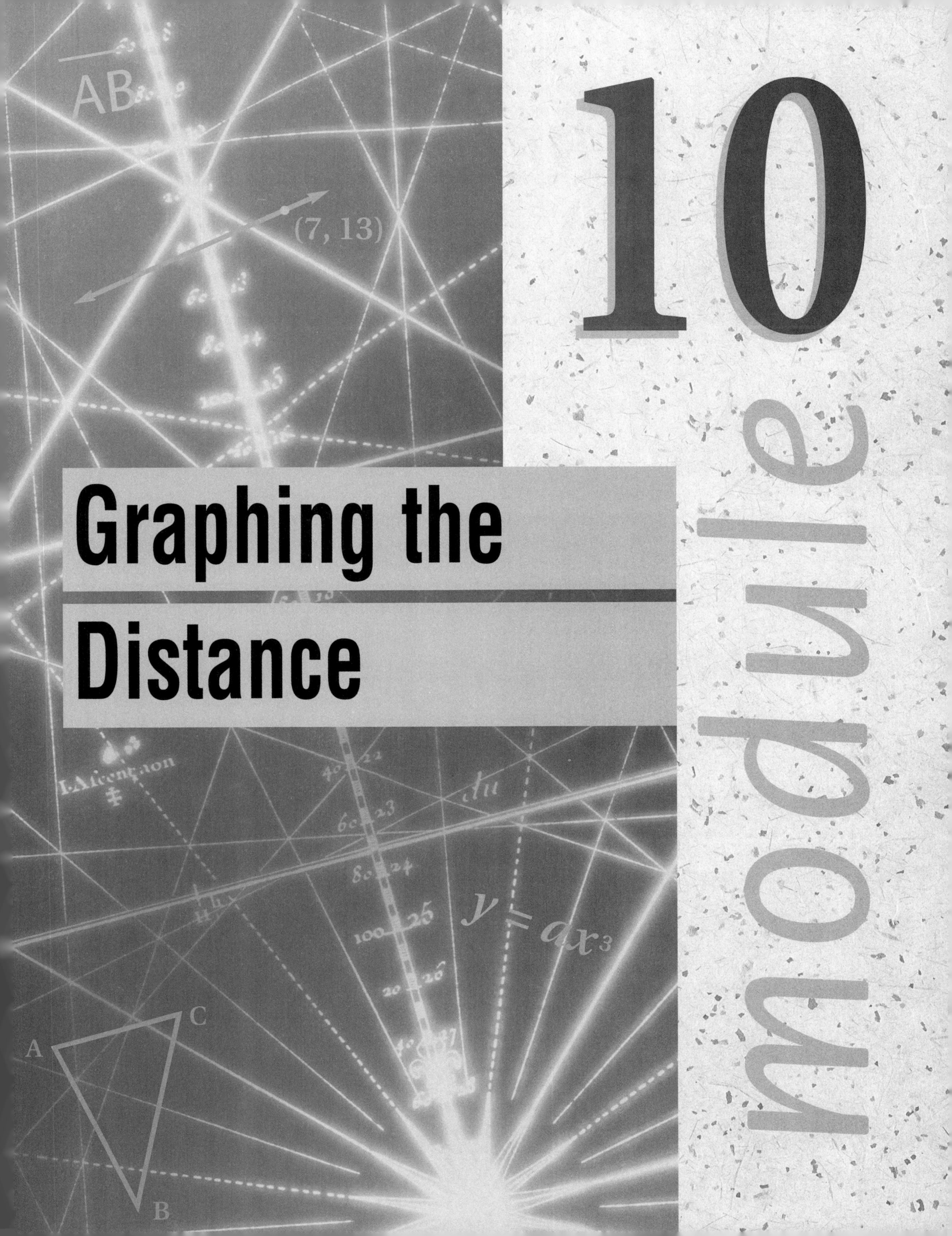
10
module
Graphing the
Distance
AB
(7, 13)
A
B
C

Introduction

Have you ever wondered how scientists at the National Aeronautics and Space Administration (NASA) plan the launch of a space shuttle? Or how traffic officers reconstruct the scene of an accident? In this module, you investigate objects in motion and the relationship between distance traveled and time.

ACTIVITY 1

Scientists use **distance-time graphs** to analyze motion. A distance-time graph displays the distance between two objects (or an object and a fixed point) as a function of time. Typically, time is represented on the x-axis and distance on the y-axis. You can observe many interesting and useful patterns by comparing the distance-time graphs of different kinds of motion.

Exploration 1

A **sonar range finder** uses sound waves to measure the distance from itself to another object. In this exploration, you use a sonar range finder to collect data, then use that data to create distance-time graphs.

a. Connect a sonar range finder to a science interface device as demonstrated by your teacher. As shown in Figure **10-1,** hold the range finder parallel to the plane of a wall or another flat, vertical surface. As a person holding the range finder moves, the science interface device collects data. You can then transfer this data to a graphing utility.

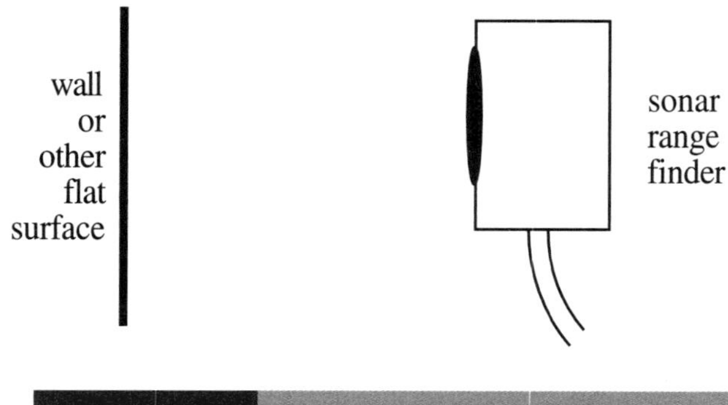

FIGURE 10-1 Positioning the sonar range finder.

b. Practice using a range finder, science interface, and graphing utility to generate distance-time graphs. Move the range finder toward the wall, then away from it, and observe the resulting graphs. Draw one of the graphs on a sheet of graph paper.

c. Use the range finder to create distance-time graphs that match the ones shown below. (This might take a few trials.) Record the method you used to create each graph.

1.

distance

time

2.

distance

time

3.

distance

time

4.

distance

time

d. Figure **10-2** below shows a distance-time graph of data collected during the launch of a model rocket, where the distance is the rocket's height above the ground. After the rocket's engine ignited, it flew straight up. A few seconds after the engine burned out, it began to fall straight back toward the ground. Later, its parachute opened and slowed its descent.

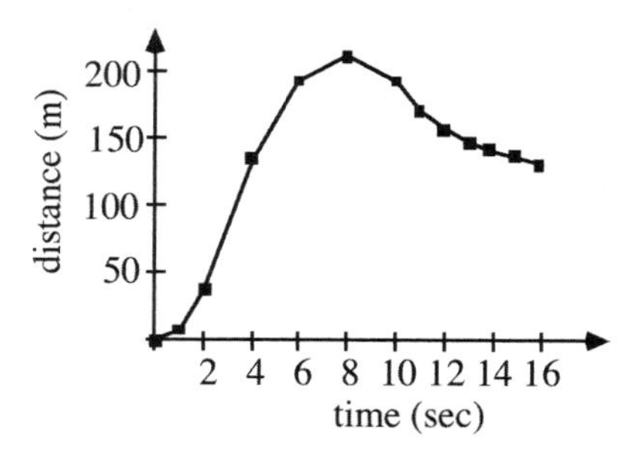

FIGURE 10-2 **Distance-time graph for a model rocket.**

Point the range finder at the floor. By raising and lowering the range finder along a vertical path, create a distance-time graph whose shape resembles the graph in Figure **10-2.**

Discussion 1

a. In Part **b** of Exploration **1,** you sketched a graph on a sheet of paper. What does each point on the graph represent?

b. On a distance-time graph, what do the x- and y-intercepts represent?

c. How does the motion of the range finder in Part **b** of Exploration **1** affect the resulting distance-time graph?

d. Describe how you moved the range finder to obtain each of the graphs in Part **c** of Exploration **1.**

e. Figure **10-3** shows a distance-time graph generated by moving a range finder toward and away from a wall. Describe what is happening to the range finder at points P, Q, and R.

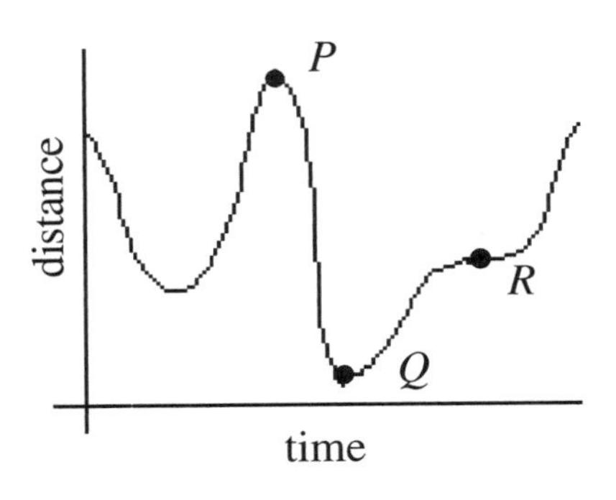

FIGURE 10-3 **A distance-time graph.**

f. How does the kind of motion represented by a "curved" section of a distance-time graph differ from the motion represented by a "straight" section?

mathematics note

The set of all real numbers between two fixed endpoints is a **real-number interval.** Each endpoint may or may not be included in the interval.

One way to describe an interval is with an inequality. For example, the set of real numbers greater than or equal to 15 but less than 30 can be described by the inequality $15 \leq x < 30$.

We also can describe a real-number interval using **interval notation.** In interval notation, a square bracket,] or [, indicates that the endpoint is included in the interval. A parenthesis,) or (, indicates that the endpoint is not included in the interval. For example, the interval described by the inequality $15 \leq x < 30$ can be written as $[15,30)$.

g. Consider the distance-time graph for a model rocket in Figure **10-2.** Use interval notation in your discussion of the following questions.

1. Over what interval of time is the distance increasing? How is this indicated by the graph?
2. Over what interval of time is the distance decreasing? How is this indicated by the graph?
3. Over what interval of time is the distance increasing the fastest? How is this indicated by the graph?
4. Over what interval of time is the distance decreasing the fastest? How is this indicated by the graph?

h. A set of real numbers greater than a given value increases without bound. Such a set of numbers is an **infinite interval.** The notation for an infinite interval uses ∞, the symbol for infinity, to indicate that the set does not end.

For example, the interval of real numbers greater than or equal to 2, or $x \geq 2$, can be represented in interval notation as $[2, \infty)$. Notice that a parenthesis,), is used with ∞.

When describing sets of real numbers less than a given value, the symbol for negative infinity $(-\infty)$ is used.

1. Describe the set of real numbers less than –6 using interval notation.
2. Would you use an infinite interval to describe time in the flight of a model rocket? Explain your response.
3. What set is described by $(-\infty, \infty)$?

i. The average speed of an object during a time interval can be calculated by dividing distance traveled by time.

TABLE 10-1 ■ *Distance-Time Data for a Model Rocket*

Time (sec)	Distance (m)	Time (sec)	Distance (m)
0	0	11	170.8
1	7.4	12	155.4
2	36.9	13	147.7
4	134.2	14	141.9
6	192.9	15	136.3
8	212.3	16	130.8
10	192.9		

1. Using the data from Table **10-1,** determine the total distance traveled by the model rocket during the interval $[6, 12]$.
2. What is the rocket's average speed during the interval $[6, 12]$?

j. Given the current location of an object moving at constant speed, what information would you need to predict the object's location in the future?

science note

Displacement is a change in the position of an object. It has both magnitude and direction.

For example, consider the distance-time data for the model rocket in Table **10-1.** At $t = 2$ sec, the rocket is 36.9 m above the ground. At $t = 6$ sec, it is 192.9 m above the ground. Its displacement during this time is $192.9 - 36.9 = 156.0$ m. In this case, the magnitude of the rocket's displacement is 156.0, while its direction is positive (away from the ground).

From $t = 6$ sec to $t = 12$ sec, however, the rocket's position changes from 192.9 m above the ground to 155.4 m above the ground. Its displacement over this period is $155.4 - 192.9 = -37.5$ m. In this case, the magnitude of the rocket's displacement is 37.5, while its direction is negative (toward the ground).

k. 1. Using the information in Table **10-1,** determine the displacement of the model rocket during the time interval [6,12].

2. Compare this displacement to the distance you determined in Part **i** of the discussion.

science note

Velocity is the rate of change in position with respect to time. Like displacement, velocity also has magnitude and direction.

Calculate the **average velocity** of an object by dividing its displacement by the change in time. For example, you can find the model rocket's average velocity between $t = 2$ sec and $t = 6$ sec as follows:

$$\frac{192.3\text{ m} - 36.9\text{ m}}{6\text{ sec} - 2\text{ sec}} = \frac{156.0\text{ m}}{4\text{ sec}} = 39\text{ m/sec}$$

l. 1. Use the data in Table **10-1** to determine the rocket's average velocity during the time interval [6,12].

2. Describe the magnitude and direction of this average velocity.

3. Compare this average velocity to the average speed you determined in Part **i** of the discussion.

Exploration 2

Highway patrol officers use radar or laser speed guns to collect distance-time data about moving objects. These devices can give very accurate information about a car's **instantaneous velocity**—its velocity at a particular instant in time. In this exploration, you examine how to use distance-time data to approximate instantaneous velocity.

a. Table **10-2** below shows some distance-time data collected from a falling object. Create a scatterplot of this data.

TABLE 10-2 ■ *Distance-Time Data for a Falling Object*

Time (sec)	Distance (m)
0	240.0
1	235.1
2	220.4
3	195.9
4	161.7
5	117.5
6	63.6
7	0.0

b. 1. Determine the average velocity for the time interval representing the entire fall.

2. Draw a line connecting the data points which correspond with the interval in Step **1.**

3. Determine the slope of the line in Step **2.** Compare its value with the average velocity for the interval.

c. One way to approximate the instantaneous velocity at a given time is to select an interval that contains that instant. Then you can use the average velocity for this interval to approximate the instantaneous velocity.

Suppose you want to approximate the instantaneous velocity at $t = 0.5$ sec. You could use the interval for the entire fall for your approximation, but is there a better choice?

1. Determine the average velocity for the time interval [0,5].

2. Draw a line connecting the data points which correspond with this interval.

3. Determine the slope of this line and compare it with the average velocity for the interval.

d. Other intervals that contain $t = 0.5$ sec might give different approximations. Repeat Part **c** for each of the following time intervals:

1. [0,3]

2. [0,2]

3. [0,1]

e. Compare the average velocities you calculated in Parts **b–d.** Which value do you think is closest to the instantaneous velocity at $t = 0.5$ sec?

f. Use the data in Table **10-1** to estimate the instantaneous velocity at $t = 4.5$ sec as accurately as possible.

Note: Save your scatterplot for use in Discussion **1** of Activity **3.**

Discussion 2

a. In Table **10-2,** what does an entry of 0 represent in each column?

b. What does a negative value for average velocity indicate about the motion of the object?

c. 1. Does the line you drew in Part **b** of Exploration **2** provide a good model for the data?

2. What information does the line provide?

d. Using the graph from Part **a** of Exploration **2,** how can you tell when the object was moving at its greatest velocity?

e. Describe how you could approximate the instantaneous velocity of the object at $t = 6.5$ sec.

Warm-Up

1. Use interval notation to describe the set of real numbers represented by each of the following inequalities.

a. $-2 \le x < 5$

b. $x \ge 9$

c. $12 > x > 7$

d. $-4 \ge x$

2. Write a corresponding inequality for each interval below.

 a. $[-12,-4]$

 b. $(-\infty,3]$

 c. $(-32,-45)$

 d. $[0,\infty)$

3. The graph below shows some distance-time data for an object.

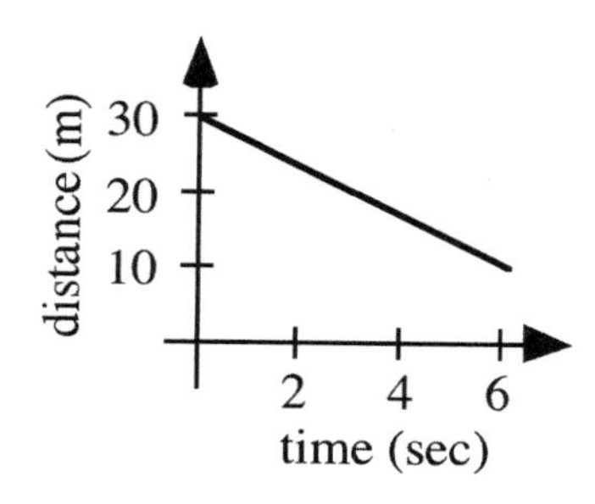

 a. What is this object's average velocity for any time interval shown on the graph?

 b. What is the relationship between this object's average velocity and the slope of the line? Explain your response.

4. Use the following graph and table to complete Parts **a–c** below.

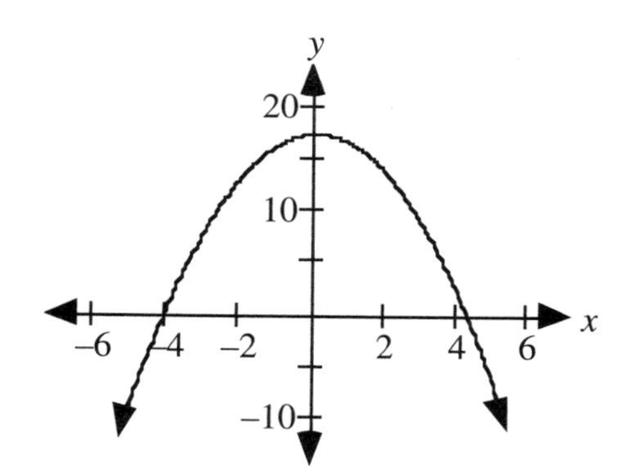

x	y
–5	–10
–4	0
–2	13
0	16
2	14
4	2
5	–5

 a. Describe the x-intercepts, if any. Explain how you used the table to help determine your response.

 b. Consider the interval of x-values $[-5,0)$. Are y-values increasing or decreasing over this interval? Explain your response.

 c. In general, the change in y-values over a given interval of x-values is the **average rate of change.**

 Consider the intervals of x-values $(0,2)$, $(2,4)$, and $(4,5)$. Is the average rate of change constant over these intervals? Explain your response.

Assignment

1.1 Describe a real-world motion that could be represented by each of the distance-time graphs below.

a.

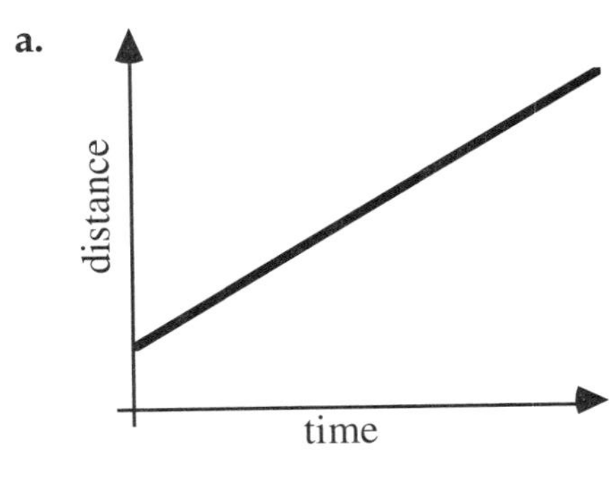

b.

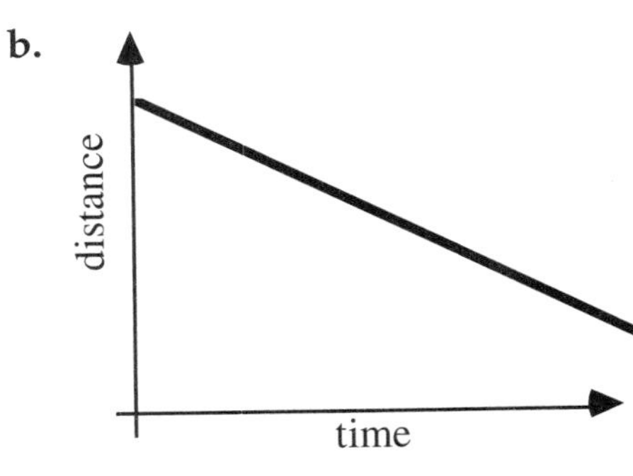

c.

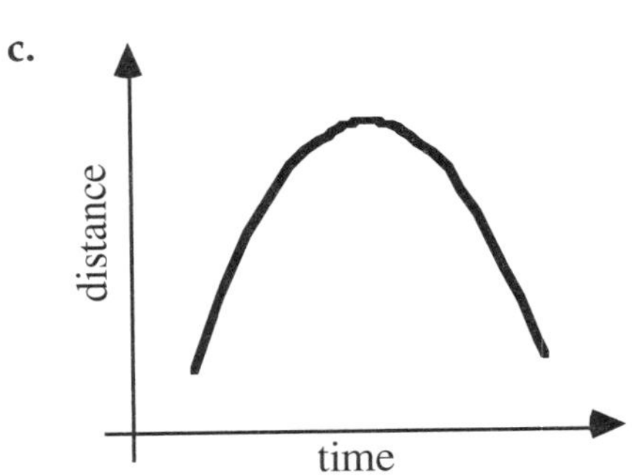

d.

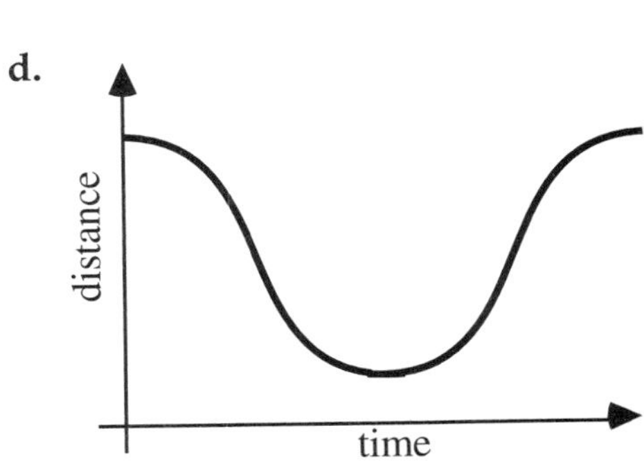

1.2 Sketch a copy of the distance-time graph in Figure **10-2.** On your copy, indicate the points at which you think the following events occurred:

a. the rocket takes off

b. the rocket's engine burns out

c. the rocket reaches its highest altitude

d. the parachute opens.

1.3 The table below contains data collected during the flight of a model rocket. Use the table to complete Parts **a–c.**

Time (sec)	Distance (m)	Time (sec)	Distance (m)
0	0	11	170.8
1	7.4	12	155.4
2	36.9	13	147.7
4	134.2	14	141.9
6	192.9	15	136.3
8	212.3	16	130.8
10	192.9		

a. Determine the rocket's average speed during the time interval [6,10].

b. Determine the average velocity of the rocket during the same interval.

c. Explain why your responses to Parts **a** and **b** are different.

1.4 **a.** Determine the average velocity of the rocket in Problem **1.3** during the time interval [6,8].

b. Estimate the instantaneous velocity of the rocket at $t = 3$ sec. Describe how you determined your estimate.

1.5 The table below shows a space shuttle's distance from earth at various times during its initial vertical ascent.

Time (sec)	Distance (m)	Time (sec)	Distance (m)
24	1791	136	53,355
48	7274	160	66,809
72	15,539	184	78,374
96	27,920	208	88,117
120	43,326		

SOURCE: Johnson Space Center, Houston, Texas.

a. Create a distance-time graph of this data.

b. Based on this data, over what time interval does the space shuttle appear to start slowing down? Justify your response.

c. What is the average velocity of the space shuttle over the time interval [24,120]?

d. **1.** Estimate the shuttle's instantaneous velocity, in meters per second, 195 sec after liftoff. Describe how you determined your estimate.

2. Express your response to Step **1** in kilometers per hour.

* * * * *

1.6 Sketch a distance-time graph that illustrates the motion of Little Red Riding Hood in the following paragraph:

Little Red Riding Hood left home and walked briskly down the road towards Grandmother's house. Along the way, she stopped to pick some violets growing beside the road. The Wolf saw her picking flowers and offered to show her a shortcut. He led Little Red Riding Hood on a winding path through the woods. After the path crossed the road for the third time at the place where she had picked the flowers, Little Red Riding Hood realized that she'd been tricked. She got back on the road and ran the rest of the way to Grandmother's house.

1.7 The table below shows the distances between an object and a fixed point over time.

Time (sec)	Distance (m)	Time (sec)	Distance (m)
1	2	14	303
2	5	15	303
3	33	16	313
4	55	17	323
5	94	18	333
6	160	19	104
7	273	20	41
8	283	21	20
9	293	22	11
10	303	23	7
11	303	24	5
12	303	25	3
13	303		

a. Create a distance-time graph of this data.

b. Which ordered pair (t,d), where d represents distance and t represents time, corresponds to the moment when the object first stopped moving away from the fixed point? Explain your response.

c. **1.** When did the object start moving back toward the fixed point?

2. How did its velocity change at this time?

d. Calculate the average velocity of the object during the time interval [4,10]. What does this value tell you about the object's motion?

e. Calculate the average velocity of the object during the time interval [18,23]. What does this value tell you about the object's motion?

In the months before each launch, NASA engineers determine a space shuttle's longitude, latitude, altitude, and weight for every 0.04 sec of the flight. How are they able to predict these values with such accuracy and confidence?

At least some of the credit for scientists' ability to make such predictions must go to the English mathematician and physicist, Sir Isaac Newton (1642–1727). Newton used three concise laws of motion to describe the rules that govern the movement of objects both on earth and in space.

science note

A **force** is a physical quantity that can affect the motion of an object. Two familiar forces are gravity and friction.

According to Newton's **first law of motion,** an object in a state of rest or moving in a straight line at a constant speed will continue in that state unless acted on by a force.

Exploration

We can model a distance-time graph with a linear equation when the distance between an object and a fixed point changes at a constant rate. In this exploration, you use a range finder to explore the movement of a ball at a constant velocity.

a. Obtain a track, a ball, and the range-finder apparatus from your teacher. As shown in Figure **10-4,** place the track on a level surface and position the range finder at one end. Place the ball on the track approximately 0.5 m from the range finder.

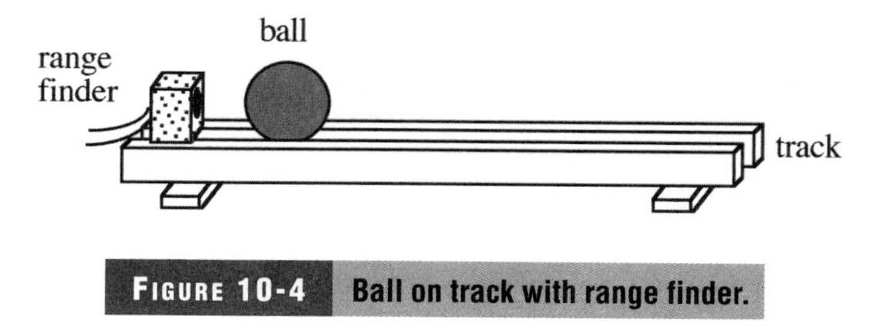

FIGURE 10-4 **Ball on track with range finder.**

b. Push the ball away from the range finder just hard enough so that it rolls to the end of the track. Collect distance-time data as the ball rolls.

c. Repeat Part **b** several times, increasing the force of the initial push each time. Observe how changing the ball's speed affects the resulting distance-time graphs.

d. Select a data set and graph from Part **c** that appears to describe the motion of the ball accurately. Determine the average velocity of the ball over the time interval represented by the graph.

mathematics note

A model might not exactly fit every data point, as Figure **10-6** demonstrates. However, even when a model does not fit every point, it still can provide a reasonable approximation of the data.

A **residual** is the difference between an observed value and the predicted value. In Figure **10-5,** the residual for each data point is the difference between the y-coordinate of the data point and the corresponding y-value of the model. Because data points may be located above or below the model, the values of residuals may be positive or negative.

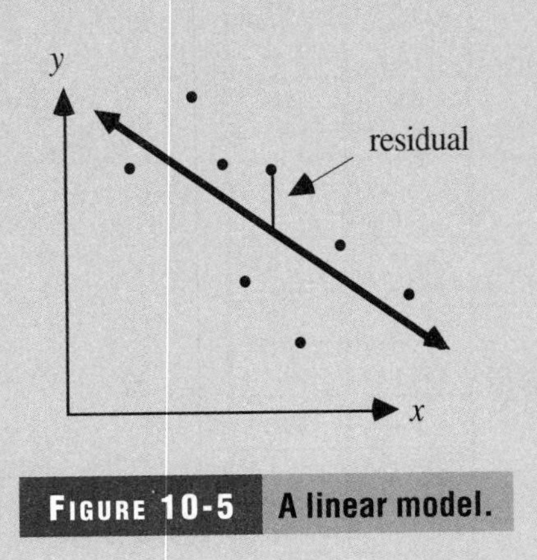

FIGURE 10-5 A linear model.

In a previous module ("What Will We Do When the Well Runs Dry?"), you used the sum of the absolute values of the residuals to help you choose linear models for data sets.

The **square of a residual,** like the absolute value of a residual, is a measure of the distance from a data point to the model. In general, the smaller the sum of the squares of the residuals, the more closely a model approximates the data.

The linear model that results in the least sum of the squares of the residuals is called a **linear regression** or **least-squares line.**

e. Determine a linear equation that appears to model your data set.

   Calculate the sum of the squares of the residuals for your model. Adjust the equation until the sum of the squares of the residuals indicates that the model closely approximates the data.

f. Use technology to find the linear regression for your data set. **Note:** Save your data, graphs, and equations for use in the assignment.

Discussion

a. How did the ball's speed affect the graphs in Part **c** of the exploration?

b. In Parts **d** and **e** of the exploration, you found the ball's average velocity and determined a linear function to model its distance-time data.

1. Describe how you determined the equation in Part **e**.
2. What does the slope of the line indicate about the ball's movement?
3. What does the y-intercept of the line represent?
4. Should the line pass through the origin? Why or why not?
5. How does your equation compare with the linear regression for the data set?

c. If you placed the ball at the far end of the track and pushed it toward the range finder, what would the resulting distance-time graph look like?

d. 1. How can you tell if an equation provides a good model of a distance-time graph?

2. If the function that models the ball's distance-time data is written in the form $f(x) = mx + b$, which part of the equation represents the ball's average velocity? Explain your response.
3. How could you determine the ball's instantaneous velocity in this situation?

e. Suppose that after collecting distance-time data for a ball on a ramp, the resulting graph can be modeled by a function of the form $d(t) = c$, where c is a constant. Describe the motion of the ball.

f. Describe some real-world situations that could be modeled with linear graphs of distance versus time.

Warm-Up

1. Complete a table of values for each of the following linear equations. Your table must include both the x- and y-intercepts, along with $x = -4$, $x = 6$, $y = -2$, and $y = 12$.

a. $y = 3x - 5$

b. $y = \frac{1}{2}x + 3$

c. $2x + 5y = 1$

2. Determine the equation of the line that contains the points in each of the following tables.

a.

x	y
−2	−7
0	3
2	13
5	28

b.

x	y
−3	11
−1	5
0	2
3	−7

c.

x	y
−4	4
−2	3
0	2
4	0

3. Consider the three linear functions $y = 2x - 7$, $5x - 3y = 4$, and $3x = 2y + 6$.

   a. Which of these functions has the greatest y-intercept?

   b. Which of these functions has the greatest average rate of change?

   c. Which of these functions has the greatest x-intercept?

Assignment

2.1 Describe how distance, velocity, and time are related when a ball is moving along a straight track at a constant rate.

2.2 Use the linear equation you found in Part **e** of the exploration to answer the following questions.

a. How far was the ball from the range finder after 1.7 sec?

b. When was the ball 0.75 m away from the range finder?

c. **1.** If the track were long enough, how far from the range finder would the ball be after 10 min?

2. Do you think your prediction is accurate? Why or why not?

2.3 The function below describes the motion of a ball on a level track, where $d(t)$ represents distance in meters from a range finder and t represents time in seconds:

$$d(t) = 0.75t + 0.5$$

a. Make a table showing the ball's distance from the range finder after 0 sec, 1 sec, 2 sec, and 3 sec.

b. Add a column to your table that shows the average velocity of the ball during the following time intervals: [0,1], [1,2], and [2,3].

c. What is the instantaneous velocity of the ball at $t = 2$ sec?

d. How do your responses to Parts **b** and **c** relate to the equation that describes the ball's motion?

2.4 Describe a function that could be used to model the distance-time graph of each of the following:

a. a ball that is not moving

b. a ball moving at a constant velocity of 1 m/sec.

2.5 The table below shows a space shuttle's distance from earth at some specific times after liftoff.

Time (sec)	Distance (m)	Time (sec)	Distance (m)
72	15,539	136	53,355
96	27,920	160	66,809
120	43,326	184	78,374

SOURCE: Johnson Space Center, Houston, Texas.

a. Create a distance-time graph of this data.

b. 1. Determine a linear equation that closely models the data.

2. What is the average velocity of the shuttle during the interval [72, 184]?

c. Use the equation you found in Part **b** to predict the shuttle's altitude after 520 sec.

d. Would it be reasonable to use this linear model to predict the shuttle's altitude at any time during its flight? Explain your response.

2.6 The table below shows some distance-time data collected as a model rocket returned to the ground under its parachute.

Time (sec)	Distance (m)	Time (sec)	Distance (m)
12	155.4	15	136.3
13	147.7	16	130.8
14	141.9	17	125.2

a. Determine an equation that closely models the data.

b. Use your equation to predict when the rocket will reach the ground.

c. Do you think your prediction is reasonable? Why or why not?

2.7 Each of the linear functions below models a distance-time data set collected using a range finder:

1. $d(t) = 3.5t + 1.3$
2. $d(t) = -1.2t + 1.3$
3. $d(t) = 3.0t + 1.3$
4. $d(t) = 3.5t + 2.0$
5. $d(t) = 1.2t + 2.0$

a. Which functions represent objects moving at the same average velocity?

b. Which functions represent objects moving at the same average speed?

c. Which function(s) represent(s) the object that is moving the fastest?

d. Which function(s) represent(s) the object that is moving the slowest?

e. Which function(s) correspond(s) to the object that started nearest to the range finder? farthest from the range finder?

In the previous activity, you examined distance-time graphs of a ball moving at a constant speed. These graphs could be modeled by linear functions. But what type of function would you use to model a distance-time graph for an object whose speed was increasing or decreasing?

mathematics note

Quadratic expressions in a single variable are expressions in which the greatest exponent on the variable is 2. Because of this fact, they are also called **second-degree** expressions.

A quadratic expression in x can be written in the general form $ax^2 + bx + c$, where $a \neq 0$. The **coefficients** of x are a, b, and c.

For example, $3x^2 - 5x + 2$ is a quadratic expression of x written in the general form. The coefficients of x are 3, –5, and 2. The expression $rsx^2 + 2tx + v$ also is a quadratic expression. In this case, the coefficients of x are rs, $2t$, and v.

A function f is a **quadratic function** if $f(x)$ is defined as a quadratic expression in x. Quadratic functions also are called second-degree functions.

For example, $f(x) = -5x^2 + 3x - 7$ is a quadratic function.

A quadratic function can be written in the general form $f(x) = ax^2 + bx + c$, where $a \neq 0$.

Exploration 1

Before using quadratic functions to model distance-time data, you must discover more about their graphs.

The graph of a quadratic function is a **parabola.** For example, Figure **10-6** below shows two parabolas. When a parabola opens upward, its **vertex** occurs at the lowest point in the graph. When a parabola opens downward, its vertex occurs at the highest point in the graph.

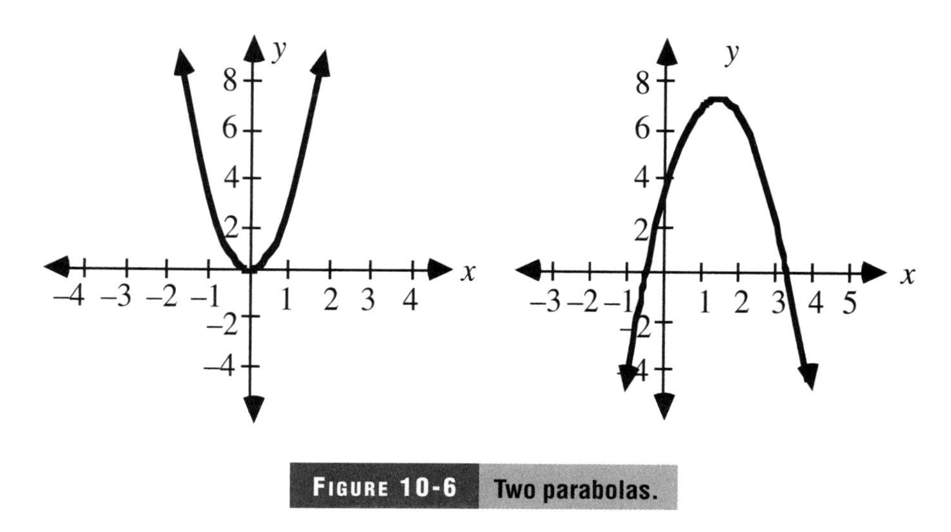

FIGURE 10-6 Two parabolas.

a. 1. Create a graph of the quadratic function $f(x) = x^2 - 6x + 14$.

2. Use your graph to identify the coordinates of the vertex.

3. A parabola is symmetric about a line, known as the **axis of symmetry.** Describe how you could locate the vertex using the axis of symmetry.

4. Write the equation for the axis of symmetry.

mathematics note

Quadratic functions may be written in several different forms, each with its own advantages. A **vertex form,** for instance, allows you to more easily identity the vertex.

A **vertex form** of a quadratic function is $f(x) = a(x - c)^2 + d$, where a, c, and d are real numbers and $a \neq 0$.

For example, the quadratic function $f(x) = x^2 - 6x + 14$ can be written in vertex form as $f(x) = (x - 3)^2 + 5$.

b. 1. Compare the graphs of $f(x) = x^2 - 6x + 14$ and $f(x) = (x - 3)^2 + 5$.

   2. Describe how the vertex form of a quadratic indicates the location of the vertex.

c. 1. How can you modify the function $f(x) = (x - 3)^2 + 5$ to move its graph 2 units upward? (*Hint:* If the vertex moves, the rest of the parabola also must move.) Record your observations.

   2. How can you modify the function $f(x) = (x - 3)^2 + 5$ to move its graph 6 units to the left? Record the new function.

   3. How can you modify the function $f(x) = (x - 3)^2 + 5$ to move its graph down 4 units and to the right 2 units? Record the new function.

d. 1. Write a quadratic function in the form $f(x) = (x - c)^2 + d$ on a sheet of paper.

   2. Create a graph of your equation.

   3. Without revealing your equations, exchange graphs with a classmate.

   4. Use your classmate's graph to determine the equation of the function.

Discussion 1

a. In Exploration **2** of Activity **1,** you graphed some distance-time data for a falling object. What shape best describes the graph?

b. Describe how you can use the vertex form of a quadratic function to determine the coordinates of the parabola's vertex.

c. A **family** of functions is a set of functions that have a common **parent.** The parent of the family of quadratic functions is $p(x) = x^2$.

   Describe how to write the function $p(x) = x^2$ in vertex form.

d. Describe how to write each of the following quadratic expressions in vertex form.

   1. $(x + 2)^2$

   2. $(x - 5)^2$

   3. $x^2 + 3$

   4. $x^2 - 4$

e. The **distributive property of multiplication over addition** provides the basis for multiplying two numbers together.

   To find the product of 4 and 25, for example, you could express 25 as (20 + 5) and distribute the 4 as follows:

$$\begin{aligned} 4(20 + 5) &= (4 \bullet 20) + (4 \bullet 5) \\ &= 80 + 20 \\ &= 100 \end{aligned}$$

Similarly, you could multiply 23 and 17 by expressing 23 as (20 + 3) and 17 as (20 – 3). Using the distributive property of multiplication over addition:

$$\begin{aligned}(20 + 3)(20 - 3) &= 20(20 - 3) + 3(20 - 3) \\ &= (400 - 60) + (60 - 9) \\ &= 391\end{aligned}$$

1. Describe how to use the distributive property to find the product of 3 and $(x - 7)$.

2. Describe how to use the distributive property to multiply $(x - 4)$ and $(x + 4)$.

3. Describe how to use the distributive property to expand $(x + 5)^2$.

f. 1. How could you use the distributive property to express $f(x) = (x - 3)^2 + 5$ in the general form $f(x) = ax^2 + bx + c$? (Recall from the order of operations that you must work with the exponent first.)

2. How does your result compare with the function you graphed in Part **a:** $f(x) = x^2 - 6x + 14$?

Exploration 2

In the following exploration, you continue your investigation of the graphs of quadratic functions.

a. Using a graphing utility, create a graph of the parent function of the quadratic family, $f(x) = x^2$.

b. Express each of the following functions in vertex form.

1. $f(x) = x^2 + 1$
2. $f(x) = x^2 - 1$
3. $f(x) = (x - 1)^2$
4. $f(x) = (x + 1)^2$

c. Create a graph of each quadratic function in Part **b** and compare it to the graph of the parent function.

d. To examine the influence of the value of a on functions of the form $f(x) = ax^2$, graph each function below on the same coordinate system as $f(x) = x^2$. Record your observations.

1. $f(x) = -x^2$
2. $f(x) = 3x^2$
3. $f(x) = \frac{1}{3}x^2$
4. $f(x) = -2x^2$

e. Write each of the functions in Part **d** in vertex form, $f(x) = a(x - c)^2 + d$.

f. Experiment with other negative and positive values for the constants a, c, and d in functions of the form $f(x) = x^2 + d$, $f(x) = (x - c)^2$, and $f(x) = ax^2$. Compare the graph of each function to the graph of $f(x) = x^2$. Record your observations.

Discussion 2

a. How does the value of a appear to affect the graphs of functions of the form $f(x) = ax^2$?

b. How does the value of c appear to affect the graphs of functions of the form $f(x) = (x - c)^2$?

c. How does the value of d appear to affect the graphs of functions of the form $f(x) = x^2 + d$?

d. How would the graph of $f(x) = -0.5(x - 3)^2 + 4$ differ from the graph of $f(x) = x^2$?

e. Figure **10-7** below shows a scatterplot of the data in the table on the left. The scatterplot can be modeled by a quadratic function.

x	y
–4	1
–3	2
–2	1
–1	–2
0	–7
1	–14
2	–23
3	–34
4	–47

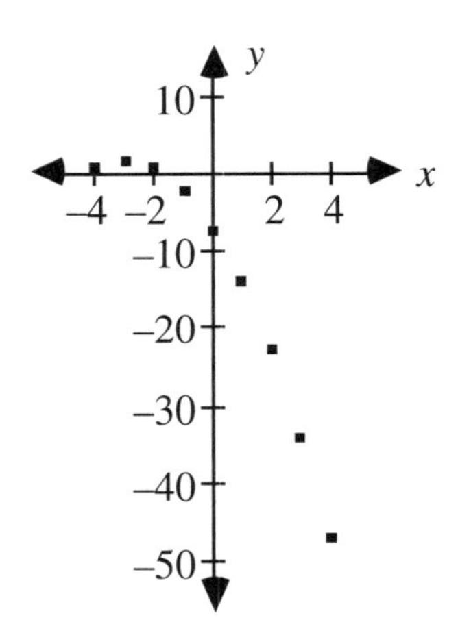

FIGURE 10-7 **Data and scatterplot.**

1. Is it possible to identify the function's y-intercept from the table? If so, describe how. If not, describe how you could approximate it.
2. Is it possible to identify the function's x-intercepts from the table? If so, describe how. If not, describe how you could approximate them.
3. Describe how you would approximate the coordinates of the vertex.
4. Describe how you could use the coordinates of the vertex to obtain the function $g(x) = a(x + 3)^2 + 2$.

5. To determine a function that models this data, you now must identify an appropriate value for a.

   One method for finding a value for a is to select a data point (not the vertex) from the table, then substitute the values for x and $g(x)$ in $g(x) = a(x + 3)^2 + 2$. For example, using the data point $(1, -14)$, you can solve for a as follows:

$$\begin{aligned} g(x) &= a(x + 3)^2 + 2 \\ -14 &= a(1 + 3)^2 + 2 \\ -14 &= 16a + 2 \\ -16 &= 16a \\ -1 &= a \end{aligned}$$

   Given this value for a, what function could be used to model this data?

f. 1. Select a different data point and determine another quadratic function $h(x)$ that could be used to model the data in Figure **10-7.**

   2. Compare $g(x)$ and $h(x)$.

   3. How could you determine which is a better model for the data?

g. Describe how you could rewrite any quadratic function in vertex form in the general form $f(x) = ax^2 + bx + c$.

Warm-Up

1. Write each of the quadratic functions below in the general form $f(x) = ax^2 + bx + c$.

   a. $r(x) = (x - 3)^2$

   b. $g(x) = (x + 5)^2 - 6$

   c. $h(x) = 2(x - 4)^2 - 7$

   d. $s(x) = -5(x + 1)^2 - 3$

   e. $t(x) = -(x + 2)^2 + 1$

2. Each of the following pairs of points satisfies a quadratic function. The first point in each pair is the vertex; the second is another point on the parabola. Write an equation for each function in vertex form.

   a. (2,3), (1,0)

   b. (2,–4), (–3,3)

   c. (0,0), (4,–8)

   d. (–3,2), (0,–4)

3. Use the following table of data to complete Parts **a–e** below.

x	y	x	y
−5	8	1	−10
−4	0	2	−6
−3	−6	3	0
−2	−10	4	8
−1	−12	5	18
0	−12		

a. Identify the x-intercept(s).

b. Identify the y-intercept(s).

c. Determine the approximate interval(s) where the function appears to be increasing.

d. Determine the approximate interval(s) where the function appears to be decreasing.

e. Identify the point(s) where the function changes from increasing to decreasing or decreasing to increasing.

4. Determine a quadratic function that could be used to model the data in Problem **3.** Explain your response.

Assignment

3.1 Determine a function of the form $f(x) = a(x - c)^2 + d$ that represents each of the following changes to the function $f(x) = x^2$. Use graphs to support your responses.

a. a move 3.5 units to the right and 1.4 units up

b. a reflection in the x-axis

3.2 Does the order in which you make changes to the graph of a function affect the result? To investigate this question, complete Parts **a–c.**

a. Create a graph of the function $f(x) = x^2$. Move the graph 3.5 units to the right and 1.4 units up, then reflect it in the x-axis.

b. Create another graph of the function $f(x) = x^2$. Reflect the graph in the x-axis, then move it 3.5 units to the right and 1.4 units up.

c. Compare your graphs from Parts **a** and **b.** What do you observe?

3.3 **a.** Write the function whose graph shows the following changes to the graph of $f(x) = x^2$: a reflection in the x-axis, followed by a move 3 units to the right and 2 units down.

b. To verify your response, graph $f(x) = x^2$ and the function from Part **a** on the same coordinate system.

c. Rewrite your function in Part **a** in the general form of a quadratic.

3.4 Determine a function of the form $f(x) = a(x - c)^2 + d$ whose graph is represented by the bold curve.

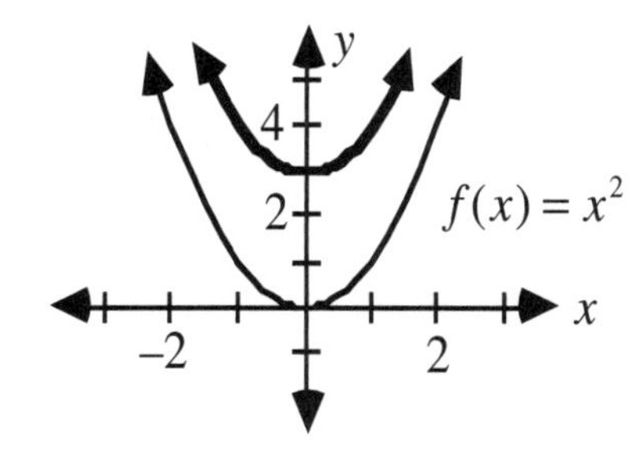

3.5 The distance-time data in the table below can be modeled by a quadratic function.

Time (sec)	Distance (m)	Time (sec)	Distance (m)
0.0	3.0	0.8	7.8
0.2	4.8	1.0	8.0
0.4	6.2	1.2	7.8
0.6	7.2	1.4	7.2

a. Create a scatterplot of the data.

b. Determine a quadratic function that models the data and graph it on the same coordinate system as in Part **a.**

c. Write the function in Part **b** in the general form of a quadratic.

3.6 **a.** Write the function whose graph results in the following changes to the graph of $f(x) = x^2$: a reflection in the x-axis, followed by a move 2 units to the left and 6 units up.

b. To verify your response, graph $f(x) = x^2$ and the function from Part **a** on the same coordinate system.

c. Rewrite the function in Part **a** in the general form of a quadratic.

3.7 Determine a function of the form $f(x) = a(x - c)^2 + d$ whose graph is represented by the bold curve.

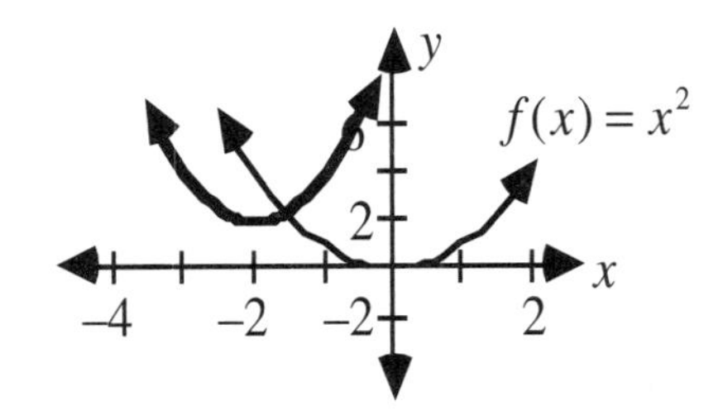

3.8 The data in the table below can be modeled by a quadratic function.

x	$f(x)$	x	$f(x)$
0.0	1.0	0.7	2.1
0.1	1.5	0.9	1.6
0.3	2.1	1.1	0.5
0.5	2.3	1.2	0.1

a. Create a scatterplot of the data.

b. Determine a quadratic function that models the data and graph it on the same coordinate system as in Part **a.**

c. Rewrite the function in Part **b** in the general form of a quadratic.

According to legend, Isaac Newton "discovered" gravity after watching an apple fall from a tree. In this activity, you explore how the **acceleration** due to gravity affects the distance-time graphs of freely falling objects.

science note

Acceleration is the rate of change in velocity with respect to time.

For example, consider a car driving along a straight section of highway. Over time, the velocity of the car can increase, decrease, or remain the same. When the car's velocity increases, its acceleration is positive. When the car's velocity decreases, its acceleration is negative. If the car's velocity remains constant, its acceleration is 0.

You can determine the average acceleration of an object over a particular time interval by dividing the change in velocity by the change in time. For example, consider a model rocket launched straight into the air. At $t = 3$ sec, its velocity is 48.65 m/sec. At $t = 5$ sec, its velocity is 29.33 m/sec. Estimate the rocket's average acceleration during this period as follows:

$$\frac{29.33 \text{ m/sec} - 48.65 \text{ m/sec}}{5 \text{ sec} - 3 \text{ sec}} = -9.65 \text{ m/sec}^2$$

This means that during the time interval [3,5], the rocket's velocity decreased by an average of 9.65 m/sec for every second that passed.

Discussion 1

a. When you rolled a ball along a level track in Activity **2,** its velocity remained almost constant over time. If one end of the track was raised, and the ball rolled down the incline, do you think that its velocity also would remain constant? Explain your response.

b. As the ball continues down the track, how would the distances traveled in equal time intervals compare?

c. What do you think a graph of the distance-time data collected for a ball rolling down an inclined track will look like?

d. Describe the shape of a scatterplot that you would model with each of the following:

1. a linear regression
2. a quadratic regression

Exploration

In this exploration, you collect distance-time data for a ball rolling down an incline. You then use quadratic functions to model this data.

a. Obtain a track, a ball, and the range-finder apparatus from your teacher. Set up the track and range finder as in Activity **2**, then use books or blocks to raise the end of the track with the range finder on it.

b. Place the ball approximately 0.5 m from the range finder and gently release it. (Do not push the ball down the track.) You should begin collecting distance-time data just before the ball is released.

c. Repeat Part **b** several times, then select a data set and graph that you think accurately describes the motion of the ball down the track.

d. 1. Edit your data set so that it contains only information collected as the ball was actually moving, beginning with the moment of its release.

   2. Determine a quadratic equation that appears to model this data set.

e. Recall that a **residual** is the difference between an observed value and the corresponding value predicted by a model, and that the sum of the squares of the residuals can be used to evaluate how well a model fits a data set.

   Calculate the sum of the squares of the residuals for your model. Adjust the equation until the sum of the squares of the residuals indicates that the model closely approximates the data. **Note:** Save your data set, graph, and equation for use later in the module.

f. In Activity **2**, you used linear regression equations to model data. Many calculators and computer software programs also can generate other types of regression equations, including exponential, power, and quadratic (or second-degree) regressions.

   Use technology to determine a quadratic regression equation for your data set in Part **d.**

g. If the track were extremely steep, the ball's motion would be virtually a **free fall.** In physics, the term *free fall* refers to an object falling without air resistance and affected only by the force of gravity.

   Remove the range finder from the track and point it at the floor from a height of approximately 60 cm. Hold the ball directly beneath the range finder at a height of about 10 cm. Release the ball.

   You should begin collecting distance-time data just before the ball is released and stop after the ball hits the ground. Repeat this experiment several times, then select a data set and graph that you think accurately describes the motion of the ball.

h. Repeat Parts **d–f** using the data for the falling ball.

Discussion 2

a. 1. How did raising one end of the track affect the speed of the ball over time?

   2. How is this effect displayed on the distance-time graphs?

b. 1. Describe how to express the quadratic functions you found in Parts **d** and **h** of Exploration **2** in the general form of a quadratic function.

2. Compare each of these equations to the quadratic regression equation for the same data set.

c. How do the distance-time graphs and equations you found in this exploration compare with those you used to model a ball rolling on a level track in Activity **2**?

d. Use your graphs from this exploration and the one in Activity **2** to answer the following questions.

1. Describe the shape of a distance-time graph when an object's acceleration is 0.

2. What influence does an object's acceleration have on the shape of its distance-time graph?

3. How does the magnitude of the acceleration affect the equations used to model the distance-time data?

science note

The acceleration due to gravity is a constant typically denoted by g. On earth's surface, the acceleration due to gravity is about 9.8 m/sec^2 in a direction toward the earth's center. For comparison, the acceleration due to gravity on the moon's surface is about 1.6 m/sec^2.

When an object is acted on only by gravity, its distance from the ground is described by the following function:

$$d(t) = -\frac{1}{2}gt^2 + v_0t + d_0$$

where $d(t)$ represents the object's distance from the ground after t sec, g is the acceleration due to gravity, v_0 is the object's velocity in the vertical direction at $t = 0$, and d_0 is the object's distance above the ground at $t = 0$.

For example, consider a tennis ball dropped from a height of 10 m. Because the ball is dropped and not thrown, its initial velocity in the vertical direction is 0, or $v_0 = 0$. Its initial distance above the ground is 10 m, therefore $d_0 = 10$. On earth, the value of g is about 9.8 m/sec^2. To calculate the ball's height above the ground after 1 sec, substitute these values into the equation for $d(t)$ as follows:

$$\begin{aligned} d(1\text{ sec}) &= -\frac{1}{2}(9.8\text{ m/sec}^2)(1\text{ sec})^2 + (0\text{ m/sec})(1\text{ sec}) + 10\text{ m} \\ &= -4.9\text{ m} + 0\text{ m} + 10\text{ m} \\ &= 5.1\text{ m} \end{aligned}$$

e. 1. Using the general formula described in the previous science note, write a quadratic function that should describe the distance from the ground over time of the falling ball in Part **h** of Exploration **2.**

2. Compare this function to the ones you determined in the exploration. Why do you think there are differences in these equations?

Warm-Up

1. Create a scatterplot of the data in each table below.

a.

x	y
−5	10
−4	1
−3	−9
−2	−10
−1	−11
0	−12
1	−10
2	−5
3	−1
4	6
5	19

b.

x	y
−5	22
−4	21
−3	19
−2	18
−1	13
0	11
1	5
2	2
3	−1
4	−2
5	−7

c.

x	y
−5	15
−4	3
−3	−10
−2	−11
−1	−9
0	−14
1	−10
2	−7
3	0
4	8
5	21

2. Describe an appropriate type of function to model each scatterplot in Problem **1.** Use technology to find the regression equation.

3. Solve each of the following equations for y when $x = -2$, $x = 0$, and $x = 3$.

a. $y = -11x^2 + 4x + 12$

b. $y = x^2 - 2.3x - 19$

c. $y - 12 = 4x - 11x^2$

Assignment

4.1 The table below shows the space shuttle's distance above the earth at various times after liftoff.

Time (sec)	Distance (m)	Time (sec)	Distance (m)
0	0	72	15,539
24	1791	96	27,920
48	7274		

SOURCE: Johnson Space Center, Houston, Texas.

a. Create a distance-time graph of this data.

b. Find an equation that closely models the data. Graph this equation on the same coordinate system as in Part **a.**

c. Use your model to estimate the shuttle's distance above the earth at each of the following times:

1. 50 sec

2. 600 sec

d. This shuttle will orbit the earth at an altitude of approximately 160 km. Given this fact, do your predictions in Part **c** seem reasonable? Explain your response.

e. Determine the approximate number of seconds required for the shuttle to reach an altitude of 160 km.

4.2 The data in the following table was generated using a ball, a ramp, and a range finder.

Time (sec)	Distance (m)	Time (sec)	Distance (m)
0	0.022	1.0	0.426
0.2	0.022	1.2	0.733
0.4	0.022	1.4	1.124
0.6	0.071	1.6	1.600
0.8	0.206	1.8	2.164

a. Determine an equation that models the data collected while the ball was rolling.

b. Predict the position of the ball 2 sec after its release.

c. If the ramp were long enough, how long would it take the ball to reach a position 4 m from the range finder?

4.3 Use the data given in Problem **4.2** to complete Parts **a–c** below.

a. Estimate the ball's instantaneous velocity at each of the times listed in the following table.

Time (sec)	Velocity (m/sec)
0.5	
0.7	
0.9	
1.1	
1.3	

b. Use the values found in Part **a** to estimate the ball's average acceleration during each of the intervals listed in the table below.

Time Interval (sec)	Acceleration (m/sec^2)
[0.5, 0.7]	
[0.7, 0.9]	
[0.9, 1.1]	
[1.1, 1.3]	

c. How does the acceleration of the ball appear to change over time?

4.4 Sketch a distance-time graph that could represent each of the situations described below.

a. A ball moves away from a range finder with an acceleration of 0.

b. A ball moves away from a range finder with a positive acceleration.

c. A ball moves away from a range finder with a negative acceleration.

4.5 The distance-time graph below shows data collected during the flight of a model rocket. After its engine burns out, the primary force acting on the rocket is gravity.

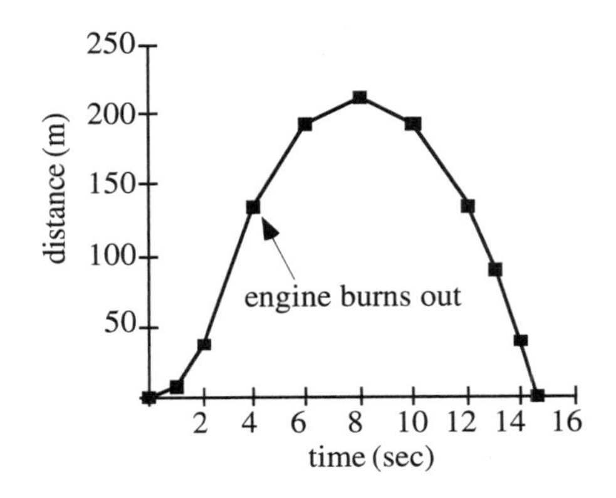

a. Identify the locations on the graph where the velocity of the rocket is positive, zero, or negative.

b. Based on your responses to Part **a,** which of the graphs below represents a graph of velocity versus time for the interval $[4, 14]$? Justify your choice.

1.

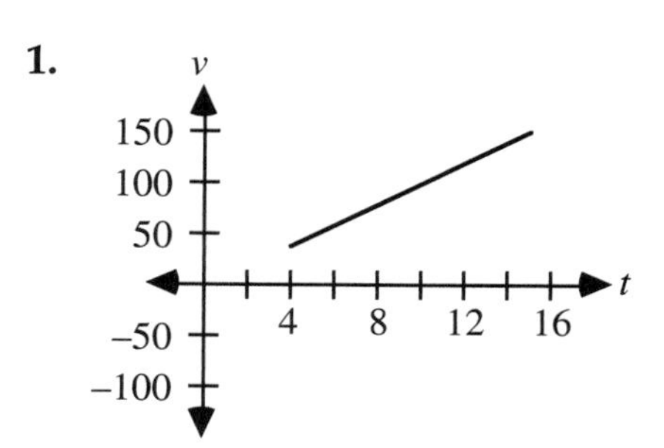

2.

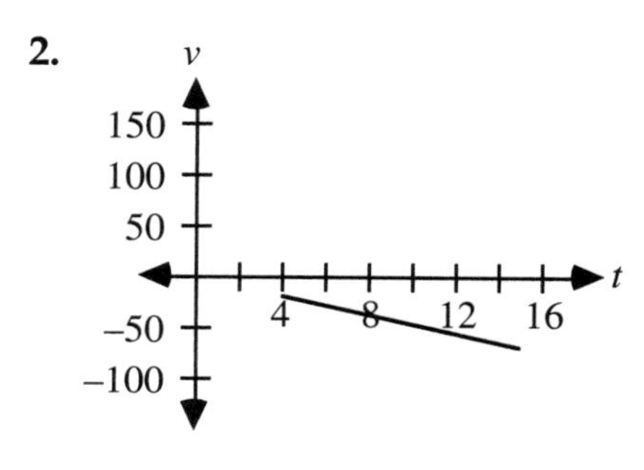

3.

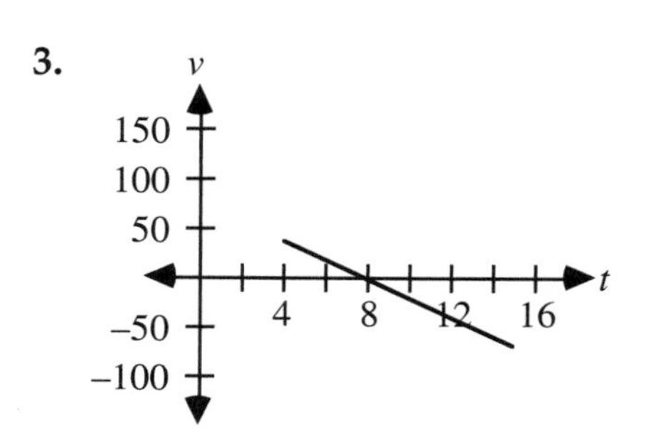

4.

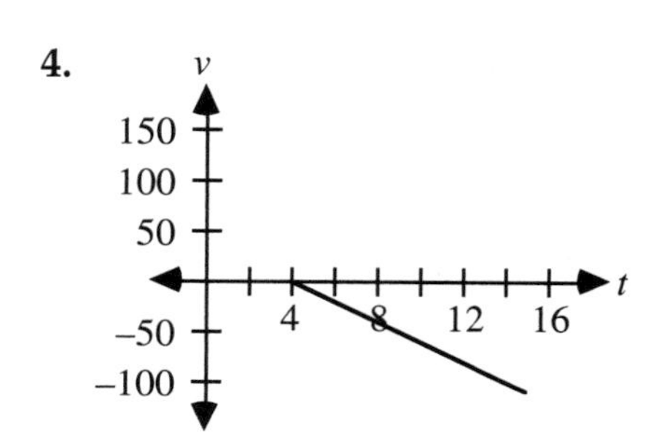

c. Using the graph you selected in Part **b,** describe a graph of the rocket's acceleration versus time over the same interval. Justify your response.

4.6 The table below shows the distance above the ground at various times for a bouncing ball.

Time (sec)	Distance (m)	Time (sec)	Distance (m)
0.00	0.0	0.48	0.933
0.08	0.301	0.56	0.878
0.16	0.549	0.64	0.762
0.24	0.736	0.72	0.583
0.32	0.865	0.80	0.342
0.40	0.929	0.88	0.0

a. Find a quadratic equation that closely models this data.

b. According to your model, when does the ball reach its highest point?

c. What is the velocity of the ball at the time it reaches this point?

d. What is the velocity of the ball at $t = 0$?

4.7 Suppose that you have used a range finder to collect distance-time data for a freely falling object. Your data can be modeled by the function $d(t) = 4.9t^2$, where $d(t)$ represents distance in meters and t represents time in seconds.

a. Describe the motion of the object, including its initial velocity and initial distance from the range finder.

b. Use the model equation to estimate when the object was 4 m from the range finder.

4.8 Sir Isaac Newton once said that if he had seen farther than other scientists and mathematicians, this was because he had "stood on the shoulders of giants." One of those giants was Galileo Galilei (1564–1642), who died in the year of Newton's birth. In fact, Newton's first law of motion was actually a variation on Galileo's concept of inertia.

a. Besides describing inertia, Galileo theorized that, in the absence of air resistance, two objects of different sizes and weights dropped from the same height would reach the ground at the same time. What does Galileo's theory predict about the motions of an apple falling from a tree and the ball you dropped in the exploration?

b. On one of the Apollo missions to the moon, an astronaut demonstrated Galileo's theory by dropping a hammer and a feather from the same height. Given that the acceleration due to gravity on the moon is $1/6$ that on earth, what function could be used to describe the two objects' distance from the lunar surface with respect to time?

c. If the hammer and feather were dropped from a height of 2 m, how long would it take them to reach the lunar surface?

d. If this demonstration were conducted on earth, how long would it take the hammer to reach the ground?

4.9 The data in the table below shows a rocket's distance above the ground at various times after launch. At $t = 2$ sec, the rocket's engine burned out. After this time, gravity is the primary force acting on the rocket.

Time (sec)	Distance (m)	Time (sec)	Distance (m)
2	36.9	8	212.3
4	134.2	10	192.9
6	192.9	11	170.8

a. Find a polynomial equation that closely fits the data.

b. Interpret the significance of each coefficient in your equation.

4.10 The table below shows a space shuttle's distance above the ground during the first seconds after liftoff. Find an equation that models this data. Explain why you think your model fits the data well.

Time (sec)	Distance (m)	Time (sec)	Distance (m)
0.00	0.00	7.68	153.31
1.92	6.10	9.60	249.63
3.84	33.53	11.52	371.86
5.76	81.69	13.44	519.99

SOURCE: Johnson Space Center, Houston, Texas.

Research Project

Select one of the following topics.

a. In addition to his three laws of motion, Isaac Newton also proposed a law of universal gravitation. Together, these few principles revolutionized the sciences of physics and astronomy. Write a report on Newton's contributions to the study of motion, including an explanation of the relationship among force, mass, and acceleration.

b. Scientists at NASA closely analyze each launch of the space shuttle and make a wealth of information available to the public. Contact the Johnson Space Center regarding a past or future shuttle flight. Write a report on the launch, including an analysis of the flight-path data.

Summary Assessment

1. The distance-time data shown below was obtained by moving a book toward and away from a range finder taped to a desk.

Time (sec)	Distance (m)	Time (sec)	Distance (m)
0.0	1.393	2.4	1.856
0.4	1.145	2.8	1.838
0.8	0.851	3.2	1.549
1.2	0.682	3.6	1.308
1.6	0.859	4.0	0.841
2.0	1.328		

   a. Create a distance-time graph of this data.

   b. Describe what happens to the velocity of the book during the interval from 0 sec to 4 sec.

   c. Identify at least three different time intervals in which the book's average velocity is 0.

   d. During which 0.4-sec interval is the book moving the fastest?

   e. Find an equation that models the motion of the book during each of the following intervals:

      1. from 0 sec to 0.8 sec

      2. from 0.4 sec to 2.0 sec.

2. The following distance-time data was recorded for a falling ball:

Time (sec)	Distance (m)	Time (sec)	Distance (m)
0.00	0.42	0.45	0.84
0.05	0.42	0.50	1.00
0.10	0.42	0.55	1.19
0.15	0.42	0.60	1.40
0.20	0.42	0.65	1.63
0.25	0.44	0.70	1.89
0.30	0.50	0.75	2.17
0.35	0.59	0.80	2.06
0.40	0.70		

a. Create a distance-time graph for this data.

b. Describe the time interval for which the ball was actually falling.

c. Find an equation that models the distance-time graph for this interval.

d. Explain how the terms of the equation you found in Part **c** relate to the movement of the ball.

e. Calculate the average velocity of the ball during each of the following intervals:

   1. [0.25,0.35]

   2. [0.65,0.75]

f. Explain why the two average velocities you found in Part **e** are different.

Module Summary

- A **distance-time graph** displays the distance between two objects as a function of time.
- The set of all real numbers between two fixed endpoints is a **real-number interval.** Each endpoint may or may not be included in the interval.
- One way to describe an interval is with an **inequality.**
- A real-number interval also can be described using **interval notation.** In interval notation, a square bracket,] or [, indicates that the endpoint is included in the interval. A parenthesis,) or (, indicates that the endpoint is not included in the interval.
- A set of real numbers greater or less than a given value increases or decreases without bound. Such a set of numbers is an **infinite interval.**
- The notation for an infinite interval uses ∞, the symbol for infinity, along with a parenthesis, to indicate that the set does not end. When describing sets of real numbers less than a given value, the symbol for negative infinity ($-\infty$) is used.
- **Displacement** is a change in the position of an object. It has both magnitude and direction.
- **Velocity** is the rate of change in position with respect to time. It also has both magnitude and direction.
- The **average velocity** of an object can be calculated by dividing its displacement by the change in time.
- The **instantaneous velocity** of an object is its velocity at a particular instant in time. To estimate the instantaneous velocity at a given instant t, one can use the average velocity of the object during a small interval containing t.
- A **force** is a physical quantity that can affect the motion of an object. Two familiar forces are gravity and friction.
- According to Newton's **first law of motion,** an object in a state of rest or moving in a straight line at a constant speed will continue in that state unless acted on by a force.
- A **residual** is the difference between an observed value and the predicted value. Because data points may be located above or below the model, the values of residuals may be positive or negative.
- The **square of a residual** is a measure of the distance from a data point to the model. In general, the smaller the sum of the squares of the residuals, the more closely a model approximates the data.
- The linear model that results in the least sum of the squares of the residuals is called a **linear regression** or **least-squares line.**

* **Quadratic expressions** in a single variable are expressions in which the greatest exponent on the variable is 2. Because of this fact, they are also called **second-degree** expressions.
* A quadratic expression in x can be written in the general form $ax^2 + bx + c$, where $a \neq 0$. The **coefficients** of x are a, b, and c.
* A function f is a **quadratic function** if $f(x)$ is equal to a quadratic expression in x. Quadratic functions also are called second-degree functions.
* A quadratic function can be written in the general form $f(x) = ax^2 + bx + c$, where $a \neq 0$.
* The graph of a quadratic function is a **parabola.** When a parabola opens upward, its **vertex** occurs at the lowest point in the graph. When a parabola opens downward, its vertex occurs at the highest point in the graph. A parabola is symmetric about a line, known as the **axis of symmetry.**
* A **vertex form** of a quadratic function is $f(x) = a(x - c)^2 + d$, where a, c, and d are real numbers and $a \neq 0$. The coordinates of the vertex are (c, d).
* A **family** of functions is a set of functions that have a common **parent.** The parent of the family of quadratic functions is $p(x) = x^2$.
* **Acceleration** is the rate of change in velocity with respect to time.
* The acceleration due to gravity is a constant typically denoted by g. On earth's surface, the acceleration due to gravity is about 9.8 m/sec^2 in a direction toward the earth's center.
* When an object is acted on only by gravity, its distance from the ground is described by the following function:

  $$d(t) = -\frac{1}{2}gt^2 + v_0 t + d_0$$

  where $d(t)$ represents the object's distance from the ground after t sec, g is the acceleration due to gravity, v_0 is the object's velocity in the vertical direction at $t = 0$, and d_0 is the object's distance above the ground at $t = 0$.

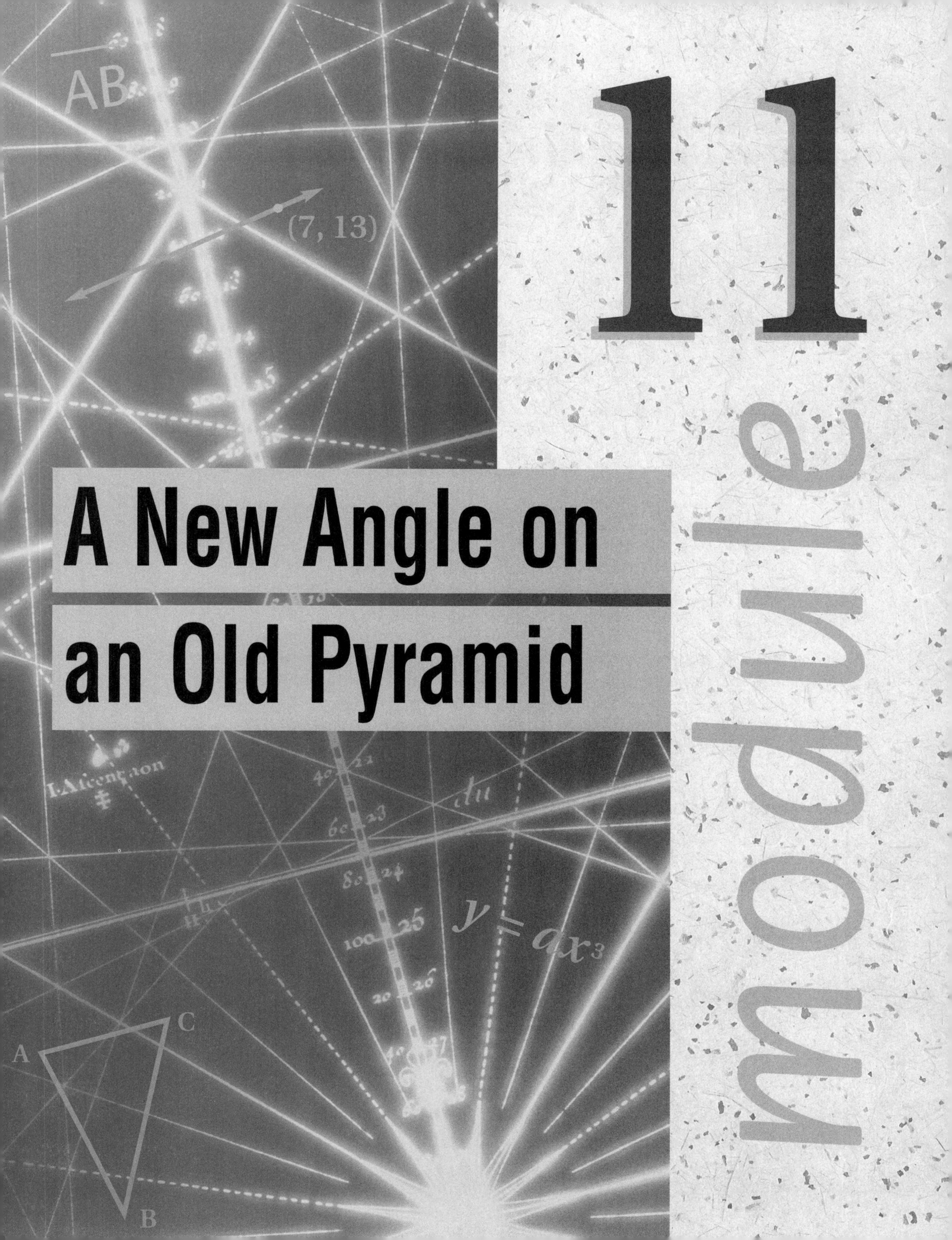
11
module
A New Angle on
an Old Pyramid

Introduction

Tutankhamen and Khufu were kings of ancient Egypt. Khufu ruled around 2500 B.C., and Tutankhamen (King Tut) governed about 1200 years later. King Tut's artifacts are among the most popular items displayed in museums today. King Khufu built the Great Pyramid at Giza, one of the "seven wonders" of the ancient world.

Still standing after 4500 years, the Great Pyramid is an amazing architectural monument. Designed as Khufu's burial tomb, the structure is a regular square pyramid which originally stood 147 m high. Each side of its square base measured 230 m, as Figure **11-1** shows.

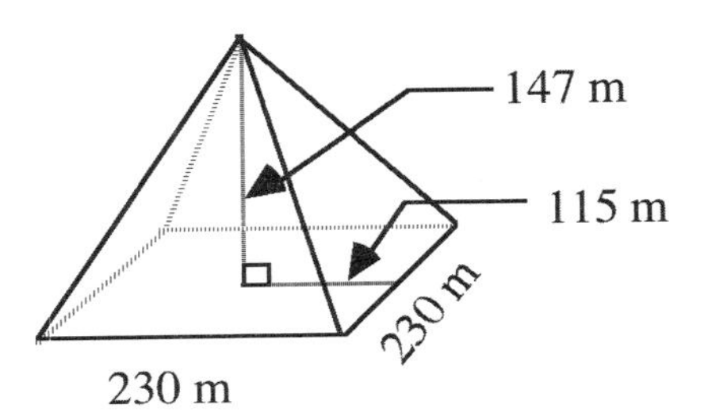

Figure 11-1 Dimensions of the Great Pyramid.

The Great Pyramid consists of about 2.3 million stone blocks, each with a mass of approximately 1000 kg. An estimated 100,000 laborers worked, possibly for 20 summers, to complete this engineering marvel. They used two basic kinds of stones: rectangular blocks and casing blocks. The casing blocks gave the faces of the pyramid a smooth, continuous slope.

The base of the Great Pyramid is nearly a perfect square. To build a structure of this size to such exacting specifications, the Egyptian engineers and surveyors must have applied some mathematics. Due to the lack of written records, however, historians are unsure about what mathematics the builders actually knew. In this module, you investigate some mathematical ideas that historians believe might have been used to build the pyramid.

ACTIVITY 1

Modern engineers use precise measuring tools to stake out the corners of a building's foundation before beginning construction. How did the Egyptians locate the corners of the Great Pyramid without the benefit of such tools? In this activity, you review some of the difficulties involved in performing this task.

Exploration

When two or more people make the same measurement, they may obtain different values. In some cases, a small difference in one measurement can have big consequences for another. In this exploration, you use proportions to investigate this possibility.

a. On a large sheet of paper, construct one corner of a square by following Steps **1–3** below. When marking points and line segments on the paper, make them dark enough to show through another sheet of paper.

   1. Mark a point C near the lower left-hand corner of the paper, 5 cm from each edge.

   2. Draw a line segment from point C to the lower right-hand corner of the paper. As shown in Figure **11-2,** place point D on the segment 30 cm from point C.

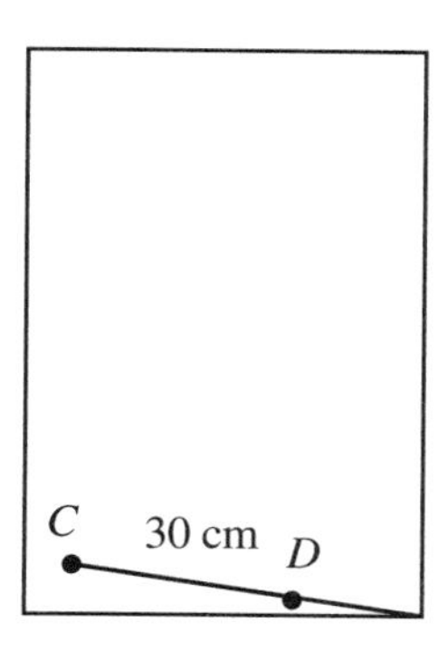

FIGURE 11-2 Segment from point *C* to point *D*.

   3. Use a protractor and a meterstick to draw a line segment that passes through point C, is perpendicular to $\overline{CD}$, and has length of 1 m. Label the point at the end of the segment as P.

b. Compare the corner you created with those of others in the class by completing the following steps.

1. Select one group's sheet of paper from Part **a** on which to record the class results.
2. Place the selected sheet on top of another sheet and align the two drawings of $\overline{CD}$.
3. Mark the location of point P on the lower sheet on the top sheet.
4. Repeat Steps **2** and **3** until the information for the entire class has been collected on the selected sheet.

c. 1. On the common sheet of paper, identify the two locations of P that are farthest apart. Measure the distance between these points to the nearest millimeter.

2. Label these two points X and Y.
3. Express the length of $\overline{XY}$ in centimeters.
4. Draw $\triangle CXY$. The common sheet should now resemble the diagram in Figure **11-3.**

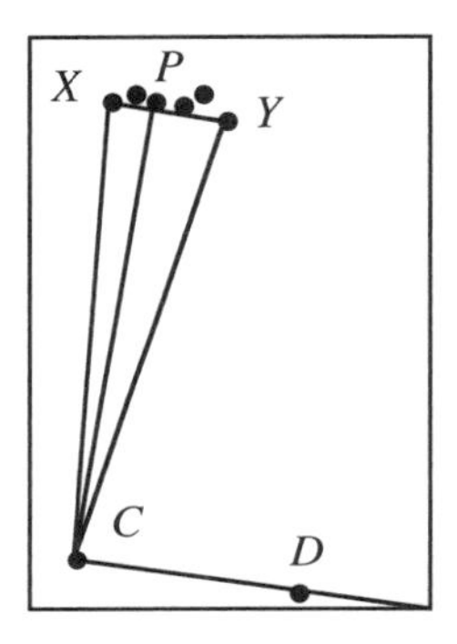

FIGURE 11-3 $\triangle CXY$ **on the common sheet of paper.**

d. Imagine that R is a point on $\overrightarrow{CX}$ 100 m from C, and S is a point on $\overrightarrow{CY}$ 100 m from C. Predict the distance between R and S.

Discussion

a. Why was there a difference between the corner you drew and those drawn by others in your class?

b. What type of triangle is $\triangle CXY$? What are its special features?

c. Two figures are **similar** when they have the same shape and corresponding sides are proportional. The symbol used to indicate similarity is $\sim$. When $\triangle ABC$ is similar to $\triangle DEF$, explain why the notation $\triangle ABC \sim \triangle EDF$ is an incorrect way of expressing this similarity.

mathematics note

In plane geometry, when the angles of one triangle are congruent to the corresponding angles of another triangle, the triangles are similar. This is referred to as the **Angle-Angle-Angle (AAA) property.**

The symbol used to indicate congruence is $\cong$. For example, consider triangles ABC and DEF in Figure **11-4.** As shown by the markings, $\angle A \cong \angle D$, $\angle B \cong \angle E$, and $\angle C \cong \angle F$. Because their corresponding angles are congruent, $\triangle ABC \sim \triangle DEF$.

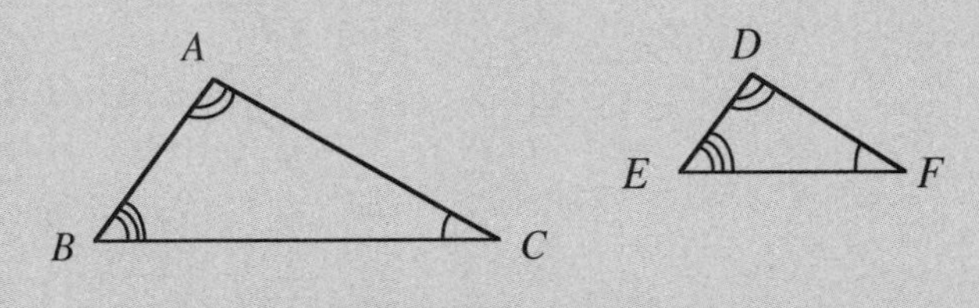

FIGURE 11-4 Two similar triangles.

These triangles are similar, therefore the measures of their corresponding sides are proportional, as shown below.

$$\frac{AB}{DE} = \frac{AC}{DF} = \frac{BC}{EF}$$

d. In the exploration, which triangle is similar to $\triangle CXY$? Explain your response.

e. How could you use the pair of similar triangles identified in Part **d** of the discussion to determine the distance between R and S?

mathematics note

A **conditional statement** is one that can be written in **if-then form.** A conditional consists of two parts: the **hypothesis** and the **conclusion.** The hypothesis is the "if" part of the conditional. The conclusion is the "then" part.

For example, consider the conditional statement, "If an animal is a German shepherd, then the animal is a dog." In this case, the hypothesis is "an animal is a German shepherd." The conclusion is "the animal is a dog."

f. 1. How would you write the AAA property as a conditional statement?

2. What is the hypothesis of the AAA property?

3. What is the conclusion of the AAA property?

Warm-Up

1. The ratio of the lengths of two corresponding sides of two similar polygons is called the ________________.

2. In the diagram below, $ABCD \sim WXYZ$. Use this fact to determine each of the following:

   a. the scale factor of $ABCD$ to $WXYZ$

   b. the lengths WX, XY, and YZ

   c. the perimeters of $ABCD$ and $WXYZ$

   d. the ratio of the perimeters of the quadrilaterals.

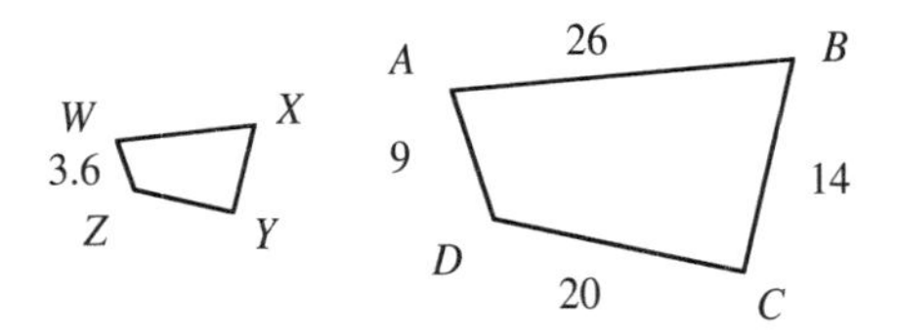

3. Use proportions to determine the values of x and y in the following triangles. (Angles which are marked in the same manner are congruent.)

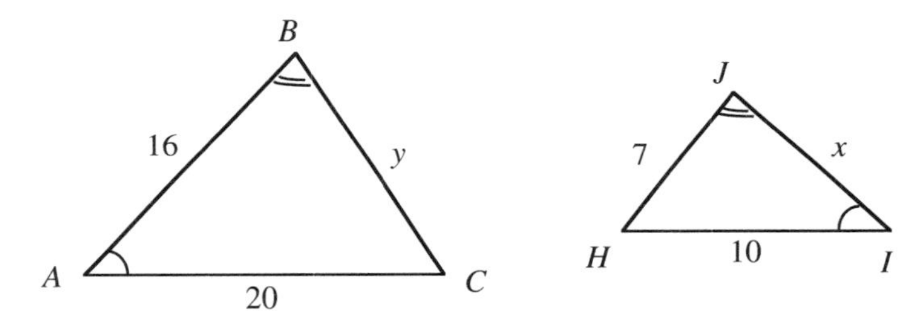

Assignment

1.1 Suppose that King Khufu ordered two different surveyors to stake the corners of the Great Pyramid. At 1 m from the first corner, the distance between the two surveyors' lines equaled the distance you measured in Part **c** of the exploration. How far apart will their two lines be after 230 m, the side length of the base of the Great Pyramid? Explain how you determined your response.

1.2 The Great Pyramid is a regular square pyramid. This means that the base is square, the altitude passes through the center of the base, and the four lateral faces are congruent isosceles triangles. To investigate some of the properties of these lateral faces, complete Parts **a–e** below.

   a. Cut an isosceles triangle from the template supplied by your teacher. Fold the triangle so that the line formed by the fold divides the triangle into two congruent parts, each a mirror image of the other. This line is a **line of symmetry.**

b. Use a protractor and a ruler to determine the relationship between the line of symmetry and the base of the triangle.

c. What is the relationship between the triangle's altitude drawn from the vertex and its line of symmetry? Describe this situation using a conditional statement.

d. When the isosceles triangle is folded along its line of symmetry, what type of triangle is formed? Describe this situation using a conditional statement.

e. What is the relationship between the line of symmetry for the isosceles triangle and its vertex angle? Describe this situation using a conditional statement.

1.3 Two pyramids are similar when their bases are similar and their faces are similar. The diagram below shows two regular square pyramids. As shown by the corresponding markings, $\angle CAB$ and $\angle FDE$ are congruent. Are these pyramids similar? Explain your response.

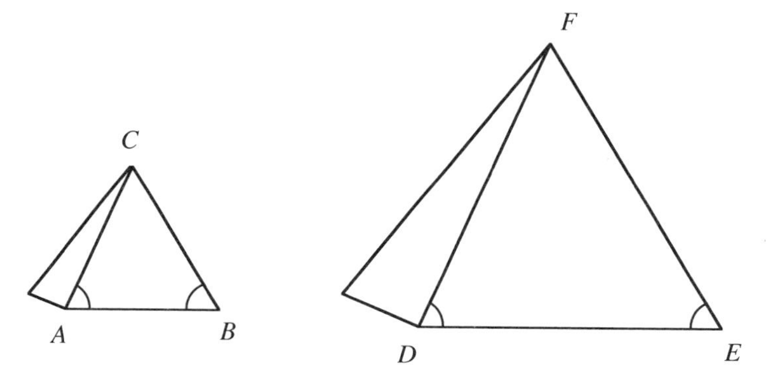

1.4 What is the least amount of information necessary to determine if two triangles are similar? Explain your response.

1.5 **a.** The diagram below shows a cross section of a regular square pyramid where h is the height of the pyramid. The ancient Egyptians were aware that the ratios h/k and b/a are equal. Explain why this relationship is true.

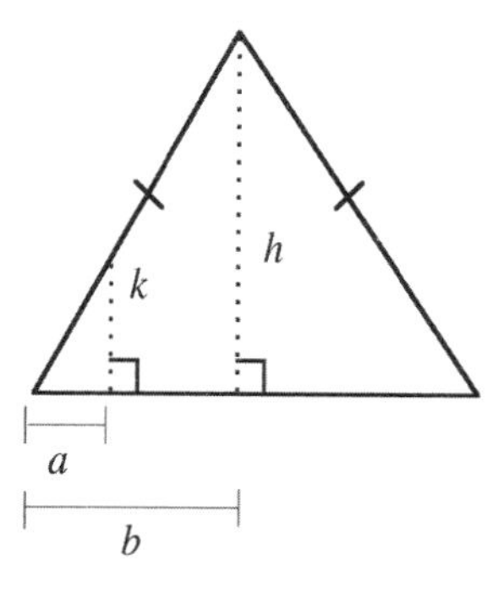

b. Describe a simple rule for determining when two right triangles are similar.

c. Write your rule in Part **b** as a conditional statement.

1.6 One source of information on ancient Egyptian mathematics is the Rhind Papyrus, a scroll about 5.5 m long and 33 cm wide. Written about 1650 B.C. by a scribe named Ahmes, the Rhind Papyrus is a practical handbook of mathematical problems.

As shown in the diagram on the right (not drawn to scale), one of these problems asks for the height of a square pyramid given certain measurements.

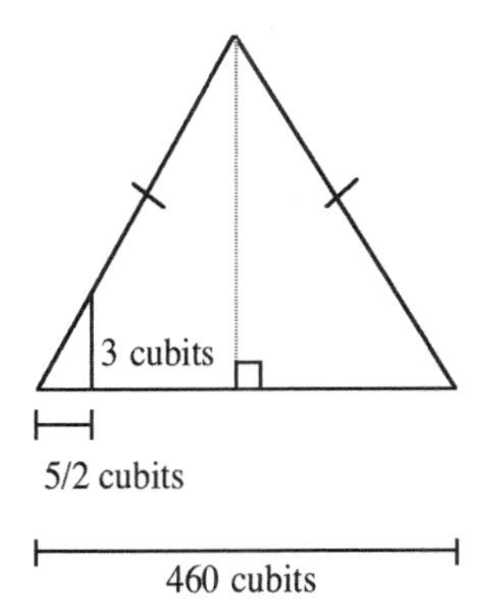

Find the height of the pyramid in cubits. **Note:** In ancient Egypt, the *cubit* was a unit of measurement based on the distance from the elbow to the tip of the fingers in an average person's forearm.

1.7 When placing the giant stone blocks on some levels of the Great Pyramid, workers had to align the blocks edge to edge and corner to corner. The task was similar to installing a tile floor—except on a much larger scale. In the diagram below, two square tiles have been placed with one pair of corners touching. The other pair of corners, however, has a gap of 1 mm. If the next tiles are aligned exactly with these two (as shown in the diagram), then how wide will the gap be after 3 m of tile have been installed? Explain your answer using similar triangles.

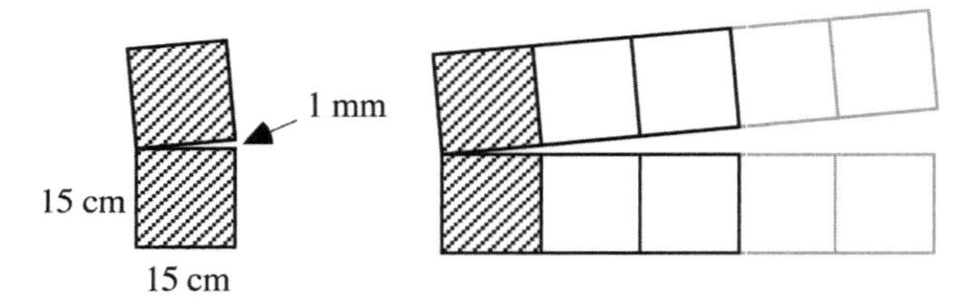

1.8 Your math class has been asked to determine the height of the school flagpole. Since you have no tools to actually measure the flagpole, the class devised a method which involves similar triangles. The diagram below shows a sketch of this situation.

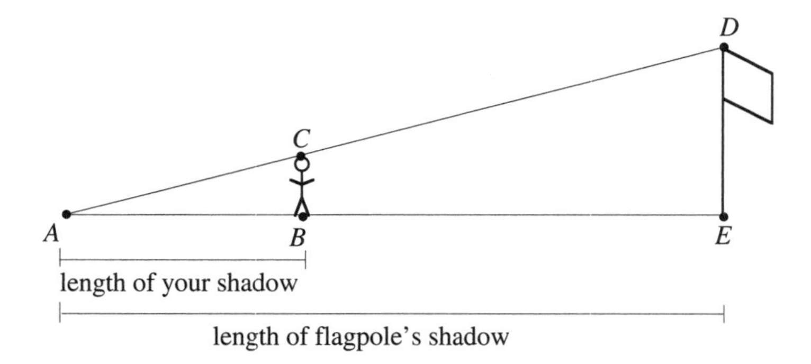

a. Explain why triangles ABC and AED are similar.

b. Describe how to use the properties of similar triangles to find the height of the flagpole.

1.9 A pinhole camera consists of a sealed box with a pinhole opening at one end and a piece of film at the opposite end. When light enters the box through the pinhole, an inverted image is projected on the film.

Consider a pinhole camera 20 cm long, as shown in the diagram below, containing a square piece of film, 5 cm on each side. The object to be photographed occupies a square 42 cm on each side.

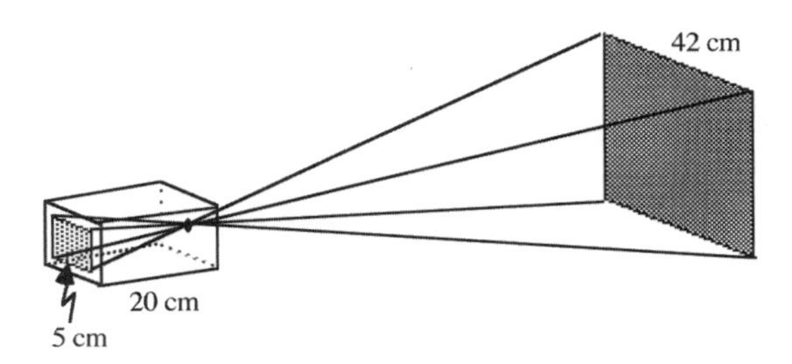

If the photographer wants the image to exactly fill the film, how far away should the camera be placed? Explain your reasoning. (*Hint:* The lines in the diagram indicate the corresponding vertices of the object and the image. The two pyramids formed are similar.)

1.10 When two triangles are similar, are their corresponding altitudes proportional? Write your answer as a conditional statement. Use diagrams to help support your response.

The ancient Egyptians did not measure angles in degrees, so they must have used other methods than those in Activity **1** to make their corners "right." One theory suggests that the Egyptians used a rope subdivided by knots into 12 congruent segments. To make a corner, the rope was formed into a triangle with sides of 3, 4, and 5 units. As Figure **11-5** shows, the special characteristics of this kind of triangle might have allowed the Egyptians to form a right angle. In this activity, you examine such triangles and develop a method for deciding when a corner is "right."

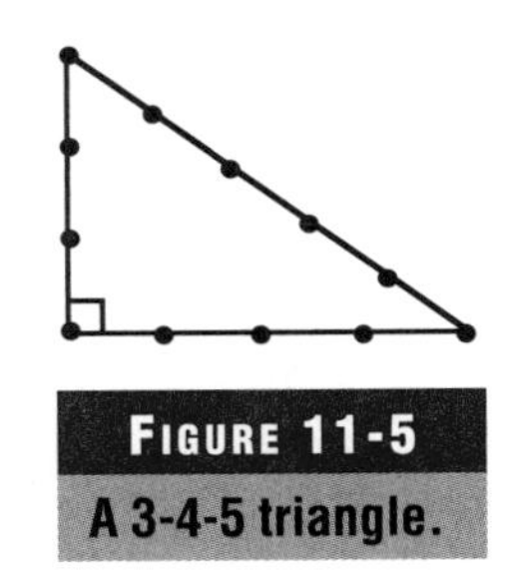

FIGURE 11-5
A 3-4-5 triangle.

mathematics note

The **Pythagorean theorem** states that, in a right triangle, the square of the length of the longest side (the hypotenuse) equals the sum of the squares of the lengths of the other sides (the legs).

In Figure **11-6,** for example, $\angle C$ is a right angle, $\overline{AB}$ is the hypotenuse, and $\overline{BC}$ and $\overline{AC}$ are the legs. Since $\triangle ABC$ is a right triangle, $a^2 + b^2 = c^2$, where a and b are the lengths of the legs and c is the length of the hypotenuse.

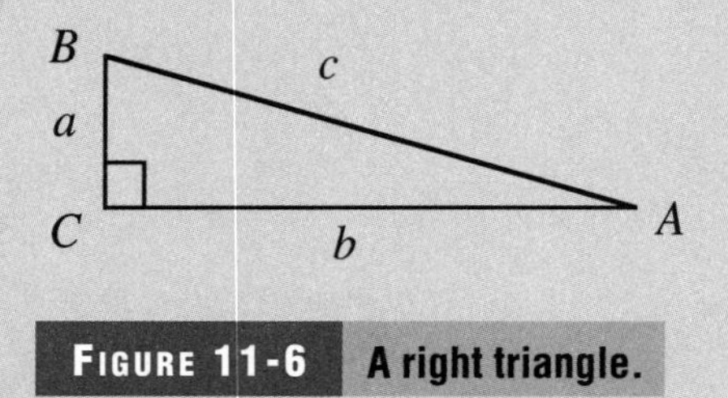

FIGURE 11-6 A right triangle.

Notice that the vertices of the triangle in Figure **11-6** are labeled with capital letters, while the sides opposite these vertices are identified with the corresponding lowercase letters. This is a conventional way to label the parts of triangles.

For example, consider $\triangle RST$ in Figure **11-7.** In this triangle, $s = 13$ m, $t = 5$ m, and $r = 12$ m. Because $\triangle RST$ is a right triangle, $s^2 = t^2 + r^2$ or $13^2 = 5^2 + 12^2$.

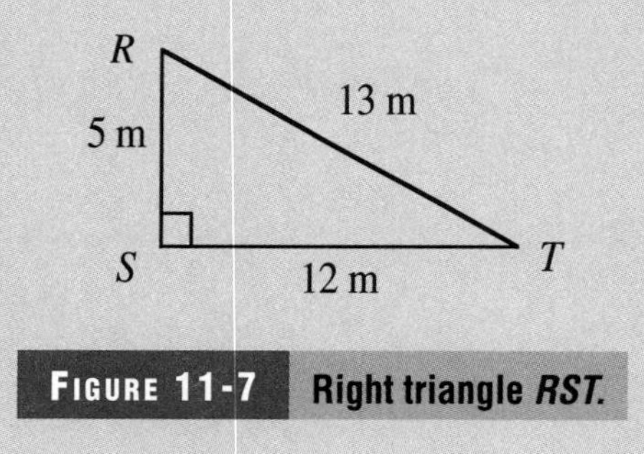

FIGURE 11-7 Right triangle ***RST.***

Exploration

In this exploration, you use a geometry utility and the Pythagorean theorem to investigate triangles. Although the Pythagorean theorem is evident in the rope triangle described above, it is the **converse** of this theorem that would have been more useful to the Egyptians.

mathematics note

The **converse** of a conditional statement in the form "If A, then B" is the statement "If B, then A." The converse of a true conditional statement may or may not be true.

For example, consider the following conditional statement:

"If the country is Egypt, then the Nile River passes through the country."

The converse of this statement is:

"If the Nile River passes through a country, then the country is Egypt."

Because the Nile flows through other countries besides Egypt, the first conditional statement in this example is true, but its converse is not.

a. 1. Write the Pythagorean theorem as a conditional statement.

2. Write the converse of the Pythagorean theorem as a conditional statement.

3. Do you think that the converse is true?

b. Use a geometry utility to test the truth of the converse of the Pythagorean theorem by completing Steps **1–5.**

1. Construct $\triangle ABC$ and two lines perpendicular to the base $\overline{AB}$, as shown in Figure **11-8.**

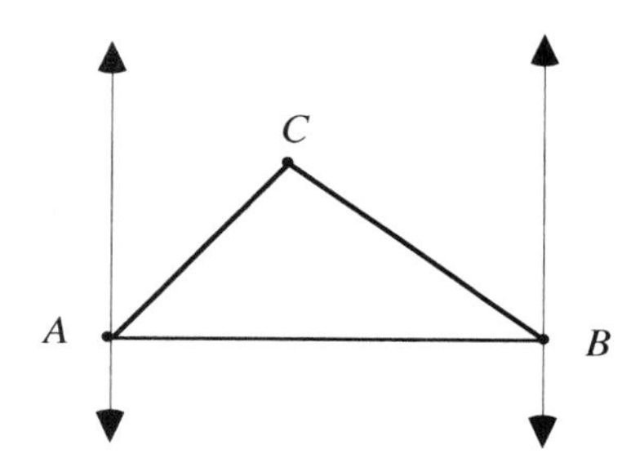

FIGURE 11-8 Construction of $\triangle ABC$.

2. Create a table with headings like those in Table **11-1** below.

TABLE 11-1 ■ *Triangle Data*

$m\angle C$	AB	AC	BC	$(AB)^2 - [(AC)^2 + (BC)^2]$

3. Record the appropriate measurements for $\triangle ABC$ in Table **11-1.**
4. Move point C to another location between the two lines (but without touching either line). Record the appropriate measurements in Table **11-1.**
5. Repeat Step **4** for several other locations of C. Include some positions that make $m\angle C$ acute (less than 90°), some that make it a right angle (exactly 90°), and some that make it obtuse (greater than 90° but less than 180°).

c. 1. When the value of $(AB)^2 - [(AC)^2 + (BC)^2]$ is positive, is $\angle C$ acute, right, or obtuse?

2. When the value of $(AB)^2 - [(AC)^2 + (BC)^2]$ is negative, is $\angle C$ acute, right, or obtuse?

3. When the value of $(AB)^2 - [(AC)^2 + (BC)^2]$ is 0, is $\angle C$ acute, right, or obtuse?

Discussion

a. How is the expression $(AB)^2 - [(AC)^2 + (BC)^2]$ related to the equation for the Pythagorean theorem, $a^2 + b^2 = c^2$?

b. 1. In an obtuse triangle, two angles are acute and one is obtuse. The longest side is opposite the obtuse angle. Based on your data in Table **11-1,** describe how the sides of an obtuse triangle are related.

2. How would you express this relationship as a conditional statement?

c. 1. In an acute triangle, all three angles are acute. Based on your data in Table **11-1,** describe how the sides of an acute triangle are related.

2. How would you express this relationship as a conditional statement?

d. Does the converse of the Pythagorean theorem appear to be true? Explain your response.

e. How could you use the converse of the Pythagorean theorem to determine if a corner is "square"?

Warm-Up

1. Each of the following sets of numbers represents the side lengths of a triangle. Identify whether the triangle is right, acute, or obtuse. Justify your responses.

   a. 9, 15, 12

   b. 8, 8, 8

   c. 14, 11, 23

2. Find the missing length in each right triangle below.

a.

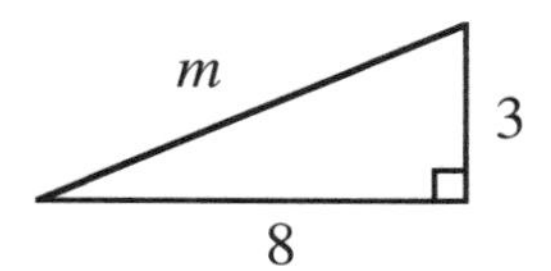

b.

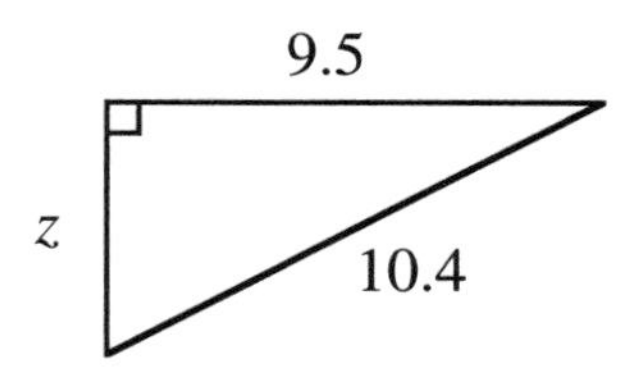

c.

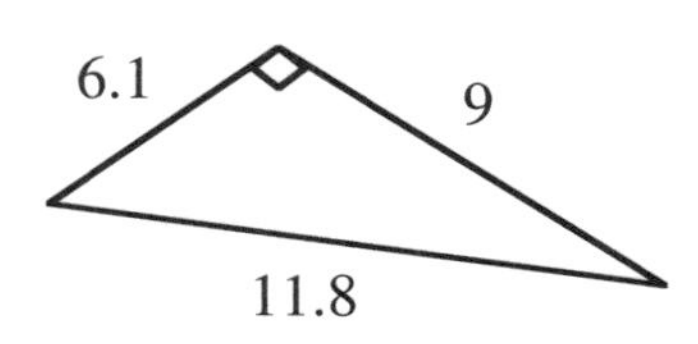

d.

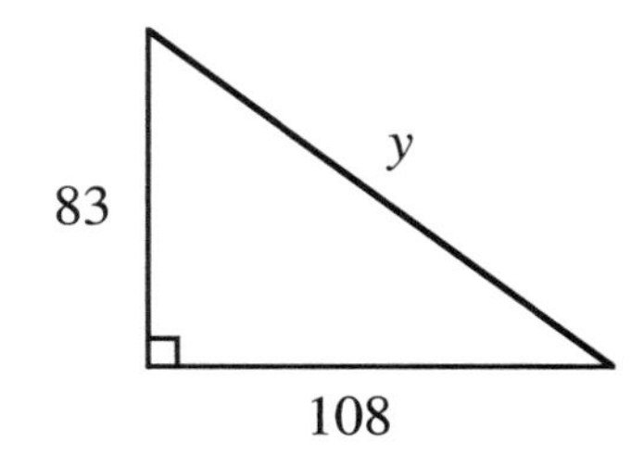

3. Consider the following conjecture: "When the diagonals of a quadrilateral are perpendicular, the quadrilateral is a rhombus."

   a. Write this conjecture as a conditional statement.

   b. Write the converse of the statement in Part **a.**

Assignment

2.1 The scholars of Babylon recorded much of their mathematics on clay tablets. Many of these tablets still exist. One remarkable tablet, designated "Plimpton 322," dates from sometime around 1900 B.C. This fragment of a once larger tablet contains several columns of numbers.

The table below shows a portion of the contents of Plimpton 322, and some numbers (in parentheses) that historians believe were in the original tablet. Each row of three numbers in the table is a *triple.*

Side 1	Side 2	Side 3
(120)	119	169
(72)	65	97
(60)	45	75
(360)	319	481

   a. Use the converse of the Pythagorean theorem to determine what type of triangle—acute, obtuse, or right—is formed when each triple in the table represents the lengths of the sides of a triangle.

   b. If you double each number in a triple from Plimpton 322, does the resulting triple still show the same relationship you described in Part **a**? Explain your response.

2.2 To create a surveying tool similar to the one the Egyptians might have used, mark 12 congruent segments on a string. Considering the length of each segment as 1 unit, form a square whose sides are exactly 3 units long. (Do not use protractors or other tools to help set your corners.) Verify that your result is a square.

2.3 Although the early Babylonians were aware of the relationship represented in the Pythagorean theorem, they had not yet developed the algebraic notation we use today. Instead, they used a sort of "geometric algebra."

The following diagram shows a right triangle ABC with squares constructed on each side. Five shaded pieces subdivide the largest square. Obtain a template from your teacher and cut out the shaded pieces from the largest square. Arrange the pieces so that they exactly fill the two smaller squares. Explain how your arrangement geometrically demonstrates the algebraic expression $a^2 + b^2 = c^2$.

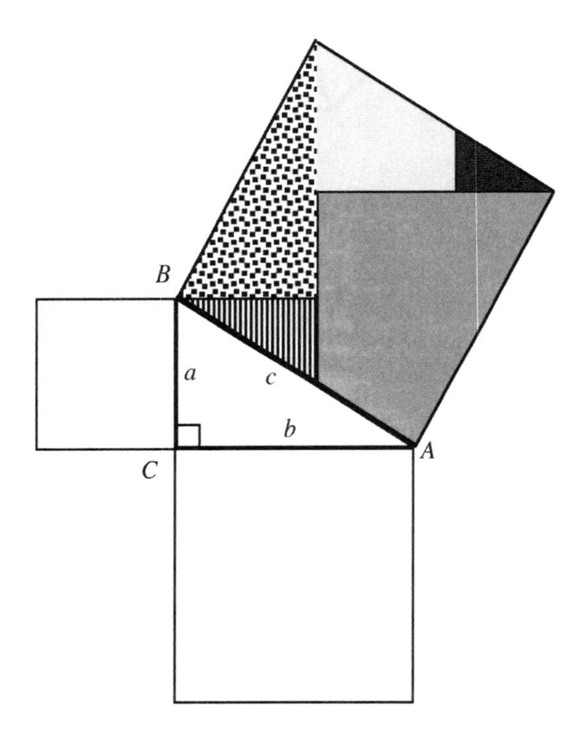

2.4 Given three segments, it is not always possible to use them to form a triangle.

a. Identify at least three different sets of three segments that do not form triangles.

b. Explain why each set of segments does not form a triangle.

c. Describe the relationship that exists among the lengths of three segments when they cannot be used to form a triangle.

d. Rewrite your response to Part **c** as a conditional statement.

2.5 Determine the unknown length x in each of Parts **a–e** below. The pyramids in Parts **c–e** are regular square pyramids.

a.

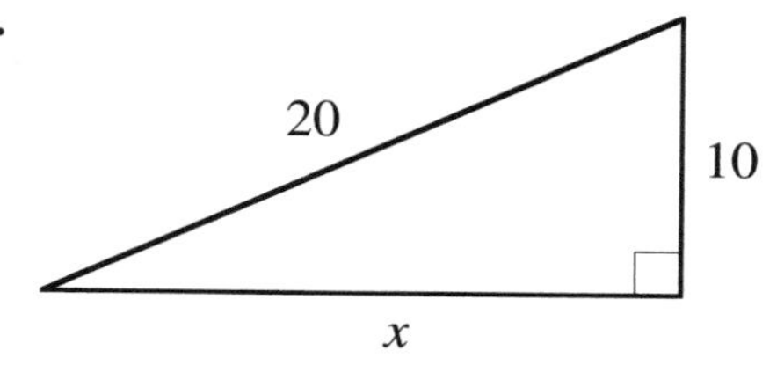

b.

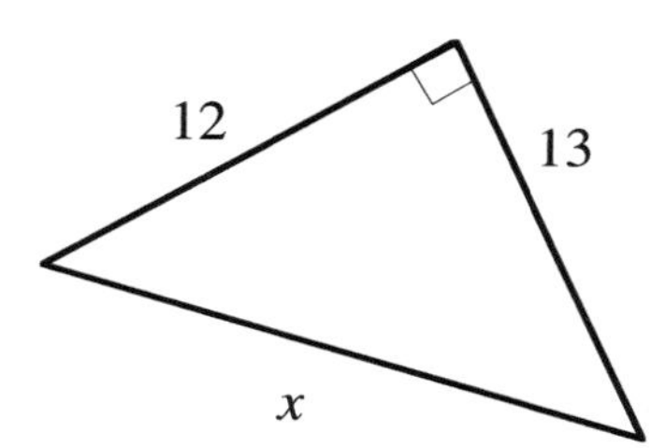

c.

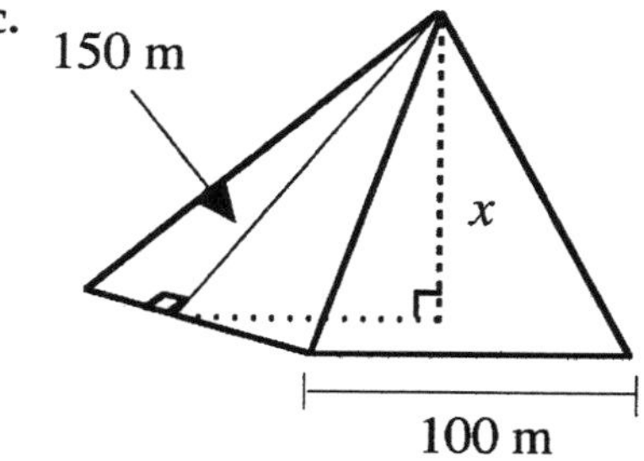

d.

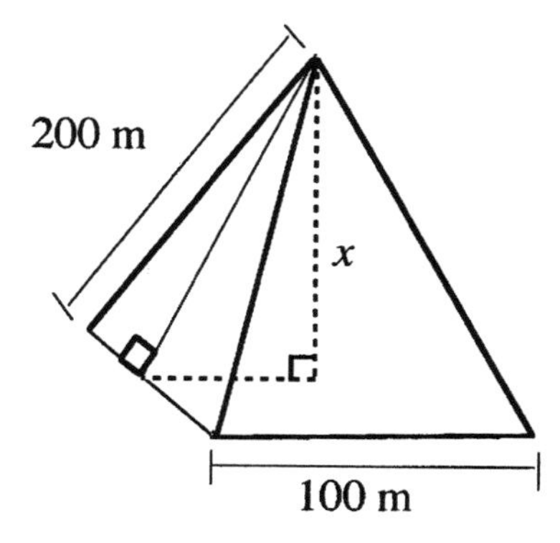

e.

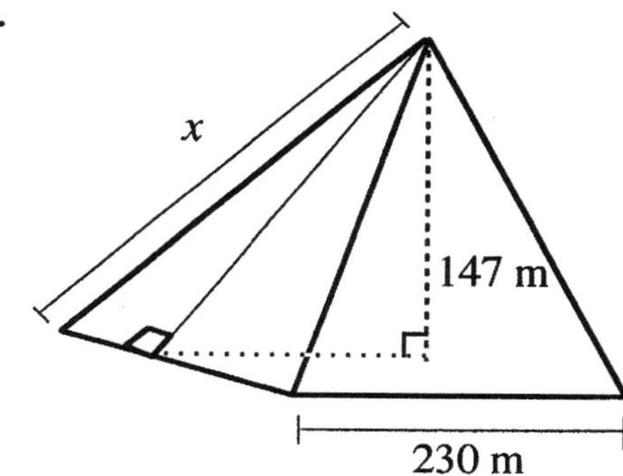

2.6 Without constructing the triangles, determine if the three lengths in each of the following sets would form an acute triangle, an obtuse triangle, a right triangle, or no triangle.

a. 5, 12, 13

b. 6, 8, 12

c. 7, 10, 19

d. 13, 8, 15

2.7 Use the properties of right triangles to find the distance between each pair of points in Parts **a–d.** (In Part **a,** an appropriate triangle has been drawn for you. In Part **d,** use an expression to represent the distance.)

a.

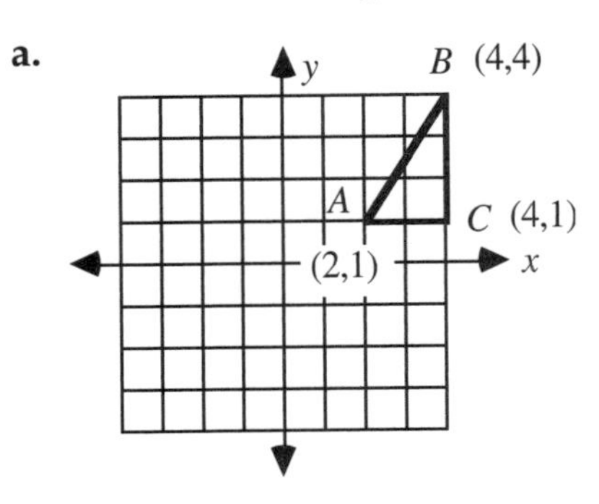

b.

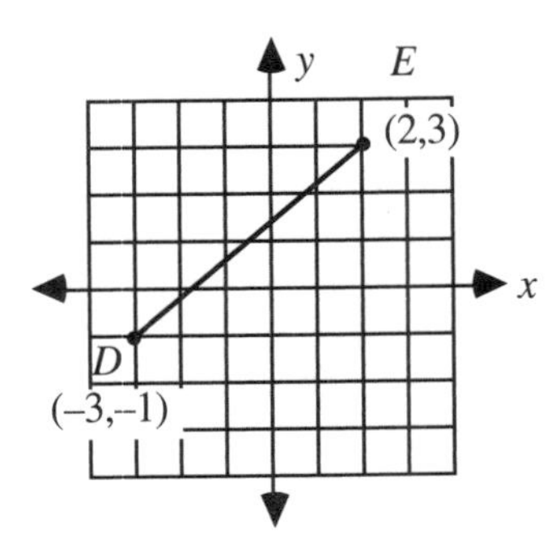

c.

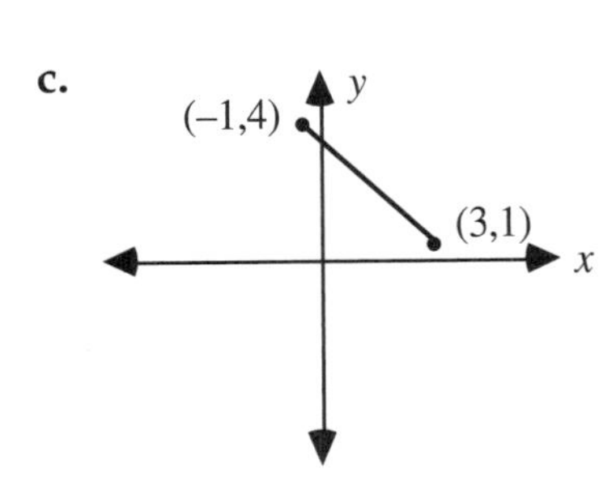

d.

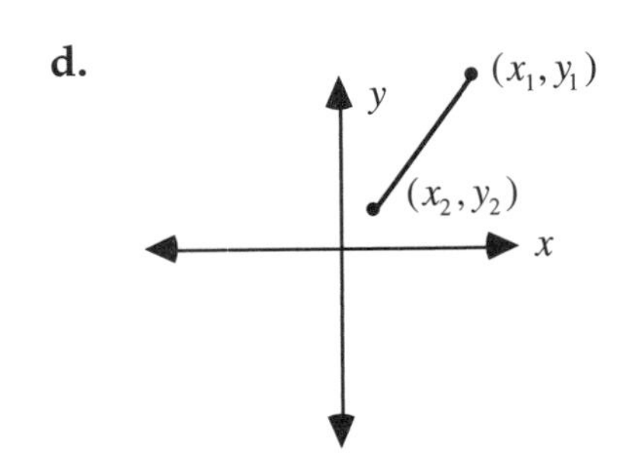

2.8 Some of the granite blocks used in the Great Pyramid are 8.2 m long and 1.2 m thick. Each block has a mass of 49 metric tons, and some of them are set 61 m above the base of the pyramid.

Egyptologists believe that the builders used inclined ramps to raise the stone blocks to these levels. As shown in the diagram below, some researchers have suggested that the incline ratio (slope or rise:run) of these ramps was 1:3.

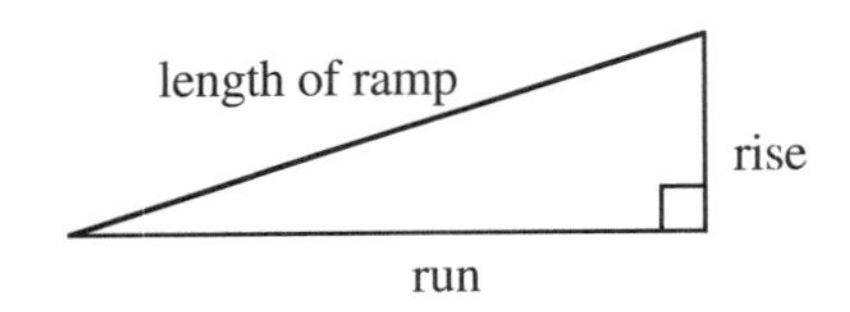

The dimensions of the completed Great Pyramid are shown in the diagram below. If the capstone (the stone on the top) is 1 m tall, how long was the ramp required to raise it?

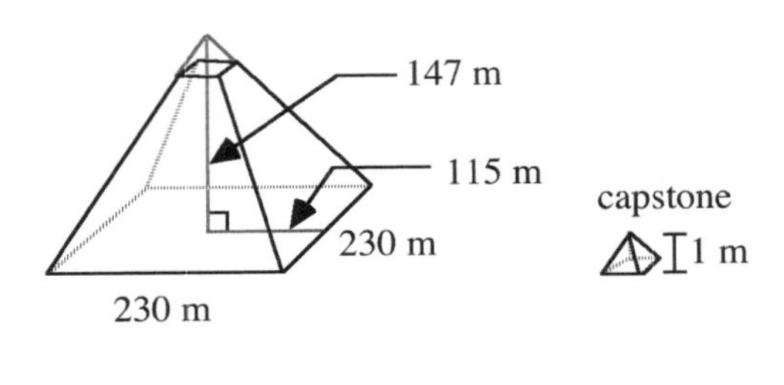

* * * * *

2.9 Leah and Harlan are building a concrete foundation for their new garage. The foundation is a square 8 m on each side. After marking the boundaries, they decide to measure the diagonals to confirm that the corners are right angles. If the corners are right angles, how long should the diagonals be?

2.10 After finishing their garage, Leah and Harlan decide to build a gazebo in their backyard. (A gazebo is a small, roofed structure with open sides.) As shown in the diagram on the right, the floor of their gazebo is a regular octagon. The floor supports lie along the perimeter and the diagonals of the octagon.

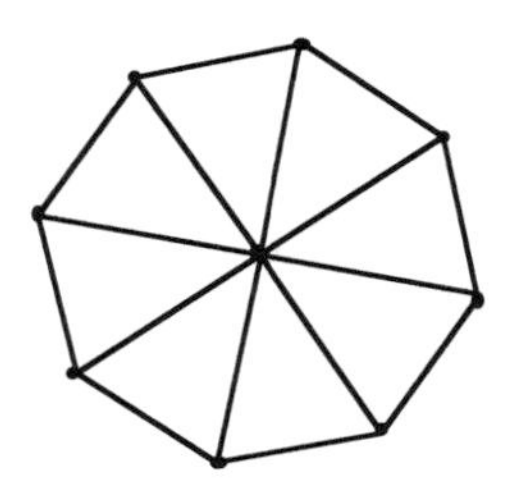

a. The diagonals of the octagon form eight congruent triangles. What type of triangles are these?

b. An altitude drawn from the center of the octagon to the base of each triangle is 2 m long. Each diagonal is 5 m long. Determine the total length of the wood required for the floor supports.

Judging from the information recorded on Plimpton 322, the ancient Babylonians (and the ancient Egyptians too, perhaps) were aware of some uses for the ratios of the sides of right triangles. These ratios are important in many modern applications, from architecture to navigation. The study of these ratios and their properties is the focus of **trigonometry**. In this activity, you explore how the ancient Egyptians might have used some basic trigonometric ideas in the construction of the pyramids.

Exploration

The Great Pyramid of Giza has 203 distinct levels or steps, like those shown below in Figure **11-9.** These steps are not all the same height.

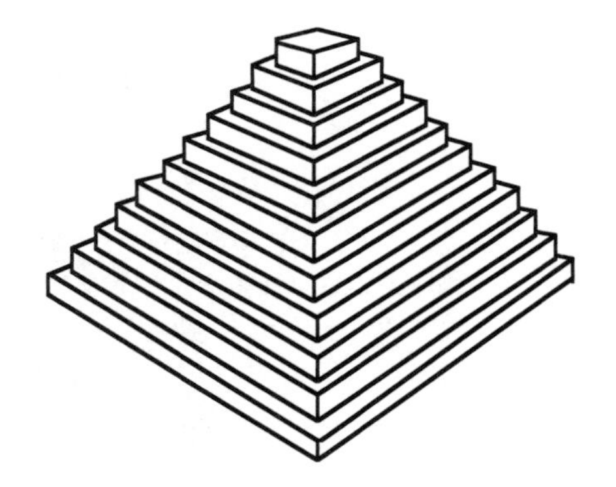

FIGURE 11-9 **Pyramid steps.**

After the steps were built, casing blocks were used to give the pyramid's walls their smooth outer surface. To create a smooth slope, the outer faces of all the casing blocks—regardless of their height—had to be slanted at the same angle to their bases. Figure **11-10** shows a portion of a pyramid wall with three casing blocks.

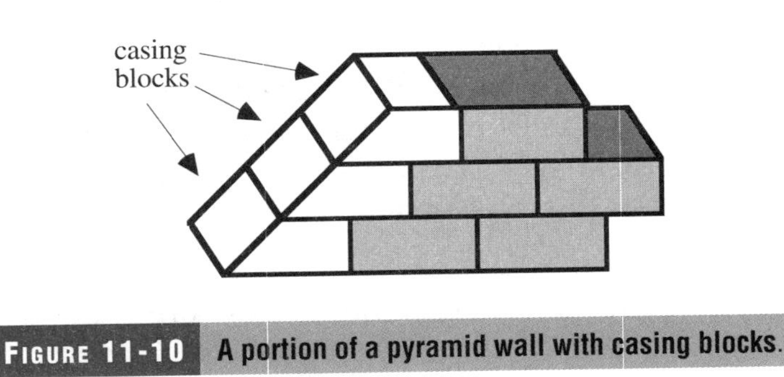

FIGURE 11-10 A portion of a pyramid wall with casing blocks.

An angle formed by two intersecting planes is a **dihedral angle.** The measure of a dihedral angle is the measure of the angle whose sides are the two rays formed by the intersections of the faces and a plane perpendicular to the edge. As shown in Figure **11-11,** the measure of the dihedral angle of the Great Pyramid is 52°.

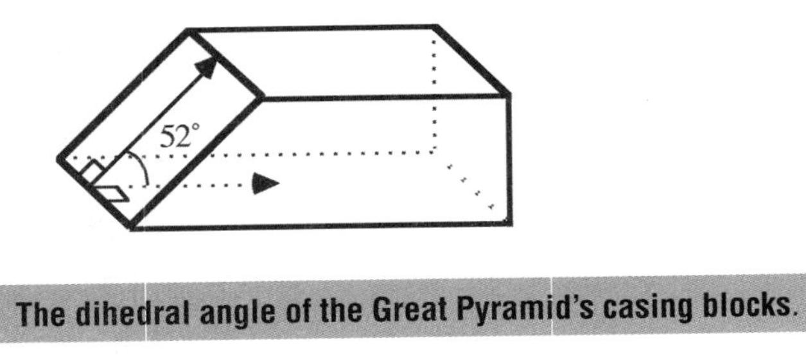

FIGURE 11-11 The dihedral angle of the Great Pyramid's casing blocks.

Figure **11-12** shows cross-sectional drawings of the casing blocks for the bottom and top steps of the Great Pyramid. The bottom step is 141 cm thick, while the top step is 56 cm thick. The heights of the remaining 201 steps lie somewhere between these two values.

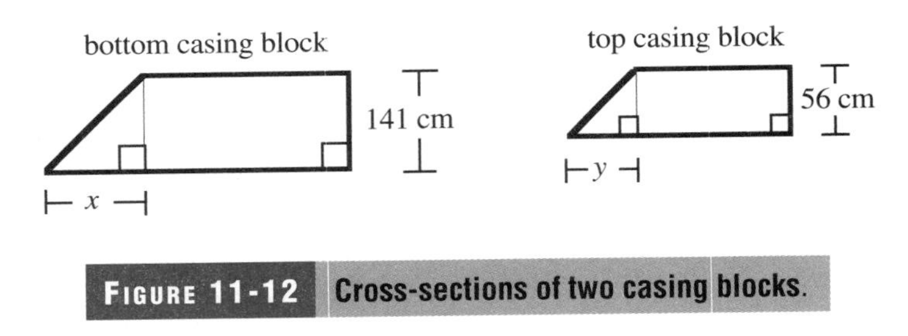

FIGURE 11-12 Cross-sections of two casing blocks.

To maintain a constant dihedral angle measure of 52°, the stonecutters had to be very precise. However, the Egyptians did not measure blocks using angles or degrees. Instead, they used a relationship called the *seqt,* the ratio of the horizontal "run" of a slope to its vertical "rise." The seqt of the bottom casing block in Figure **11-12,** for example, is $x/141$. In this exploration, you experiment with a ratio from trigonometry related to the Egyptian seqt.

a. 1. On a geometry utility, construct a horizontal line. Construct and label two points A and C on the line.

2. Construct a line perpendicular to $\overleftrightarrow{AC}$ through C. Label a point B on the perpendicular.

3. Construct $\overline{AB}$. Your construction should now resemble the one shown in Figure **11-13.**

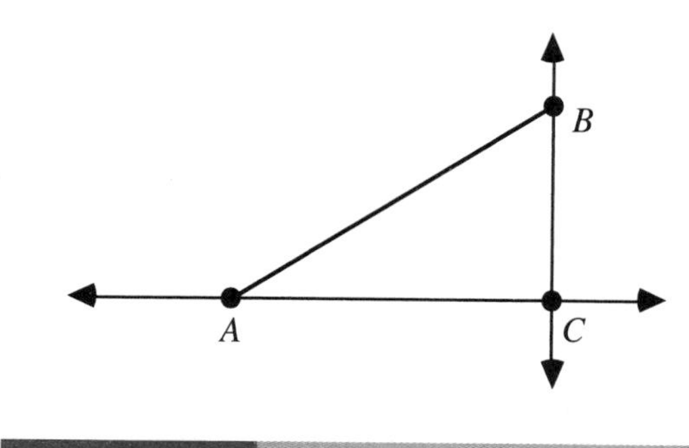

FIGURE 11-13 **Construction of right triangle.**

4. Hide the lines and construct $\overline{AC}$ and $\overline{BC}$, as shown in Figure **11-14. Note:** Save this construction for use in Activity **4.**

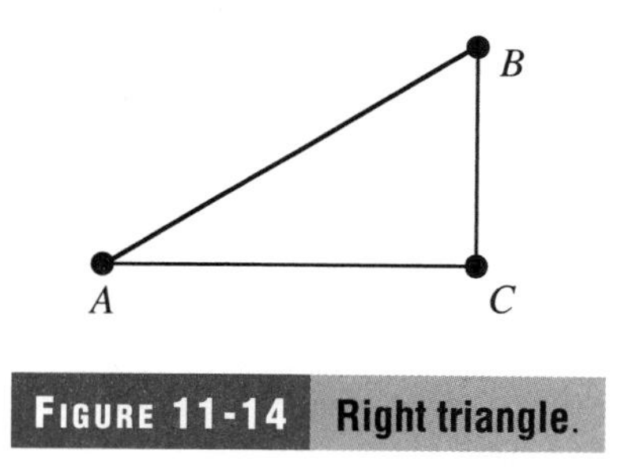

FIGURE 11-14 **Right triangle.**

5. Drag point B until $m\angle A = 52°$ (the measure of the dihedral angle of the Great Pyramid).

b. Measure the legs of right triangle ABC and calculate the ratio below.

$$\frac{\text{length of leg opposite } \angle A}{\text{length of leg adjacent to } \angle A}$$

Note: For convenience, this ratio will be referred to in this module as the ratio "opposite/adjacent."

c. Drag point C along the horizontal line to form other right triangles.

1. As the lengths of the legs change, describe any patterns you observe in the ratios of the lengths.

2. Explain why these right triangles are similar.

d. Create a table with headings like those in Table **11-2.** Drag point B to change the measure of $\angle A$ and record the ratio of the length of the leg opposite $\angle A$ to the length of the leg adjacent to $\angle A$.

TABLE 11-2 ■ *Ratios of Length of Opposite Leg to Adjacent Leg*

$m\angle A$	opposite/adjacent
52°	
15°	
30°	
45°	
60°	
75°	

mathematics note

In any right triangle, the **tangent** of the measure of an acute angle is the ratio of the length of the leg opposite the angle to the length of the leg adjacent to the angle.

For example, Figure **11-15** shows a right triangle ABC.

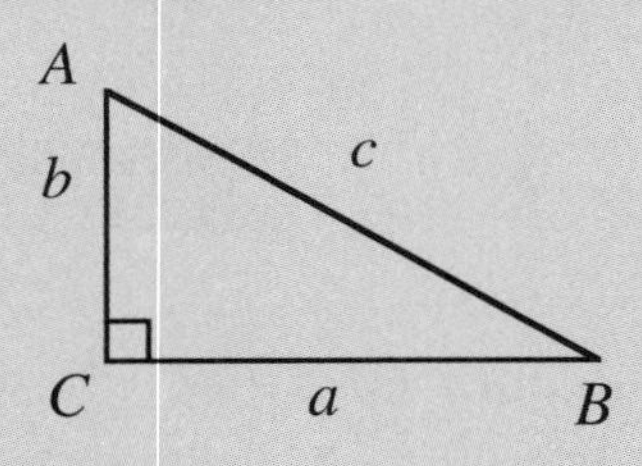

FIGURE 11-15 A right triangle ***ABC.***

In this case, the tangent of $\angle A$ is the ratio of a to b. This can be written as follows:

$$\tan \angle A = \frac{a}{b}$$

The tangent of $\angle B$ is the ratio of b to a. This can be written as $\tan \angle B = b/a$.

The tangent ratio is useful for determining unknown lengths in triangles. Consider the triangle in Figure **11-16,** for example.

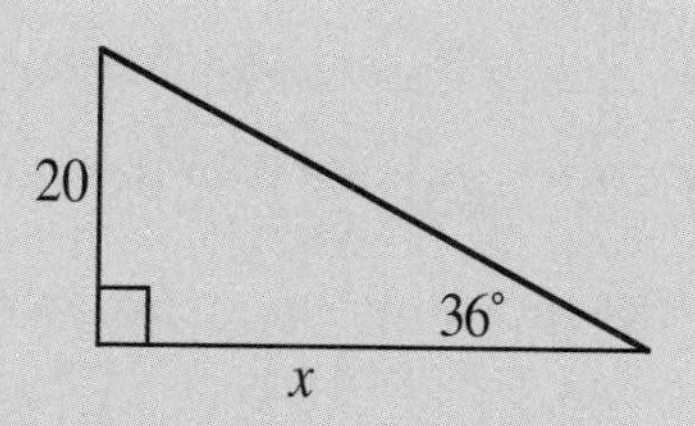

FIGURE 11-16 Triangle with the length of one leg unknown.

Since tan 36° equals the ratio of the length of the opposite leg to the length of the adjacent leg, the value of x can be found by solving the following equation.

$$\tan 36° = \frac{20}{x}$$

$$x(\tan 36°) = 20$$

$$x = \frac{20}{\tan 36°} \approx 27.53$$

e. Add a column to Table **11-2** and label it "tan $\angle A$." Using technology, find and record the tangent of each angle measure in the left-hand column. Compare your results with the ratios in the column labeled "opposite/adjacent."

f. Many calculators feature a key labeled "$\tan^{-1}$." This represents the inverse tangent command. Use technology to determine and record the inverse tangent of each value you determined in Part **e.** Describe any patterns you observe.

Discussion

a. In Part **c** of the exploration, what pattern did you observe in the ratio opposite/adjacent? Explain why this pattern occurs.

b. Compare the values you recorded in Table **11-2** with others in your class. Describe any similarities or differences you observe.

c. What happens to the tangent as the measure of an acute angle changes?

d. How is the tangent related to the Egyptian seqt?

e. 1. Given that the tangent of an angle is approximately 1.73, how could you use the values in Table **11-2** to determine the measure of the angle?

   2. Describe how this process is related to the $\tan^{-1}$ key on a calculator.

f. Why would you expect tan 45° to equal 1?

Warm-Up

1. What is the definition of a dihedral angle?

2. Determine the unknown measure in each triangle below.

a.

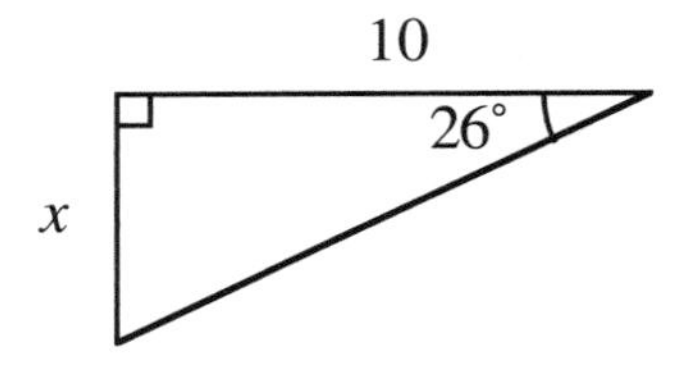

b.

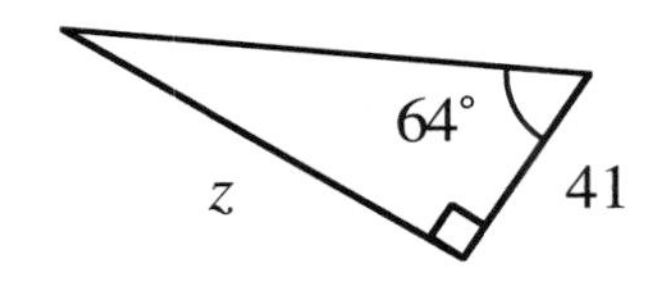

c.

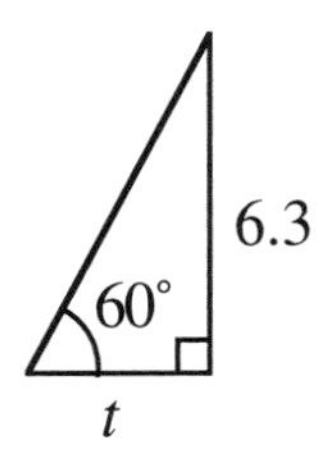

d.

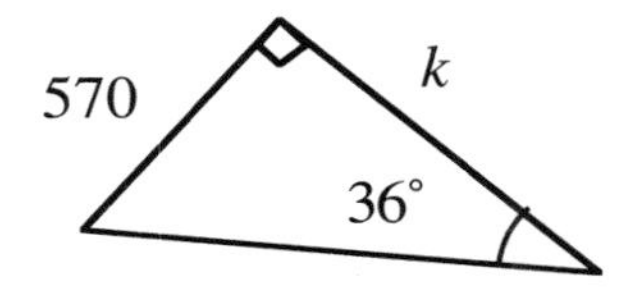

e.

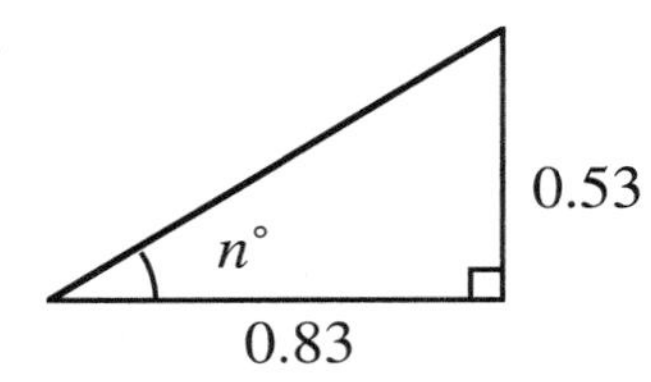

f.

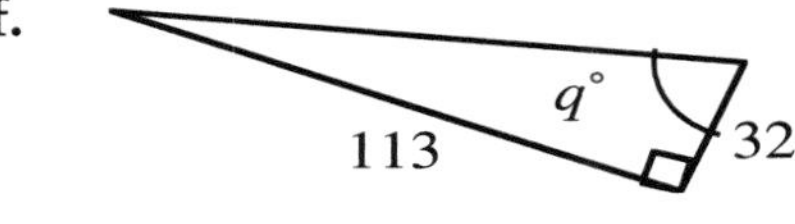

Assignment

3.1 The figure below shows a cross-sectional drawing of the Great Pyramid and a cross-sectional drawing of a casing block.

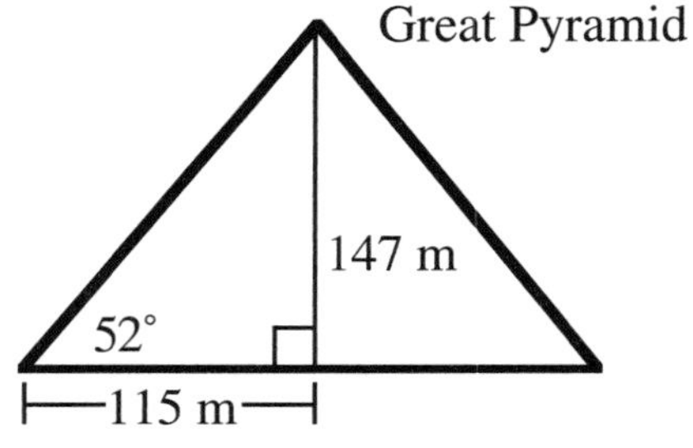

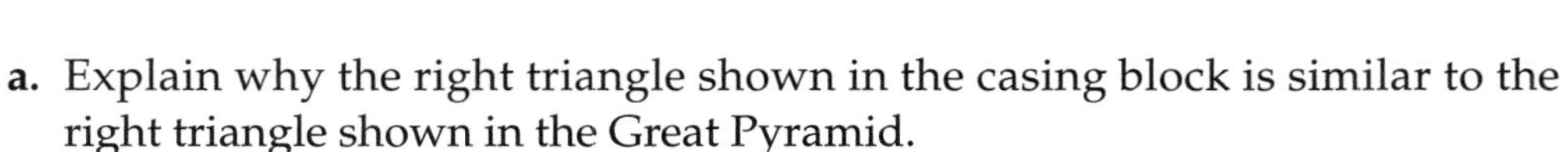

a. Explain why the right triangle shown in the casing block is similar to the right triangle shown in the Great Pyramid.

b. Determine the value of x in the casing block using each of the following methods:

1. proportions and similar triangles **2.** the tangent ratio.

3.2 The following diagrams show three casing blocks from the Great Pyramid. Determine the unknown length in each case.

a.

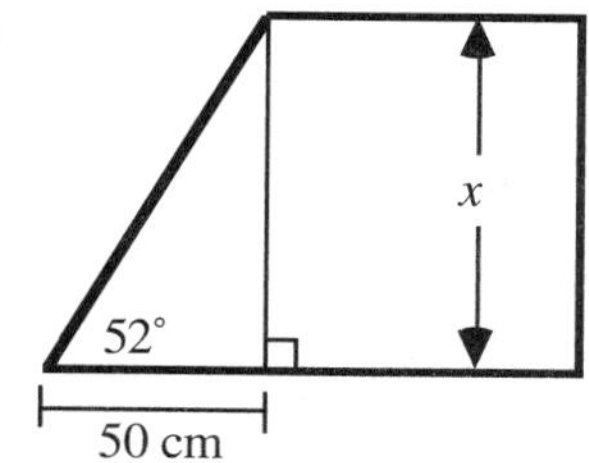

b.

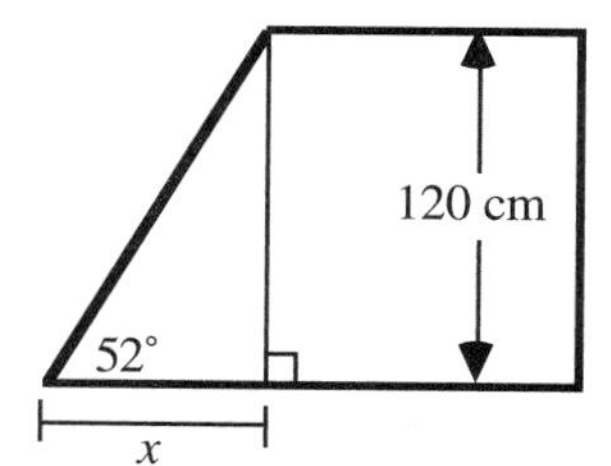

c.

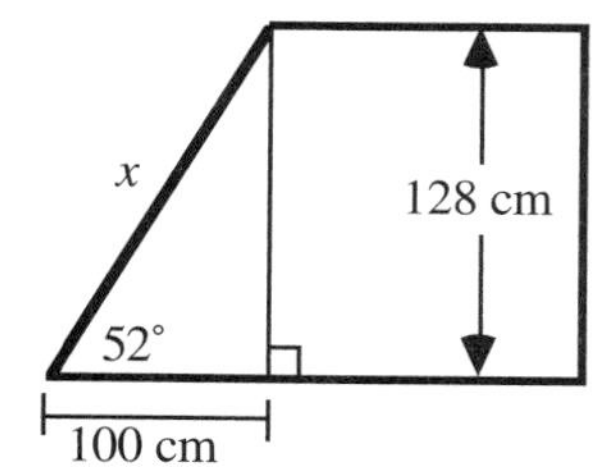

3.3 Consider a pyramid whose base has the same dimensions as the Great Pyramid's. If its casing blocks have dihedral angle measures of 71° instead of 52°, how tall is the pyramid? (*Hint:* Use the given information to sketch an appropriate triangle.)

3.4 Examine the value of the tangent ratio for angles with measures close to 90°. Describe what a calculator displays for tan 90° and explain why this occurs.

3.5 King Khufu's father, Snefru, built a pyramid at Dashur known as the Bent Pyramid. As shown in the diagram below, the base of the Bent Pyramid is a square 189 m on each side. The 50° dihedral angle measure at its base was abandoned after construction reached a height of 73.5 m. A smaller angle measure, about 37°, was used to finish the pyramid.

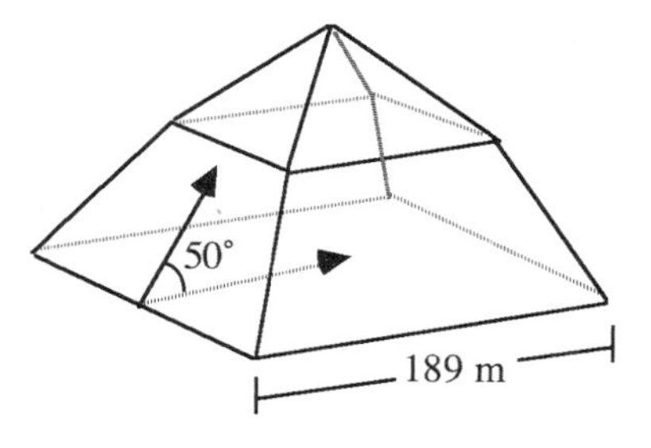

a. How tall would the Bent Pyramid have been if completed using the 50° dihedral angle measure?

b. How tall is the actual Bent Pyramid?

3.6 Find the unknown lengths and angle measures in each of the following triangles.

a.

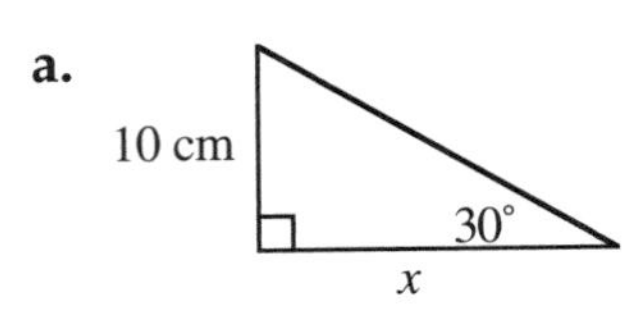

b.

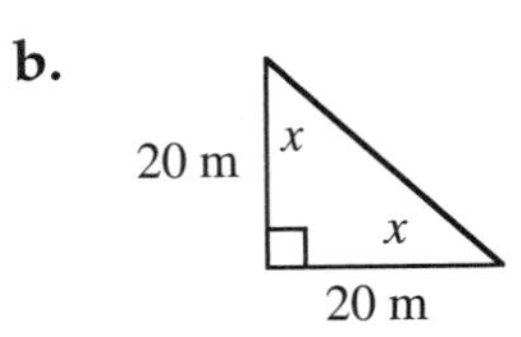

c.

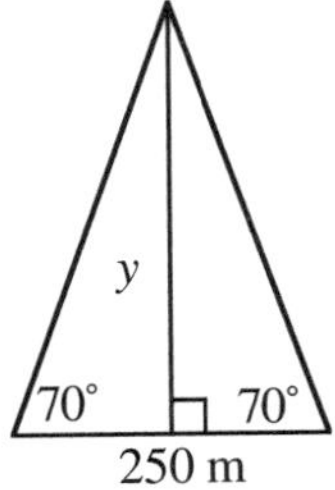

d.

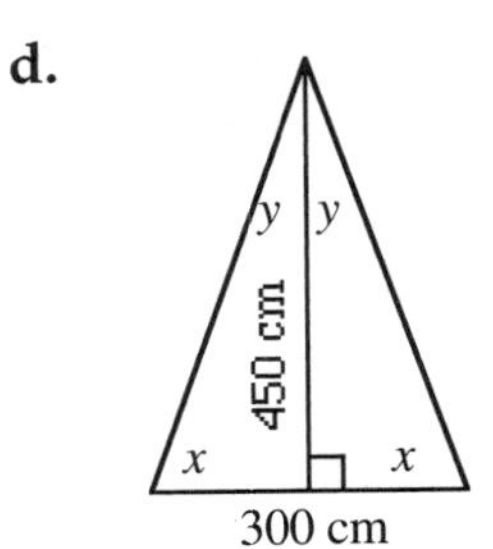

3.7 The ancient Egyptians used the ratio a/b to measure the slant of the casing block below. Express this ratio in terms of the tangent of the measure of the block's dihedral angle.

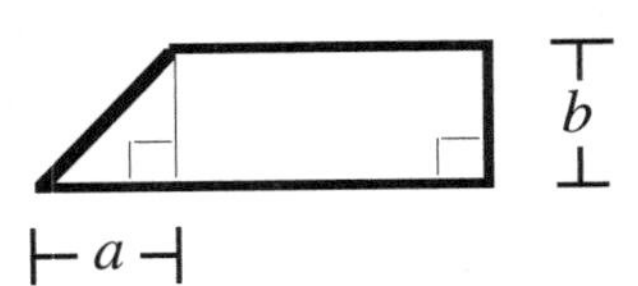

3.8 A clinometer measures angle of elevation. The simple clinometer shown in the diagram below consists of a drinking straw, a weighted string, and a protractor. Using this tool, the angle of elevation (the shaded angle in the diagram) is the difference between the angle indicated by the weighted string and 90°. Use this diagram to describe how a clinometer—along with some knowledge of trigonometry—could be used to calculate the height of a pyramid.

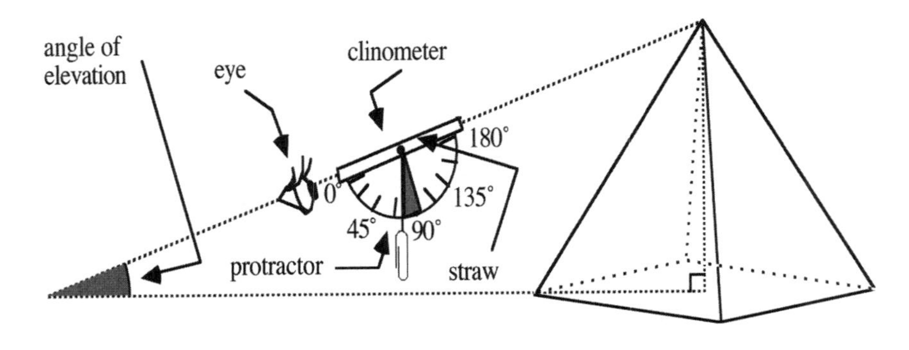

* * * * *

3.9 **a.** Find the unknown angle measures in the figure below.

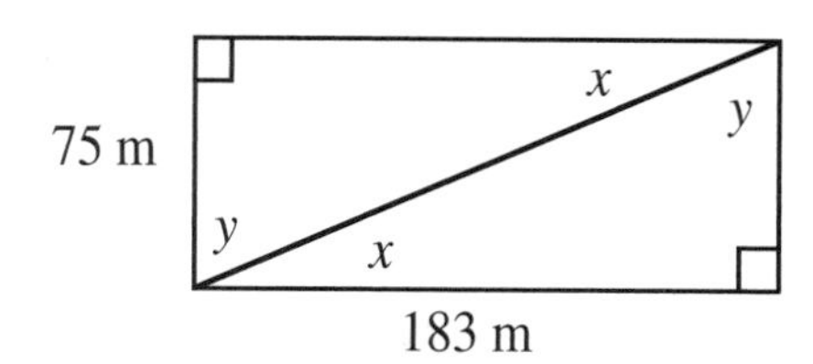

b. Find the unknown lengths in the following figure.

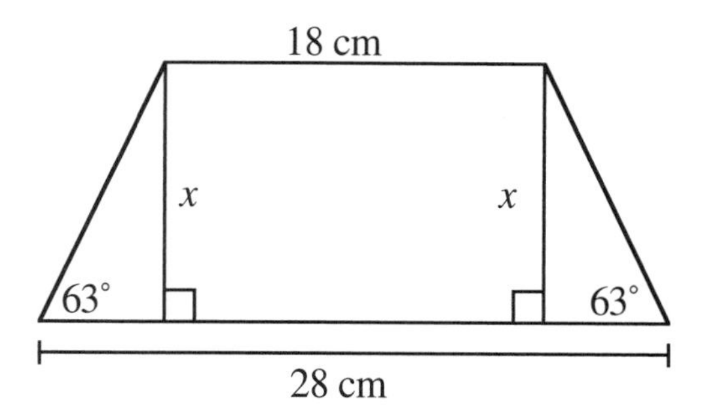

3.10 When describing the roof of a house, the ratio of the vertical distance to the horizontal distance is often referred to as *pitch*. The figure below shows a roof with a pitch of 2/5. Determine the measure of the angle which this roof makes with the horizontal.

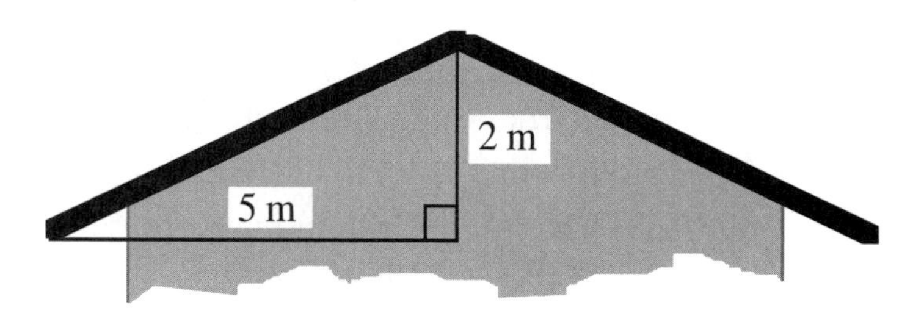

Research Project

Construct a clinometer like the one described in Problem **3.8.** Use your clinometer to estimate the height of your school, a flagpole, or some other tall object. Describe the methods you used to make each estimate. If possible, find the actual height of the object and compare this value to your estimate. Discuss some possible explanations for any differences you observe.

ACTIVITY 4

The word *trigonometry* is derived from the Greek words for "three-angle measurement." Right-triangle trigonometry involves the relationships among the sides and angles of right triangles. The tangent ratio is only one of these relationships.

As noted in Activity **3**, the Egyptians used the seqt. In Plimpton 322, the Babylonians worked with yet another such ratio. In this activity, you explore some other trigonometric ratios and examine their usefulness as problem-solving tools.

Exploration

a. Consider $\triangle ABC$ in Figure **11-17.** In Activity **3**, you found that the tangent ratio for a given measure of $\angle A$ remains the same for all right triangles that contain that angle. List all the other ratios that you think will remain constant for $\angle A$.

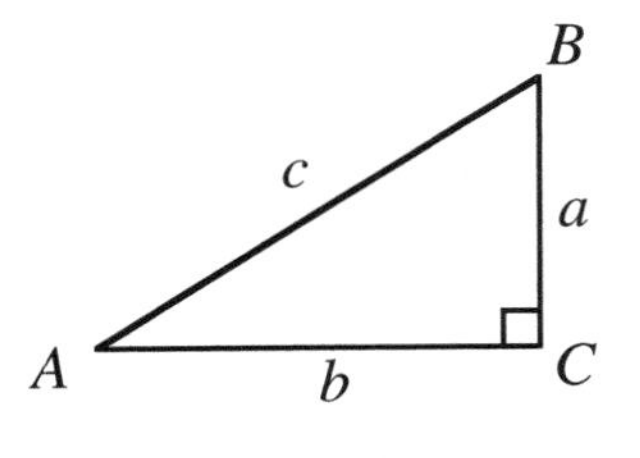

FIGURE 11-17 Right triangle ***ABC.***

b. Using your construction of a right triangle from Activity **3**, measure $\angle A$ and the sides of $\triangle ABC$. Calculate all the ratios that exist among the lengths of the sides.

c. Drag point C to create other, similar right triangles. Verify that the ratios you identified in Part **a** remain constant.

d. Create a table with headings like those in Table **11-3** below. Use your geometry utility to complete the table.

TABLE 11-3 ■ ***Ratios of Lengths in Right Triangles***

$m\angle A$	opposite/hypotenuse	adjacent/hypotenuse
5°		
15°		
30°		
45°		
60°		
75°		

mathematics note

In any right triangle, the **sine** of the measure of an acute angle is the ratio of the length of the leg opposite that angle to the length of the hypotenuse.

For example, Figure **11-18** shows a right triangle *ABC*.

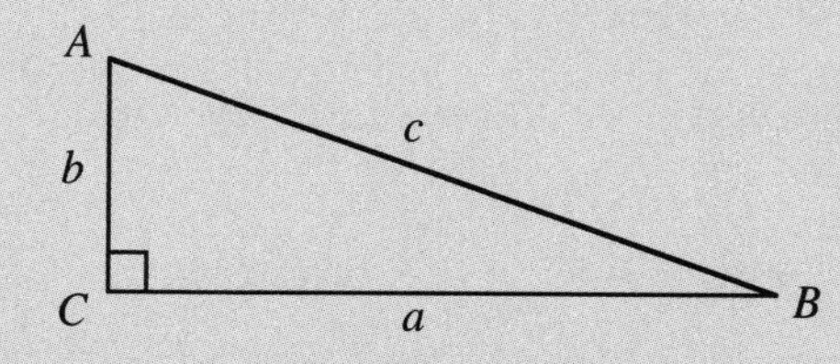

FIGURE 11-18 **A right triangle *ABC*.**

In this right triangle, the sine of $\angle A$ is the ratio of a to c. This can be written as:

$$\sin \angle A = \frac{a}{c}$$

In any right triangle, the **cosine** of the measure of an acute angle is the ratio of the length of the leg adjacent to that angle to the length of the hypotenuse. In the right triangle in Figure **11-18,** the cosine of $\angle A$ is the ratio of b to c. This can be written as:

$$\cos \angle A = \frac{b}{c}$$

For example, consider right triangle *DEF* in Figure **11-19.** In this case, $\sin \angle E = 8/10 = 0.8$ and $\cos \angle E = 6/10 = 0.6$.

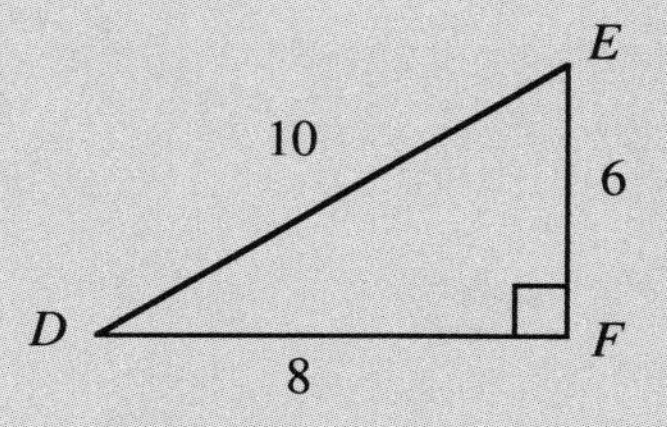

FIGURE 11-19 **Right triangle *DEF*.**

e. Add two columns to Table **11-3** using the headings "sin $\angle A$" and "cos $\angle A$." Use technology to determine the sine and cosine of each angle measure in the left-hand column. Compare your results with the ratios in the columns labeled "opposite/hypotenuse" and "adjacent/hypotenuse."

f. Use your geometry utility to determine the minimum and maximum values of $\sin \angle A$ and $\cos \angle A$ in right triangle *ABC*.

g. Many calculators feature keys labeled "$\sin^{-1}$" and "$\cos^{-1}$." These represent the inverse sine and inverse cosine commands, respectively. Use the values you determined in Part **e** to experiment with these commands. Describe any patterns you observe.

Discussion

a. Describe how the two ratios in Table **11-3** are related to $\sin \angle A$ and $\cos \angle A$.

b. What trends did you observe in the values of sine and cosine as the measure of $\angle A$ increased?

c. What is the measure of $\angle A$ when $\sin \angle A$ and $\cos \angle A$ are equal?

d. 1. Describe the information you would need to find the measure of an angle using the inverse sine command.

   2. Describe the information you would need to find the measure of an angle using the inverse cosine command.

e. In a right triangle ABC where $\angle C$ is the right angle, $\sin \angle A$ equals $\cos \angle B$. Explain why this occurs.

Warm-Up

1. Use the right triangle below to answer Parts **a–d.**

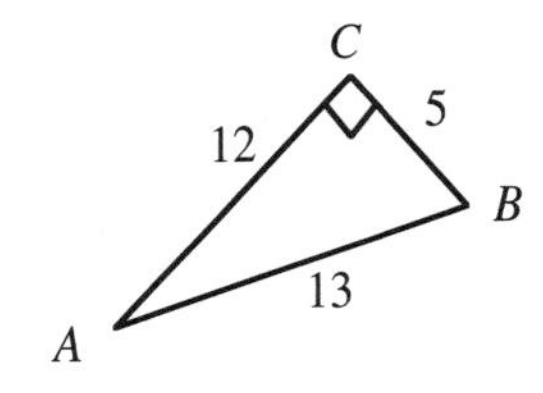

   a. For $\angle B$ which trigonometric ratio is represented by 5/13?

   b. For $\angle A$, which trigonometric ratio is represented by 5/13?

   c. For $\angle B$, which trigonometric ratio is represented by 12/5?

   d. For $\angle A$, which trigonometric ratio is represented by 12/13?

2. Determine the unknown length or angle measure in each of the three right triangles below.

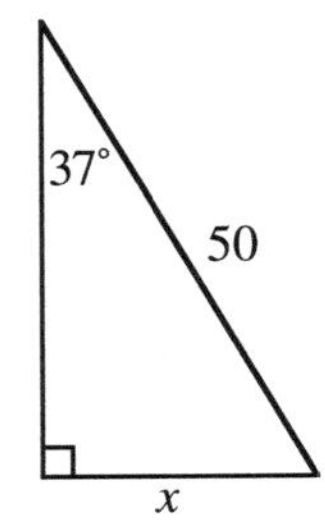

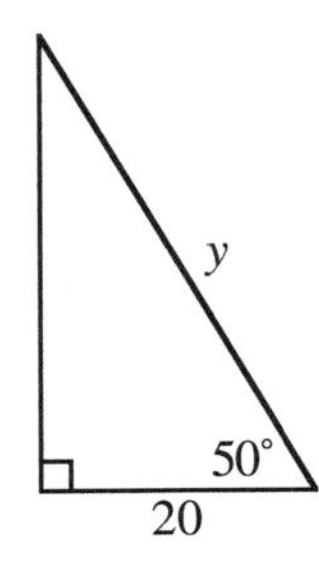

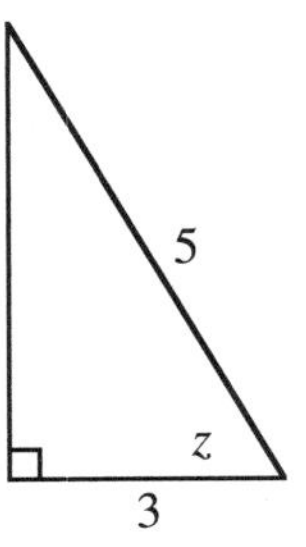

3. Find the height of an isosceles triangle if the vertex angle measures 48° and the congruent legs have a length of 5.8 cm.

Assignment

4.1 **a.** The figure below shows a cross-section of a pyramid. Use trigonometric ratios to determine the height h and the length l.

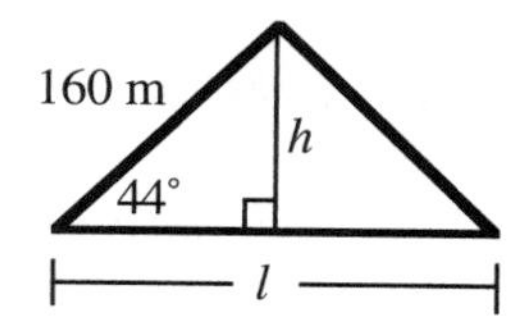

b. The figure below shows a cross-section of a casing block. Determine the unknown length x.

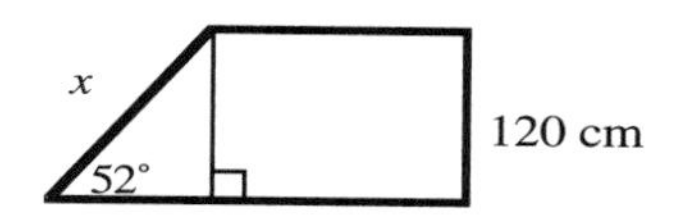

c. To move stones to the top of a pyramid, the Egyptians may have built a ramp of sand. If the pyramid in the diagram below is 100 m tall and the incline of the ramp is 25°, determine the length of the ramp.

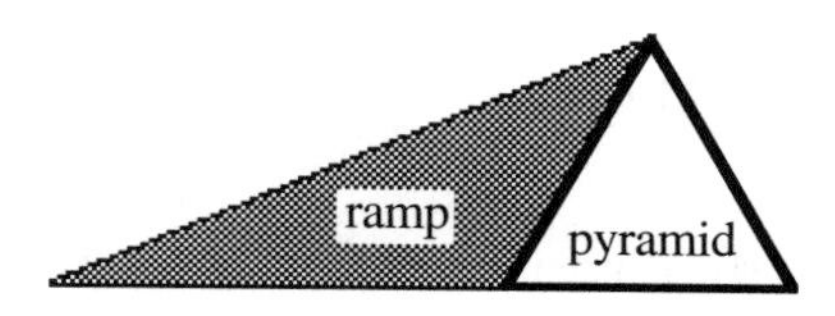

4.2 Use appropriate technology and the inverse cosine command to find the unknown angle measure x in the figure below.

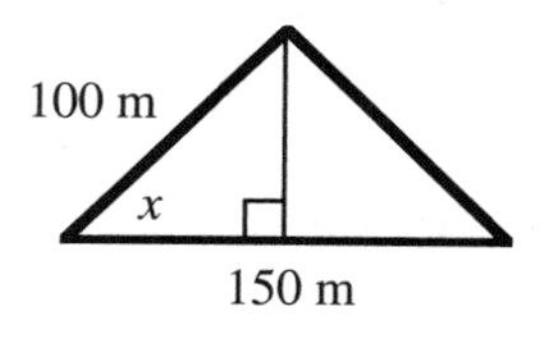

4.3 Use the definitions of the sine, cosine, and tangent ratios to prove that the following equation is true.

$$\tan \angle A = \frac{\sin \angle A}{\cos \angle A}$$

4.4 **a.** Using $\triangle ABC$ below, explain why $\sin 65° = \cos 25°$ and $\tan 65° = 1/\tan 25°$.

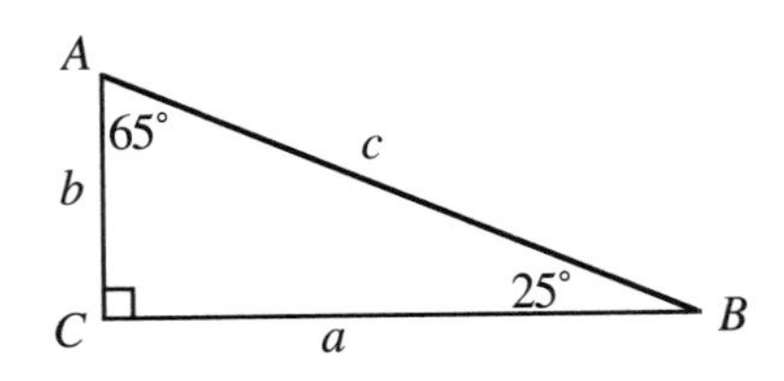

b. Generalize your response to Part **a** for all pairs of acute angles whose measures add up to 90°. Use technology to verify this conjecture.

4.5 The diagram below shows the base angles on a face of the Great Pyramid. Determine the measure of these angles.

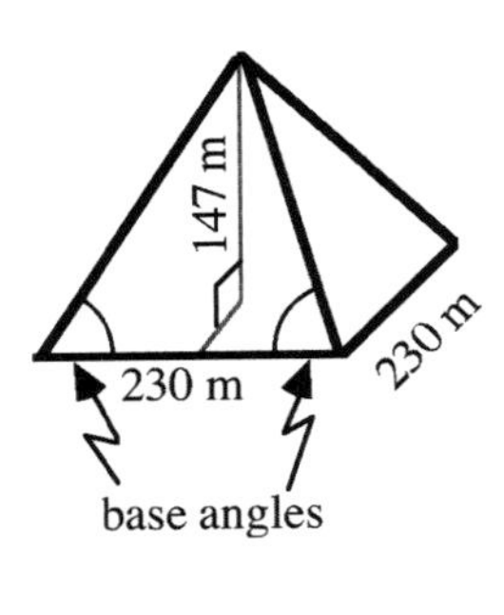

* * * * *

4.6 On a highway, a uniform grade of 4% means that there is a rise of 4 m for every 100 m of horizontal distance.

a. If you are driving up a road with a 4% grade, what angle measure does the path of your car make with the horizontal?

b. What is your change in elevation after traveling 32 m on this road?

4.7 Workers building the Great Pyramid used scaffolding to raise themselves to an appropriate height. The scaffold in the diagram below lifted stone masons to a height 4 m above the previous level. The measure of the angle between each crosspiece and vertical support is 60°. What is the length of the crosspiece? Describe how you determined your response.

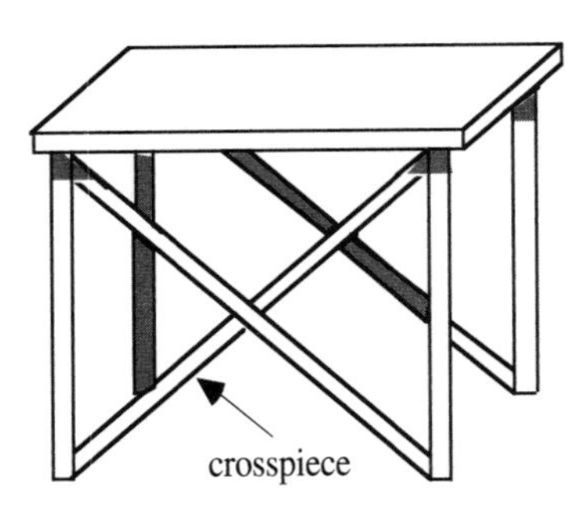

4.8 Determine the measure of the angle that the roof in the following diagram makes with the horizontal.

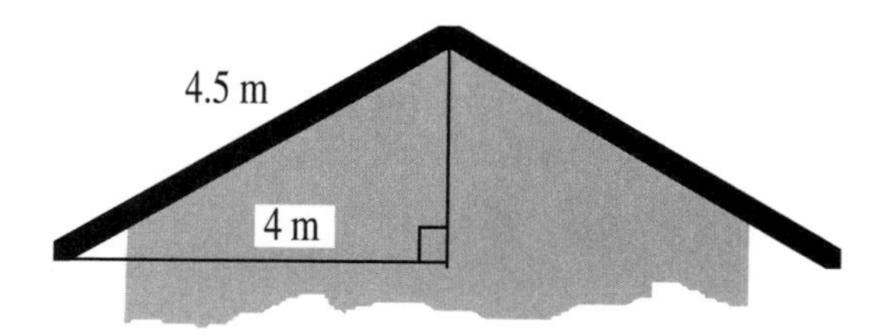

4.9 A radio tower is anchored to the ground by four cables, two of which are shown in the figure below. Each cable is bolted to the tower 20 m above the ground. The angles formed by the cables with the ground measure 60°.

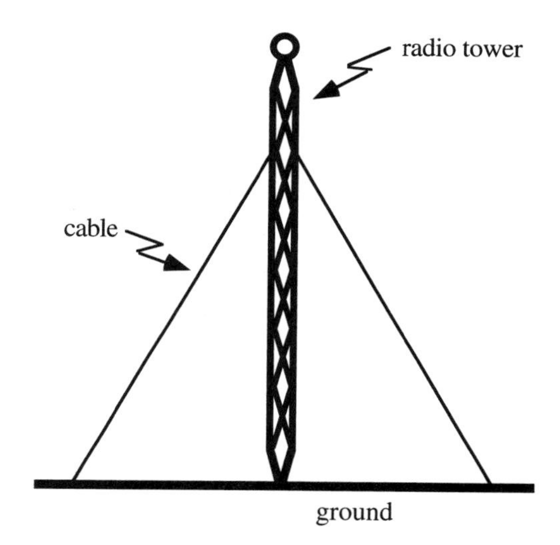

a. How many meters of cable have been used to anchor the tower?

b. How far is it from the bottom of the tower to the anchor point of each cable?

Summary Assessment

1. The annual flooding of the Nile River was an important part of life for the ancient Egyptians. Imagine that you must determine the width of the Nile at its crest near the Great Pyramid. You know the distance from the edge of the pyramid to the near bank is 1 km, and that you are 3.5 km from the opposite bank. From where you are standing, the angle of elevation to the pyramid's peak is approximately 1.5°. Use the figure below to help calculate the width of the Nile.

2. In the diagram of the Great Pyramid below, $\angle CDF$ and $\angle CEF$ are angles with one side in the plane of the pyramid's base and the other in the plane of one of its faces. The dihedral angle *CDF* measures 52°. The length of $\overline{DE}$ is 77 m. Triangles *CFD, CFE,* and *FDE* are all right triangles. Use the Pythagorean theorem and trigonometric ratios to show that the measure of the dihedral angle is different from $m\angle CEF$.

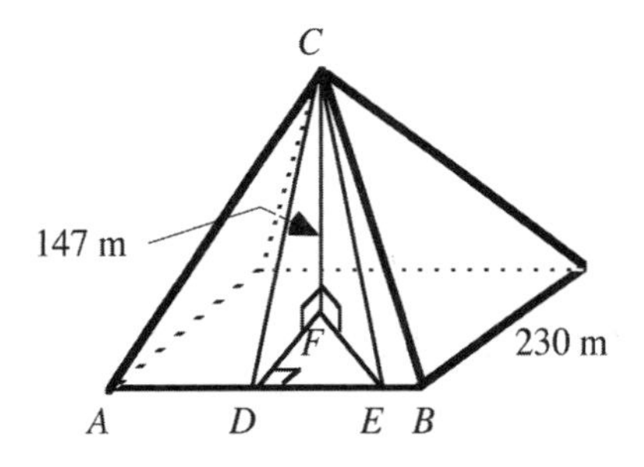

3. A truss is a combination of beams used to support the roof of a building. The diagram below shows some dimensions for a truss for a house. Use the measures indicated in the diagram to determine the lengths of segments *EF, DF,* and *CD.*

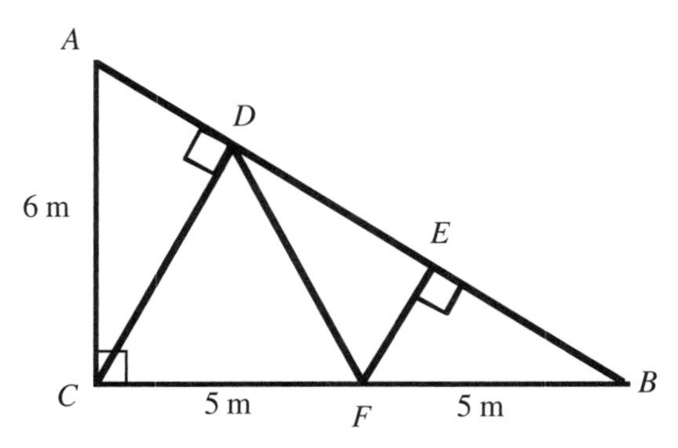

Module Summary

* Two figures are **similar** if they have the same shape and corresponding sides are proportional.
* In plane geometry, if the angles of one triangle are congruent to the corresponding angles of another triangle, then the triangles are similar. This is referred to as the **Angle-Angle-Angle (AAA) property.**
* The symbol used to indicate congruence is $\cong$.
* The **Pythagorean theorem** states that, in a right triangle, the square of the length of the longest side (the hypotenuse) equals the sum of the squares of the lengths of the other sides (the legs).
* The **converse** of a statement in the form "If A, then B" is the statement "If B, then A." The converse of a true if-then statement may or may not be true.
* An angle formed by two intersecting planes is a **dihedral angle.** The measure of a dihedral angle is the measure of the angle whose sides are the two rays formed by the intersections of the faces and a plane perpendicular to the edge.
* In any right triangle, the **tangent** of the measure of an acute angle is the ratio of the length of the leg opposite the angle to the length of the leg adjacent to the angle. For right triangle ABC in the figure below, $\tan \angle A = a/b$.

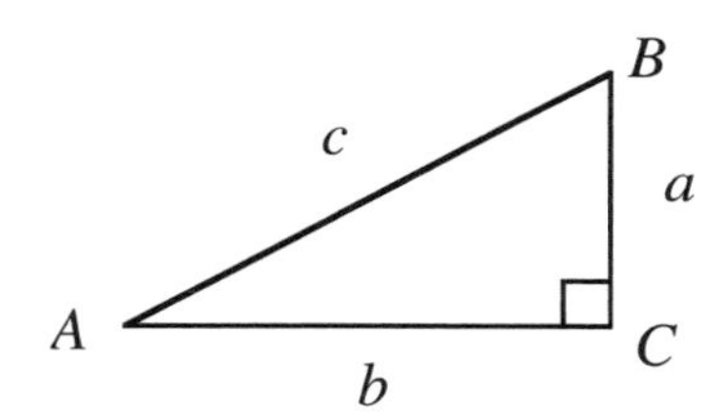

* In any right triangle, the **sine** of the measure of an acute angle is the ratio of the length of the leg opposite that angle to the length of the hypotenuse. For right triangle ABC in the figure above, $\sin \angle A = a/c$.
* In any right triangle, the **cosine** of the measure of an acute angle is the ratio of the length of the leg adjacent to that angle to the length of the hypotenuse. For right triangle ABC in the figure above, $\cos \angle A = b/c$.
* The sine, cosine, and tangent are **trigonometric** ratios.

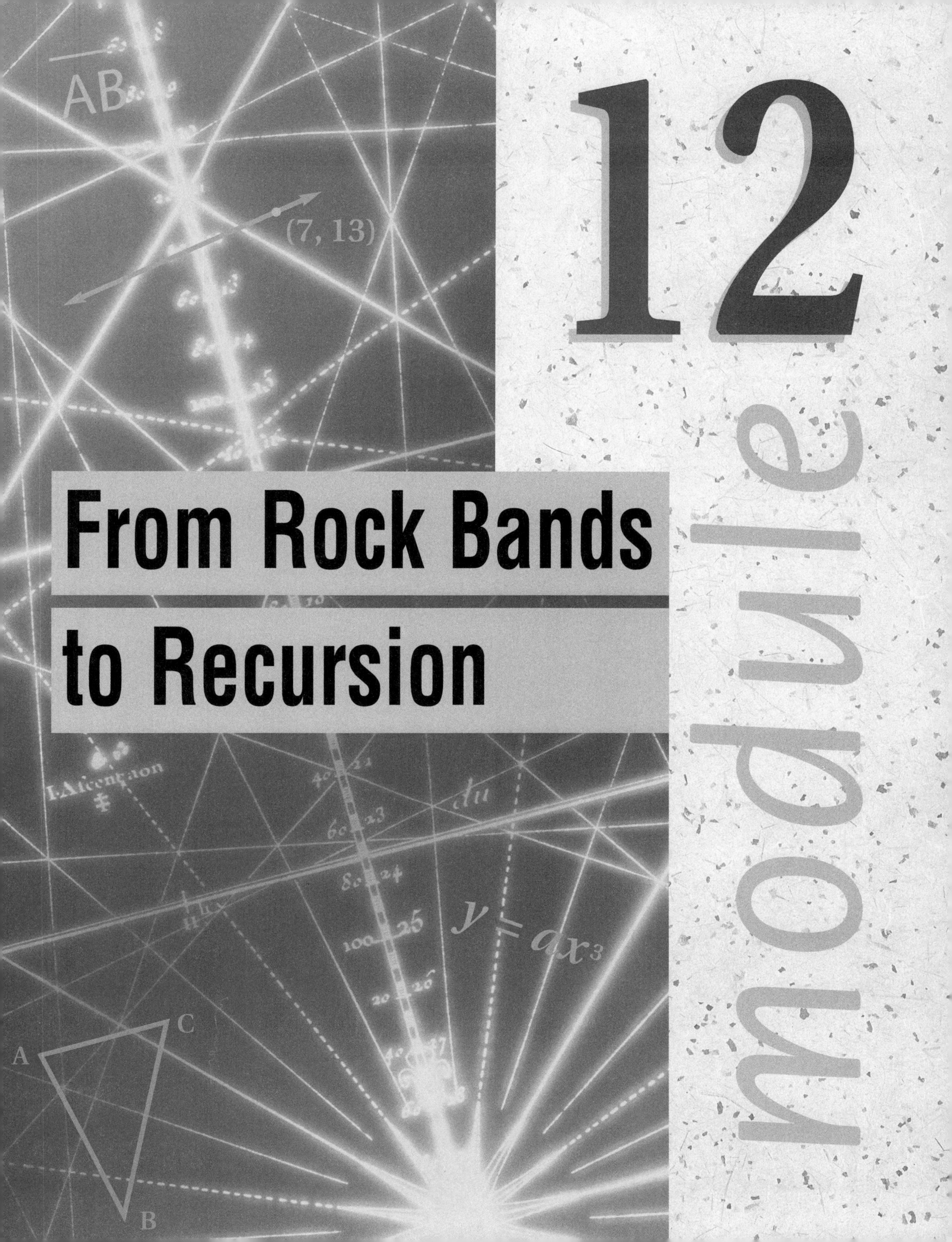

12
module
From Rock Bands
to Recursion
AB
(7, 13)
A
B
C

Introduction

Since the time you first learned to count (1, 2, 3), skip-count (2, 4, 6, 8), and stack blocks, you've been investigating patterns of numbers. For example, if you continue to stack blocks as shown in Figure **12-1,** the number of blocks in each row of a stack forms a pattern. The total number of blocks used to build each stack forms another pattern.

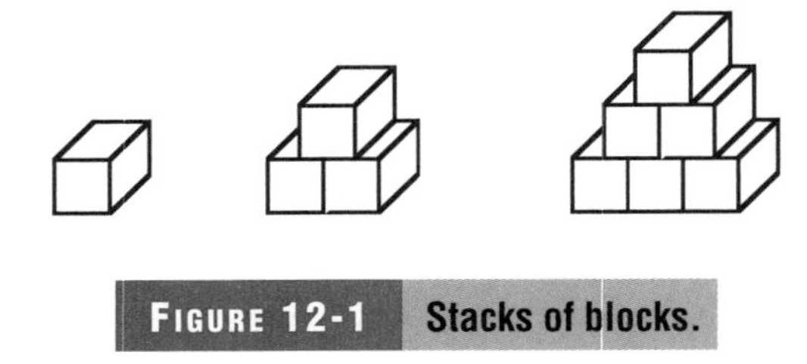

Figure 12-1 Stacks of blocks.

In this module, you go on tour with the rock band Stellar Attraction. Along the way, you use technology and mathematical formulas to examine patterns in the sales of CDs and concert tickets. You also analyze the sequence of notes played by the lead guitarist.

ACTIVITY 1

In this activity, you investigate the basic number patterns formed by the number of performances during Stellar Attraction's first world tour.

Exploration

Before starting their world tour, the band's concert career was relatively short—only 6 performances. The upcoming schedule, however, contains 2 performances per week. Table **12-1** summarizes the band's career number of performances over the next 10-week period.

TABLE 12-1 ■ *Performances by Stellar Attraction*

No. of Weeks on Tour	Total No. of Performances
1	8
2	10
3	12
4	14
⋮	⋮
10	26

a. Complete Table **12-1** for each of the next 10 weeks.

b. Record any patterns you observe in the table.

c. Use the patterns you discovered to answer the following questions.

1. After how many weeks will the band have given 24 performances?
2. How many performances will they have given after 12 weeks?
3. After 16 weeks, Stellar Attraction will have performed 38 times. What will be the total number of performances after 18 weeks?

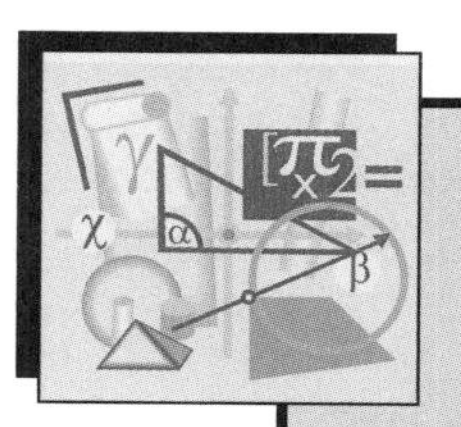

mathematics note

A **sequence** is an ordered list. Each item in the list is a **term** of the sequence.

The terms of a sequence may be represented by symbols, such as $p_1, p_2, p_3, \ldots, p_n$. These symbols are **subscripted variables,** and the natural numbers $(1, 2, 3, \ldots, n)$ are the **subscripts.** The symbol p_1 (read "p sub one") represents the first term of the sequence, the symbol p_2 (read "p sub two") represents the second term of the sequence, and so on. The symbol p_n (read "p sub n"), represents the **general,** or ***n*th, term** of a sequence.

For example, consider the following ordered list of numbers 16, 18, 20, 22, 24, ... In this sequence, $p_1 = 16$, $p_2 = 18$, $p_3 = 20$, and so on.

d. 1. Create a spreadsheet with headings like those shown in Table **12-2** below. The entries in the right-hand column represent the total number of performances at the end of each week. They also represent the terms of a sequence.

TABLE 12-2 ■ *Performances Spreadsheet*

No. of Weeks on Tour (n)	Total No. of Performances (p_n)
1	8
2	10
3	12
4	14
⋮	⋮
50	

2. Use the spreadsheet to determine the total number of performances after each week for the next 50 weeks.

mathematics note

A **recursive formula** is a rule for finding any term in a sequence by using the preceding term(s). The process of using a recursive formula is known as **recursion.**

An **arithmetic sequence** is a sequence in which every term after the first is found by adding a constant value to the preceding term.

The recursive formula for calculating any term in an arithmetic sequence is:

$$\begin{cases} a_1 = \text{first term} \\ a_n = a_{n-1} + d, \ n > 1 \end{cases}$$

where a_1 is the first term, a_n is the nth term, a_{n-1} is the term preceding a_n, and d is the **common difference** between any two consecutive terms, $a_n - a_{n-1}$.

For example, consider the sequence in which the first term (a_1) is 27 and the common difference (d) between any two consecutive terms is 5. The recursive formula for this sequence is:

$$\begin{cases} a_1 = 27 \\ a_n = a_{n-1} + 5, \ n > 1 \end{cases}$$

Using this formula, the first four terms of the sequence can be found as follows:

$$\begin{aligned} a_1 &= 27 \\ a_2 &= a_{2-1} + d = a_1 + d = 27 + 5 = 32 \\ a_3 &= a_{3-1} + d = a_2 + 5 = 32 + 5 = 37 \\ a_4 &= a_{4-1} + 5 = a_3 + d = 37 + 5 = 42 \end{aligned}$$

e. Find a recursive formula for the sequence in the right-hand column of Table **12-2.**

Discussion

a. How did you use the patterns you described in Part **b** of the exploration to complete Table **12-2**?

b. Use the sequence in the right-hand column of Table **12-2** to answer the following questions.

1. What is the value of n for p_{20}?
2. What is the value of p_{20}?
3. If $p_n = 20$, what is the value of n?
4. When $n = 8$, what is the value of p_{n-1}, the term before p_n?

c. How can you use subscript notation to express the fact that the 30th term of a sequence is 66?

d. Explain why the sequence found in each column of Table **12-2** is an arithmetic sequence.

Warm-Up

1. For each arithmetic sequence below, write a recursive formula, then list the next three terms.

   a. 7, 13, 19, 25, 31, 37, . . .

   b. 3, −4, −11, −18, −25, −32, . . .

   c. 8.3, 16, 23.7, 31.4, 39.1, 46.8, . . .

2. Consider the following recursive formula:

$$\begin{cases} a_1 = 13 \\ a_n = a_{n-1} + 6, \; n > 1 \end{cases}$$

a. What is the common difference?

b. What is the first term in the sequence?

c. What are the next three terms in the sequence?

d. What does the n in the equation represent? What does $n - 1$ represent?

3. Write recursive formulas for the arithmetic sequences described below.

a. The first term is 5 and the common difference is –8.

b. The first term is –7.6 and the common difference is 3.9.

Assignment

1.1 For their next performance, Stellar Attraction must drive from St. Louis, Missouri, to Portland, Oregon: a distance of 3290 km. They can average 100 km per hour during the trip.

a. Create a spreadsheet with headings like those in the table below. Let h represent the number of hours driven and k_h represent the number of kilometers remaining after each hour.

Hours Driven (h)	Kilometers Remaining (k_h)
1	3190
2	3090
3	2990
⋮	⋮

b. During which hour does the band arrive in Portland?

c. What is the value of k_5?

d. How many kilometers remain after the band has driven for 13 hr? Express your answer using subscript notation.

e. For how many hours has the band been driving when they are 1390 km from Portland? Express your answer in subscript notation.

f. What is the value of k_{h-1} when $k_h = 2290$?

g. Write a recursive formula that describes the pattern for k_h.

1.2 After arriving in Portland, the band finds that concert tickets have been selling well. The ticket agency sold 790 tickets on the first day. During the next 20 days, they sold an average of 213 tickets per day.

a. Let n represent the number of days that tickets have been on sale and t_n represent the total number of tickets sold after n days. Express the first 5 terms of this sequence using subscript notation.

b. Using the sequence from Part **a,** on what day did total sales exceed 2200 tickets? Express your answer using subscript notation.

c. What is the value of t_{n+1} when $t_n = 2494$?

d. Write a recursive formula that describes the pattern of ticket sales.

e. To complete Parts **a–d,** you assumed that the pattern of ticket sales was an arithmetic sequence where $t_1 = 790$ and $t_{21} = 790 + 20(213)$. Do you think that this is a reasonable assumption?

1.3 In some arithmetic sequences, the numbers increase with each successive term. In others, the numbers decrease with each successive term. What can you say about the common differences used to form these sequences?

1.4 Consider the following recursive formula:

$$\begin{cases} t_1 = 9.0 \\ t_n = t_{n-1} + 0.5, \ n > 1 \end{cases}$$

a. What is the value of the first term of this sequence?

b. What are the next four terms of this sequence?

1.5 Find a recursive formula for the arithmetic sequence 3, 7, 11, 15, ...

1.6 **a.** Create your own arithmetic sequence.

b. What is the common difference for your sequence?

c. Write a recursive formula for your sequence.

1.7 In a paragraph, compare the two sequences described by the formulas shown below.

$$\begin{cases} t_1 = 5 \\ t_n = t_{n-1} + 3, \ n > 1 \end{cases} \quad \text{and} \quad \begin{cases} r_1 = -4 \\ r_n = r_{n-1} + 3, \ n > 1 \end{cases}$$

* * * * *

1.8 The *National Geographic* magazine is published 12 times per year. Each edition of the magazine is approximately 0.8 cm thick.

a. Imagine that your parents started collecting *National Geographic* in the year you were born. How much shelf space would they need to display their collection at the end of this year?

b. Write a recursive formula that describes the amount of shelf space needed at the end of a year. Let the first term of the sequence be the width of the shelf when you were in kindergarten.

c. Use your recursive formula to predict how much shelf space will be required when you are 60 years old.

1.9 **a.** Melinda has $51.00 and spends $3.00 per week. Write a recursive formula to describe the amount of money m_n Melinda has at the beginning of week n.

b. Kris has $11.00 and saves an additional $2.00 per week. Write a recursive formula to describe the amount of money k_n Kris has at the beginning of week n.

c. When will Melinda and Kris have the same amount of money?

1.10 Consider the following recursive formula:

$$\begin{cases} t_1 = 1 \\ t_2 = 1 \\ t_n = t_{n-2} + t_{n-1} \text{ for } n > 2 \end{cases}$$

a. Find t_3.

b. Generate the first 10 terms of the sequence.

c. Create a scatterplot of the first 10 terms of the sequence versus the term number.

d. Is the sequence an arithmetic sequence? Justify your response.

The band's record company tracks the number of compact discs (CDs) that Stellar Attraction sells each week. During the week of June 10–16, the band sold 9050 copies. Sales projections indicate that the band can expect weekly sales to increase by an average of 2353 copies each week for the next year. These projections are shown in Table **12-3** on the next page.

Table 12-3 ■ *Weekly CD Sales*

Week	Week No.	CD Sales
June 10–16	1	9050
June 17–23	2	11,403
June 24–30	3	13,756
July 1–7	4	16,109
⋮	⋮	⋮
December 23–29	29	
⋮	⋮	⋮
June 2–8	52	

If the projections are accurate, how many CDs will the band sell during the last week of December? When will the total number of copies sold exceed 1 million? The predicted values for weekly sales represent an arithmetic sequence, so you could use a recursive formula to answer these questions. However, using a recursive formula can be time consuming. In this activity, you develop another type of formula that will allow you to respond more quickly.

Exploration

The two left-hand columns in Table **12-4** show the term number and terms for an arithmetic sequence. The two right-hand columns show expanded (and equivalent) forms of the term values. In this exploration, you use the patterns in this table to develop another type of formula for the sequence.

Table 12-4 ■ *Patterns within Arithmetic Sequences*

Term Number (n)	Term (p_n)	Recursive Form of p_n	Another Form of p_n
1	27	27	$27 + (0 \bullet 2)$
2	29	$27 + 2$	$27 + (1 \bullet 2)$
3	31	$27 + 2 + 2$	$27 + (2 \bullet 2)$
⋮			
7			

a. Complete Table **12-4** for the first seven terms of the sequence. Record any patterns you discover.

b. Write an expression that represents the number of 2s added to the first term to form the nth term.

c. Use the pattern in the far right-hand column to write a formula for p_n in terms of n.

d. Create a scatterplot of the data in the two left-hand columns of the table. Use the horizontal axis for the term number (n) and the vertical axis for the term value (p_n).

e. Find an equation that models the scatterplot and graph it on the coordinate system from Part **d.**

Compare this equation to the one you wrote in Part **c.**

Discussion

a. 1. In the sequence shown in Table **12-4,** how many 2s would you have to add to find p_{21}?

2. How many 2s would have to be added to 27 to find p_n?

b. 1. Describe the formula you wrote for p_n using n as a variable.

2. Use this formula to determine the values of p_{47} and p_{100}.

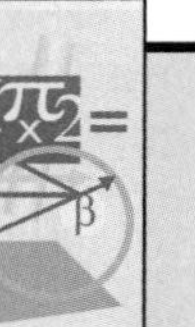

mathematics note

An **explicit formula** for calculating any specific term in an arithmetic sequence is:

$$a_n = a_1 + d(n - 1)$$

where a_n is the nth term, a_1 is the first term, and d is the common difference between any two consecutive terms, $a_n - a_{n-1}$.

For example, consider the arithmetic sequence 8, 14, 20, 26, ... In this sequence, the first term is 8 and the common difference is 6. The explicit formula for this sequence is $a_n = 8 + 6(n - 1)$. This formula can be used to find the 20th term of the sequence as follows:

$$\begin{aligned} a_{20} &= 8 + 6(20 - 1) \\ &= 8 + 6(19) \\ &= 122 \end{aligned}$$

The sum of the terms of an arithmetic sequence is an **arithmetic series.**

For example, consider the arithmetic sequence 8, 14, 20, 26. The corresponding arithmetic series is 8 + 14 + 20 + 26, or 68.

c. How does the graph of a linear equation differ from the graph of an arithmetic sequence?

d. Do you think that the scatterplot of an arithmetic sequence can always be modeled by a linear equation in slope-intercept form, $y = mx + b$? Why or why not?

e. Using the distributive property, the explicit formula for an arithmetic sequence, $a_n = a_1 + d(n - 1)$, can be written as $a_n = a_1 + dn - d$. Using the associative property, it can also be written as $a_n = dn + (a_1 - d)$.

Assuming that the equation $y = mx + b$ models the same arithmetic sequence, describe the relationship between each of the following:

1. the nth term a_n and y
2. the term number n and x
3. the difference d and the slope m
4. the first term a_1 and the y-intercept b

f. In what types of situations would an explicit formula be easier to use than a recursive formula?

g. Using the relationships described in Part **e** of the discussion, show that the explicit formula for an arithmetic sequence, $a_n = a_1 + d(n - 1)$, is equivalent to the linear equation of the form $y = mx + b$ that models the same sequence.

Warm-Up

1. Write an explicit formula for each arithmetic sequence below.

   a. 13, 18.3, 23.6, 18.9, 34.2, 39.5, . . .

   b. 22, 14, 6, −2, −10, −18, . . .

   c. −17, 2, 21, 40, 59, 78, . . .

2. Consider the explicit formula $a_n = 5 + 7.5(n - 1)$.

   a. What is the first term of the sequence?

   b. What is the common difference?

   c. What is the 23rd term of the sequence?

3. Write an explicit formula for each arithmetic sequence described below, then find its 50th term.

   a. The first term is 31 and the common difference is −16.

   b. The first term is −12 and the common difference is 7.

Assignment

2.1 Table **12-3** shows that weekly CD sales for Stellar Attraction are expected to increase by an average of 2353 copies per week for the next 52 weeks after June 10–16.

a. If this projection is accurate, how many CDs will be sold during the week of December 23–29?

b. When will the total number of CDs sold exceed 1 million?

2.2 Stellar Attraction is playing at the Jan-San Amphitheater. The amphitheater has 120 seats in the front row, 136 seats in the second row, and 152 seats in the third row. This pattern continues from row to row. The last row has 584 seats.

a. Write an explicit formula to determine the number of seats in any row of the theater.

b. How many seats are in the 16th row?

c. How many rows are in the theater?

d. How many total seats are in the theater?

2.3 Imagine that you work as an usher at the Jan-San Amphitheater. Your starting wage is $4.25 per hour. Periodically, you will receive a raise of $0.10 per hour. Write an explicit formula to calculate your hourly wage after n raises.

2.4 **a.** Before the concert begins, the Jan-San Amphitheater contains 85 employees. The doors open to the public at 6:00 P.M. Between 6:00 P.M. and 6:15 P.M., an average of 9 people per second enter the theater. Let p_n represent the number of people in the theater after n seconds.

1. List the first 5 terms of the sequence.
2. Identify the common difference d.
3. Write an explicit formula of the form $a_n = a_1 + d(n - 1)$.
4. Determine the number of people in the amphitheater at 6:15 P.M.

b. When the concession stands open, they have a supply of 8500 L of soft drinks. Soft drink sales average 110 L per minute throughout the evening. Let l_n represent the number of liters remaining after n minutes.

1. List the first 5 terms of the sequence.
2. Identify the common difference d.
3. Write an explicit formula of the form $a_n = a_1 + d(n - 1)$.
4. Determine how long the supply of soft drinks will last.

2.5 A cashier starts the evening with $50.00 in the drawer. During the next 45 minutes, an average of $2.15 per minute is added to the drawer. Let c_n represent the number of dollars in the drawer at the end of n minutes.

a. Write a recursive formula for this sequence of the form

$$\begin{cases} c_1 = \text{first term} \\ c_n = c_{n-1} + d, \ n > 1 \end{cases}$$

Explain what each term in the formula represents.

b. Write an explicit formula for this sequence of the form

$$c_n = c_1 + d(n - 1)$$

Explain what each term in the formula represents.

c. Write an equation of the form $y = mx + b$ that models this sequence. Explain what each term in the equation represents.

* * * * *

2.6 Brianna chairs the membership committee of a club with 33 members. To meet club goals, she plans to recruit 5 new members each month.

a. If Brianna meets her membership goals, how many members will the club have after the next 12 months?

b. Each club member receives a monthly newsletter. If each newsletter requires one stamp to mail, how many stamps will be needed during the next year?

2.7 **a.** Create a scatterplot of the data in the following table.

n	t_n
1	7
2	9
3	11
4	13
5	15

b. Write an equation for the line that fits the data. Graph this equation on your coordinate system from Part **a.** What does this graph tell you about an arithmetic sequence?

c. Write an explicit formula to determine t_n. How does this compare with the equation you wrote in Part **b?**

2.8 Raul works in a supermarket. He is stacking blocks of cheese for a dairy display. The diagram on the right shows the first three layers, top to bottom, in his display.

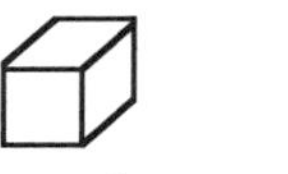
layer 1

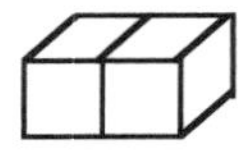
layer 2

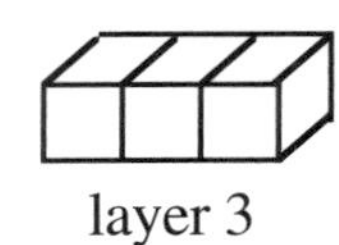
layer 3

a. Make a sketch of the next three layers in the display.

b. Let l_n represent the number of blocks in layer n. Find the first six terms of this sequence.

c. Is the sequence you wrote in Part **b** an arithmetic sequence? Justify your response.

d. Write a formula to describe this sequence.

e. Raul plans to build a display with seven layers. How many blocks of cheese will there be in the stack?

2.9 Another supermarket employee is creating a pyramid of oranges for a produce display. The diagram on the right shows the first three levels, top to bottom, in this display.

level 1

level 2

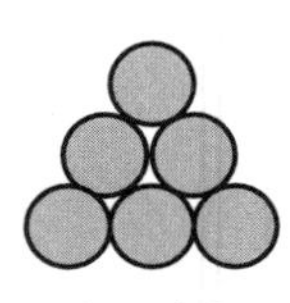
level 3

a. Make a sketch of the next three levels in the display.

b. Let l_n represent the number of oranges in level n. Find the first six terms of this sequence.

c. Is the sequence you wrote in Part **b** an arithmetic sequence? Justify your response.

d. Write both recursive and explicit formulas to describe this sequence.

e. How many oranges are there in a 10-level display?

ACTIVITY 3

In Activities **1** and **2,** you examined how arithmetic sequences can be modeled by linear equations. However, just as there are many different types of equations, there are many different types of numerical sequences. In this activity, you explore a type of sequence that can be used to model a projected increase in sales.

Exploration

Before starting their next concert tour, Stellar Attraction releases a second CD. During the first week, 500 copies are sold. The band's manager predicts sales will double each week that the band is on tour.

a. The band's concert tour will last 12 weeks. Table **12-5** shows the manager's predictions for both weekly sales and total sales during this period. Complete the table.

Table 12-5 ■ *Projected CD Sales*

Week	Weekly Sales	Total Sales
1	500	500
2	1000	1500
3	2000	3500
⋮	⋮	⋮
12		

b. Record any patterns you observe in the table.

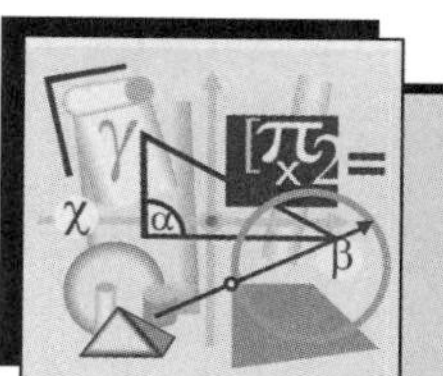

mathematics note

A **geometric sequence** is a sequence in which every term after the first is found by multiplying the preceding term by a constant value.

The recursive formula for calculating any term in a geometric sequence is:

$$\begin{cases} g_1 = \text{first term} \\ g_n = g_{n-1}(r),\ n > 1 \end{cases}$$

where g_1 is the first term, g_n is the nth term, g_{n-1} is the term preceding g_n, and r is the **common ratio** between any two consecutive terms, g_n/g_{n-1}.

For example, consider the sequence in which the first term (g_1) is 4 and the common ratio (r) between any two consecutive terms is 5. The recursive formula for this sequence is:

$$\begin{cases} g_1 = 4 \\ g_n = g_{n-1}(5),\ n > 1 \end{cases}$$

Using this formula, the first four terms of the sequence can be found as follows:

$$g_1 = 4$$

$$g_2 = g_{2-1}(r) = g_1(r) = 4(5) = 20$$

$$g_3 = g_{3-1}(r) = g_2(r) = 20(5) = 100$$

$$g_4 = g_{4-1}(r) = g_3(r) = 100(5) = 500$$

The sum of the terms of a geometric sequence is a **geometric series.**

For example, consider the geometric sequence 3, 12, 48, 192. The corresponding geometric series is 3 + 12 + 48 + 192, or 255.

c. In Table **12-5,** the numbers in the "Weekly Sales" column form a geometric sequence.

1. Find the common ratio for this sequence.
2. Write a recursive formula for this sequence.
3. Determine the corresponding geometric series.

Discussion

a. Describe the patterns you observed in the numbers in Table **12-5.**

b. Use these patterns to answer the following questions:

1. After 12 weeks, what are the predicted total sales?
2. What are the predicted weekly sales for week 10?
3. During what week are total sales predicted to exceed 1 million?

c. Why do the numbers in the "Weekly Sales" column form a geometric sequence?

d. Do the numbers in the "Total Sales" column also form a geometric sequence? Why or why not?

e. If the band extends their tour for 12 more weeks, should they expect sales to continue the predicted pattern? Explain your response.

Warm-Up

1. For each of the following geometric sequences, write a recursive formula, then list the next three terms.

a. 4, 4.8, 5.76, 6.912, 8.2944, 9.95328, . . .

b. 24, 12, 6, 3, 1.5, 0.75, . . .

c. 2, −6, 18, −54, 162, −486, . . .

2. Consider the following recursive formula:

$$\begin{cases} g_1 = 3.2 \\ g_n = g_{n-1} \bullet 5, \ n > 1 \end{cases}$$

a. What is the common ratio?

b. What is the first term?

c. What are the next four terms?

3. Write a recursive formula for each geometric sequence described below.

a. The first term is 4.4 and the common ratio is 3.1.

b. The first term is −3 and the common ratio is 7.

Assignment

3.1 Determine a recursive formula for each of the following geometric sequences:

a. 4, 28, 196, 1372, . . .

b. 9, 18.9, 39.69, . . .

c. 144, 36, 9, 9/4, . . .

3.2 **a.** Create a scatterplot of the first six terms of each geometric sequence in Problem **3.1.** Let x represent the term number and y represent the value of the term.

b. Compare the graphs of the three sequences.

3.3 As soon as the concert tour ends, Stellar Attraction's manager predicts that CD sales will begin to decline. Over the next 8 weeks, sales should fall by 75% each week.

a. Use this information to extend Table **12-5** for weeks 13–20.

b. The numbers in the "Weekly Sales" column for weeks 12–20 form a geometric sequence. Write a recursive formula for this sequence. (The first term is the weekly sales for week 12.)

c. Does your formula work after week 18? Explain your response.

d. What are the predicted weekly sales for week 20?

e. What are the predicted total sales for week 20?

3.4 Following the concert at the Jan-San Amphitheater, an enterprising group of students offers to clean the arena at the following rate: $0.01 for the first barrel of garbage, $0.02 for the second barrel, and $0.04 for the third barrel, with this doubling pattern continuing for each additional barrel.

a. Create a table with the following column headings. Complete this table for 20 barrels of garbage.

Barrel Number	Charge per Barrel	Total Charge

b. If the students want to earn at least $500, how many barrels of garbage must they collect?

c. The manager of the amphitheater has budgeted $1000 to clean up after the concert. How many barrels of garbage must the students collect to exceed this budget?

* * * * *

3.5 Consider the pattern of dots shown in the following diagram.

a. Draw the next picture in this pattern.

b. Represent this pattern as a sequence.

c. Is this sequence a geometric sequence? Explain your response.

d. Write a recursive formula for the sequence.

e. Graph the sequence as a scatterplot. Represent the term number on the x-axis and the value of the term on the y-axis.

3.6 As part of a holiday sales promotion, a clothing store plans to reduce the price of its $20.00 shirts by 10% each week.

a. Will the sale prices from week to week represent a geometric sequence? Explain your response.

b. The store originally paid $12.00 for each shirt. In what week will the store begin to lose money on the sale items?

c. The store manager decides to stop the sale in the week before shirt prices fall below $12.00. If you buy one shirt during each week of the sale, how much money will you spend?

3.7 Shahid and Yasmir borrowed money to buy their house. Their monthly payment includes the cost of the loan, insurance, and property taxes. During the first year of the loan, the monthly payment is $350.00. In each year following the first, the monthly payment rises by 2%.

a. Write a recursive formula that describes the monthly payment in any year.

b. Determine when the monthly payment will be more than $500.00.

c. Shahid and Yasmir must pay a total of $150,238.41 to pay off their loan. During what year will this occur?

ACTIVITY 4

As mentioned in Activity **3,** Stellar Attraction's manager predicted that the weekly sales of their CD would double each week. The predicted sales for the next 10 weeks form a geometric sequence. The two left-hand columns in Table **12-6** show the term number and terms for this sequence. The other three columns show expanded (and equivalent) forms of the term values.

Table 12-6 ■ *Patterns within Geometric Sequences*

Term Number (n)	Term (t_n)	Recursive Form of t_n	Expanded Recursive Form of t_n	Explicit Form of t_n
1	500	500	500	500
2	1000	500 • 2	500 • 2	$500 \bullet 2^1$
3	2000	1000 • 2	500 • 2 • 2	$500 \bullet 2^2$
4	4000	2000 • 2	500 • 2 • 2 • 2	$500 \bullet 2^3$
⋮	⋮	⋮	⋮	⋮

In this activity, you use the patterns in this table to investigate explicit formulas for geometric sequences.

Exploration

a. Develop an explicit formula for the sequence of terms, t_n, in Table **12-6.**

b. Create a three-column spreadsheet that duplicates the following three columns from Table **12-6.**

Term Number (n)	Recursive Form of t_n	Explicit Form of t_n

c. 1. Extend the spreadsheet to at least $n = 10$.

2. Compare the values in the two right-hand columns in your spreadsheet.

d. Add a fourth column to the spreadsheet that determines the ratio of each term to its preceding term, t_n / t_{n-1} where $n > 1$.

e. Create a scatterplot of the sequence. Let x represent the term number and y represent the value of each term.

f. Find an equation that models the scatterplot and graph it on your coordinate system from Part **e.**

Compare this equation to the formula you wrote in Part **a.**

Discussion

a. 1. Using the explicit form of t_n described in Table **12-6,** what power of 2 is multiplied by 500 to determine t_{19}?

2. How is the power of 2 in each row related to the value of n in that row?

b. 1. Describe a formula based on the value of n that could be used to calculate the value of t_n.

   2. Use this formula to calculate t_7.

c. What do you observe about the ratio found in Part **d** of the exploration?

d. How is this ratio related to the formula described in Part **b** of the discussion?

An **explicit formula** for calculating any specific term in a geometric sequence is:

$$g_n = g_1 r^{n-1}$$

where g_n is the nth term, g_1 is the first term, and r is the common ratio between any two consecutive terms, g_n / g_{n-1}.

For example, consider the geometric sequence 6, 24, 96, 348, 1536, ... For this sequence, the first term is 6 and the common ratio 4. The explicit formula for this sequence is: $g_n = 6(4)^{n-1}$. Using this formula, the seventh term of the sequence can be found as follows:

$$g_7 = 6(4)^{7-1} = 6(4)^6 = 6(4096) = 24{,}576$$

e. Do you think that the scatterplot of a geometric sequence can always be modeled by an exponential equation? Why or why not?

f. How does the graph of an exponential equation differ from the graph of a geometric sequence?

g. Using the laws of exponents, the equation $y = ab^x$ can be rewritten as $y = a \bullet b^1 \bullet b^{x-1}$, which is equivalent to $y = (ab)b^{x-1}$. Assuming that this equation models the same geometric sequence as the explicit formula $g_n = g_1 r^{(n-1)}$, describe the relationship between each of the following:

   1. the nth term g_n and y
   2. n and x
   3. the common ratio r and b
   4. the first term g_1 and a

h. When is an explicit formula for a geometric sequence easier to use than the recursive formula?

i. Using the relationships described in Part **g** of the discussion, show that the explicit formula for a geometric sequence, $g_n = g_1 r^{(n-1)}$, is equivalent to the exponential equation of the form $y = ab^x$ that models the same sequence.

Warm-Up

1. Write an explicit formula for each of the following geometric sequences.

   a. 4000, 2000, 1000, 500, 250, 125, . . .

   b. 13, −39, 117, −351, 1053, −3159, . . .

   c. −4, −9.6, −23.04, −55.296, −132.7104, 318.50496, . . .

2. Consider the explicit formula $g_n = 7 \bullet 3.1^{n-1}$.

   a. What is the common ratio?

   b. What is the first term?

   c. What are the next three terms?

3. Write an explicit formula for each geometric sequence described below.

   a. The first term is −2.4 and the common ratio is 1.3.

   b. The first term is 9 and the common ratio is 0.8.

Assignment

4.1 Identify each of the following sequences as geometric or not geometric. For each geometric sequence, write an explicit formula and find the 10th term. Explain why each of the remaining sequences is not geometric.

   a. 0.5, 2.5, 12.5, 62.5, . . .

   b. 15, 150, 300, 900, . . .

   c. 4, −12, 36, −108, . . .

   d. 1000, 250, 62.5, 15.625, . . .

4.2 Write the geometric series for each sequence below and find the corresponding sum.

   a. 1, 3, 9, 27, 81

   b. 2, 5, 12.5, . . . , 78.125

   c. 0.5, 1, 2, . . . , 64

   d. 125, 25, 5, . . . , 0.04

4.3 At one of Stellar Attraction's concerts, an exuberant fan hits a beach ball into the air. The ball falls onto the stage from a height of 24 m. The height of each bounce is approximately one-third the height of the preceding bounce. Predict the number of bounces the ball will take before coming to rest. Justify your response.

4.4 Describe the possible range of values for the common ratio in each of the following:

a. an increasing geometric sequence

b. a decreasing geometric sequence.

4.5 Consider the pattern of dots shown in the following diagram.

a. If this pattern is expressed as a geometric sequence, what are the values for t_1 and r?

b. Write an explicit formula that describes this pattern.

c. Use your formula to determine the value of t_{14}.

science note

Sound is produced by vibrating objects. The frequency of a sound wave equals the frequency of the vibrating object.

The international unit of frequency is the **hertz (Hz),** which represents one cycle per second. For example, a sound with a frequency of 220 Hz is produced by an object vibrating at 220 cycles per second.

4.6 When a guitar string vibrates, the guitar produces sound. The rate at which the string vibrates determines the note. A string vibrating at 220 Hz produces the note A immediately below middle C. The note A immediately above middle C vibrates at 440 Hz. The frequencies of consecutive A notes form a geometric sequence.

Note	Frequency
A	
A	
A	
A	440 Hz
middle C	
A	220 Hz
A	
A	
A	
A	

a. Complete the table for all A notes above and below middle C.

b. Write a recursive formula that describes this sequence.

c. The average young person can hear sounds with frequencies from 20 Hz to 20,000 Hz. Which of the notes in the table in Part **a** could be heard by concert fans? Defend your response.

4.7 Annaborg has been offered two summer jobs, each for 12 weeks. The job at Plouvier's Pottery pays $5.00 per hour, with a 10% increase in the hourly wage every two weeks. The job at Brocklebank's Bakery pays $6.50 per hour, with a $0.10 increase in the hourly wage every two weeks.

a. Which type of sequence, arithmetic or geometric, best describes the wages offered by Plouvier's Pottery? Justify your response.

b. Which type of sequence, arithmetic or geometric, best describes the wages offered by Brocklebank's Bakery? Justify your response.

c. Write an explicit formula that describes the wages for each job.

d. If Annaborg wants to make as much money as possible, which job should she take? Justify your response.

Summary Assessment

1. In 1990, the village of Bone Gap had a population of 350 people. By the end of 1991, the population had grown to 385. Many long-time residents grew concerned about the future of their community. At a town meeting, two different predictions were made.

   Mrs. Stephens presented the following graph and argued that residents should not be concerned about growth.

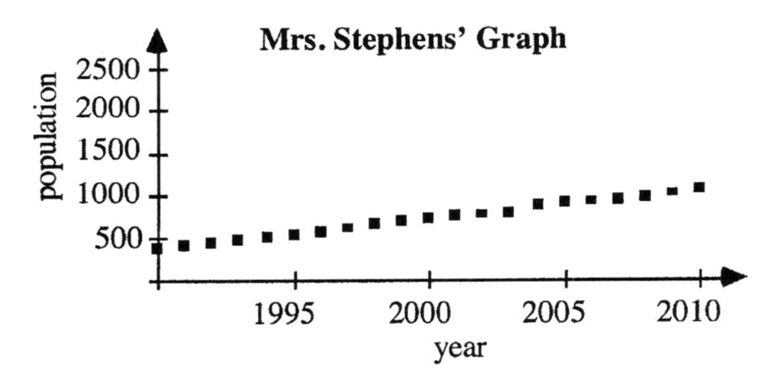

   Mr. Aloishan, however, presented the graph below and argued that life in Bone Gap would change dramatically.

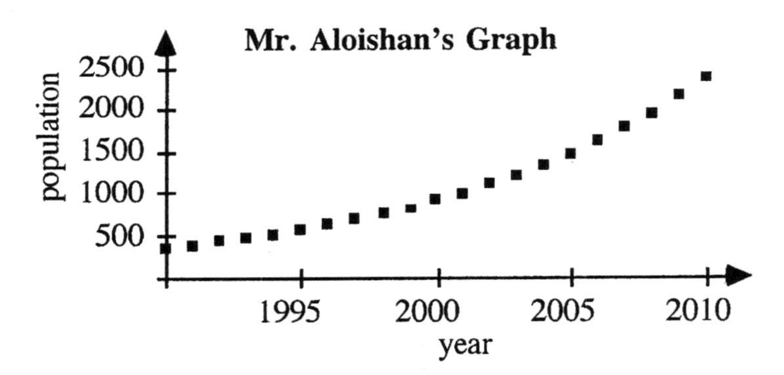

   Based on these two graphs and the initial data, explain how the two residents reached their conclusions. Include formulas for each graph.

2. Imagine that the following two plans were proposed at the time that the U.S. national debt reached $4 trillion.

   - Plan A: Balance the budget to eliminate additional accumulation of debt. Reduce the debt by $1.00 per second until the debt is canceled.
   - Plan B: Balance the budget to eliminate additional accumulation of debt. Reduce the debt by $1.00 in the first year, $2.00 in the second year, $4.00 in the third year, and continue to double the reduction until the debt is canceled.

   Use the ideas and tools in this module to analyze the two plans. Which one do you think is better? Defend your choice.

Module Summary

- A **sequence** is an ordered list. Each item in the list is a **term** of the sequence.
- The terms of a sequence may be represented by symbols, such as $p_1, p_2, p_3, \ldots, p_n$. These symbols are **subscripted variables,** and the natural numbers $(1, 2, 3, \ldots, n)$ are the **subscripts.** The symbol p_1 (read "p sub one") represents the first term of the sequence, the symbol p_2 (read "p sub two") represents the second term of the sequence, and so on. The symbol p_n (read "p sub n"), represents the **general,** or ***n*th, term** of a sequence.
- A **recursive formula** is a rule for finding any term in a sequence by using the preceding term(s). The process of using a recursive formula is known as **recursion.**
- A sequence in which every term after the first is found by adding a constant value to the preceding term is an **arithmetic sequence.**
- The recursive formula for calculating any term in an arithmetic sequence is:

$$\begin{cases} a_1 = \text{first term} \\ a_n = a_{n-1} + d,\ n > 1 \end{cases}$$

where a_1 is the first term, a_n is the nth term, a_{n-1} is the term preceding a_n, and d is the **common difference** between any two consecutive terms, $a_n - a_{n-1}$.

- An **explicit formula** for calculating any specific term in an arithmetic sequence is:

$$a_n = a_1 + d(n - 1)$$

where a_n is the nth term, a_1 is the first term, and d is the common difference between any two consecutive terms, $a_n - a_{n-1}$.

- The sum of the terms of an arithmetic sequence is an **arithmetic series.**
- A **geometric sequence** is a sequence in which every term after the first is found by multiplying the preceding term by a constant value.
- The recursive formula for calculating any term in a geometric sequence is:

$$\begin{cases} g_1 = \text{first term} \\ g_n = g_{n-1}(r),\ n > 1 \end{cases}$$

where g_1 is the first term, g_n is the nth term, g_{n-1} is the term preceding g_n, and r is the **common ratio** between any two consecutive terms, g_n/g_{n-1}.

- The sum of the terms of a geometric sequence is a **geometric series.**
- An **explicit formula** for calculating any specific term in a geometric sequence is:

$$g_n = g_1 r^{n-1}$$

where g_n is the nth term, g_1 is the first term, and r is the common ratio between any two consecutive terms, g_n/g_{n-1}.

module 13

Under the Big Top but Above the Floor

Introduction

Every year at Dantzig High School, the mathematics club sponsors a school carnival. The club designs game booths to earn money. As booths compete to attract more customers, the atmosphere grows festive. Many students dress in crazy costumes. Balloons, tinsel, and streamers are everywhere, and the aromas of pizza, popcorn, and hot dogs waft through the gym.

The first game booth that you visit is "Guess My Number." Inside the booth, Yvette stands next to a tumbling basket of numbers. Yvette picks a number from the basket. You must now guess the number by asking questions which can be answered by "yes" or "no." If you guess correctly using seven or fewer questions, you win a prize.

Exploration

In this exploration, you play Guess My Number with a classmate and try to develop a winning strategy.

a. To play Guess My Number with a classmate, each of you should select an integer in the interval $[-50, 50]$. Do not reveal your number to your classmate. Take turns asking yes-or-no questions until you discover each other's number. Record the questions asked, the answers given, and the number of questions.

   Play the game at least twice and consider some strategies you might use to guess correctly with the fewest questions.

b. Play Guess My Number at least two more times, using only questions that include inequalities (for example, "Is your number less than 5?"). Record each question using inequality symbols. Record the responses on a number line.

c. Play Guess My Number at least three more times, using questions that include inequalities.

Discussion

a. If your opponent must choose an integer in the interval $[-50, 50]$, can you develop a strategy that guarantees you will know the number in seven questions or less?

b. What do you think the minimum number of questions would be to determine an integer in the interval [–75,75]?

ACTIVITY 1

The next booth you visit is "Guess My Location." The object of this game is to determine the exact location of your opponent's point on a grid. Pablo and Lisa are ahead of you at the booth. Watch them play while you wait for your turn. Figure **13-1** shows the beginning of their game.

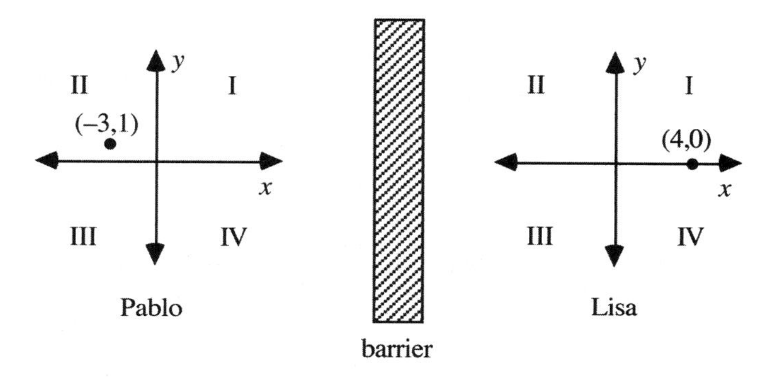

FIGURE 13-1 **Pablo and Lisa play Guess My Location.**

Pablo asks, "Is $x > 0$?"

Lisa answers, "Yes."

Pablo knows that Lisa's point must be in quadrant I, quadrant IV, or on the positive x-axis.

Lisa asks, "Is $y \leq 0$?"

"No," answers Pablo.

Lisa knows that Pablo's point is above the x-axis.

It's Pablo's turn again. "Is $y \geq 0$?" he asks.

"Yes," answers Lisa.

Pablo knows that Lisa's point can only be in the first quadrant or on the positive x-axis.

Discussion 1

a. The graph of the equation $y = -3$ is shown in Figure **13-2a** below. As the shaded region in Figure **13-2b** demonstrates, the line separates the plane into two parts or **half planes.**

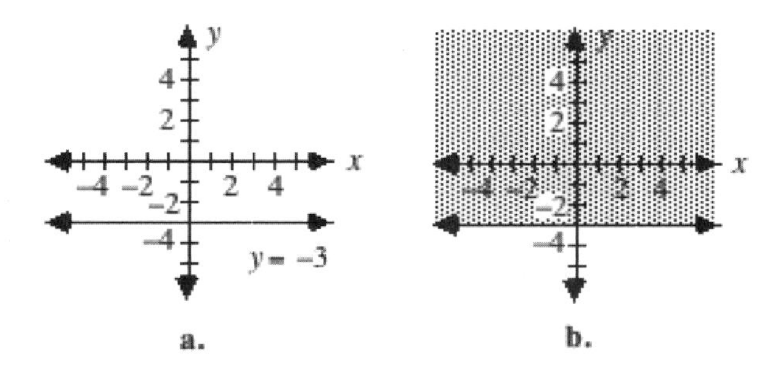

FIGURE 13-2 Graphs of $y = -3$ and the half-plane above $y = -3$.

1. What must be true about the coordinates of all the points in the shaded region in Figure **13-2b?**
2. How can you use inequality notation to describe the y-coordinates of the points either on or above the line $y = -3$?

b. The line $x = 5$ defines the boundary for the inequality $x < 5$.

1. Describe what the graph of $x = 5$ would look like on a coordinate system.
2. Would a graph of $x < 5$ be shaded to the right or to the left of $x = 5$? Explain your response.
3. Should the boundary be a part of the graph of $x < 5$? Explain your response.

mathematics note

The graph of a linear inequality is a shaded region that represents the **solution set** of the inequality. The solution set contains all the points, or solutions, that make the inequality true. The graph of a linear equation forms the **boundary line** for the region. A solid boundary indicates that the points on the line are part of the solution set. A dashed boundary indicates that the points on the line are not part of the solution set.

For example, Figure **13-3a** shows the graph of $x \geq -2$ and Figure **13-3b** shows the graph of $y < 3$.

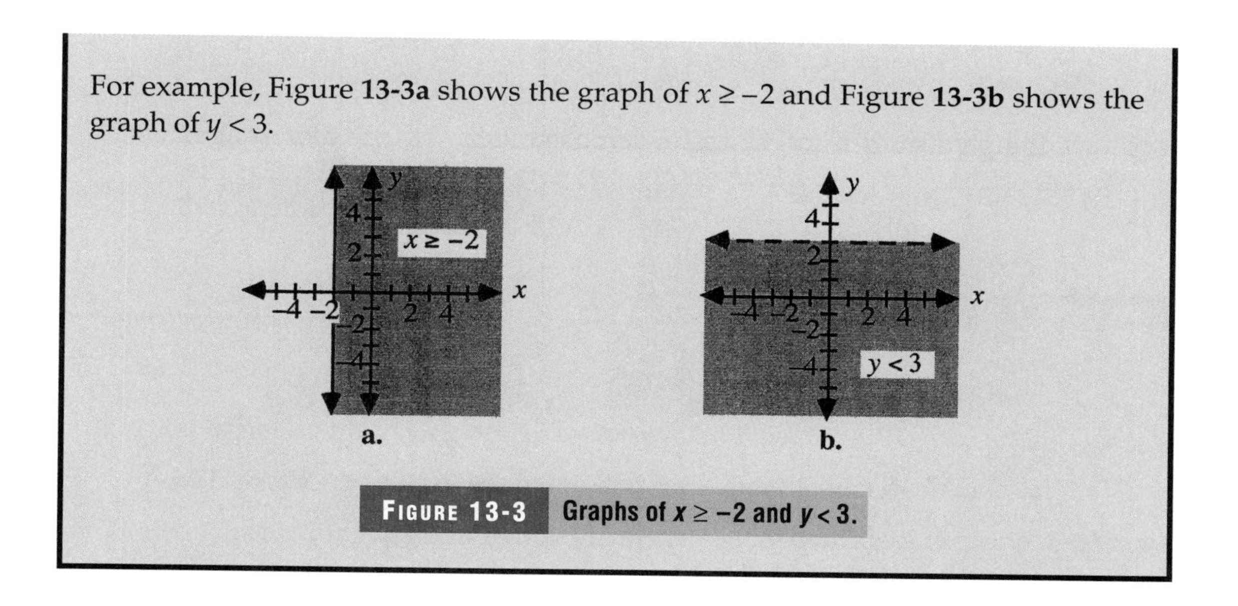

FIGURE 13-3 Graphs of $x \geq -2$ and $y < 3$.

c. How many points are in the solution set for each inequality in Figure **13-3**?

d. 1. Identify the coordinates of a point that is in the solution set of both inequalities in Figure **13-3.**

   2. How many points are in the solution set that satisfies both inequalities?

e. Explain why the point (2,−7) is in the solution set for $x \geq 2$ but not for $y < -7$.

Exploration 1

In this exploration, you play Guess My Location with a classmate. Read Parts **a–d** before beginning play

a. Each player makes a game sheet by drawing a coordinate system on a sheet of graph paper. Both game sheets should have the same scales on the x- and y-axes.

   Place a book upright between the two game sheets so that neither player can see the other's graph.

b. Both players choose and mark a point on their game sheets, without revealing the point's location to the opponent. The coordinates of the point must be integers.

c. Players take turns asking yes-or-no questions involving inequalities, to gain information about the location of the opponent's point.

   Record each question you ask as an inequality. Record each answer you receive as the graph of an inequality on your coordinate system.

d. The first player to identify the coordinates of the opponent's point wins the game. If a player guesses incorrectly, then that player loses the next turn.

Discussion 2

a. Describe the strategies you used to play Guess My Location.

b. Assume that your opponent's point is located in the third quadrant. What two mathematical statements would describe this region?

mathematics note

A **conjunction** combines two mathematical statements with the word *and.* A conjunction can be represented as the intersection of two sets.

As shown in Figure **13-4,** for example, the conjunction $x > 0$ and $y > 0$ can be represented by the intersection of their solution sets.

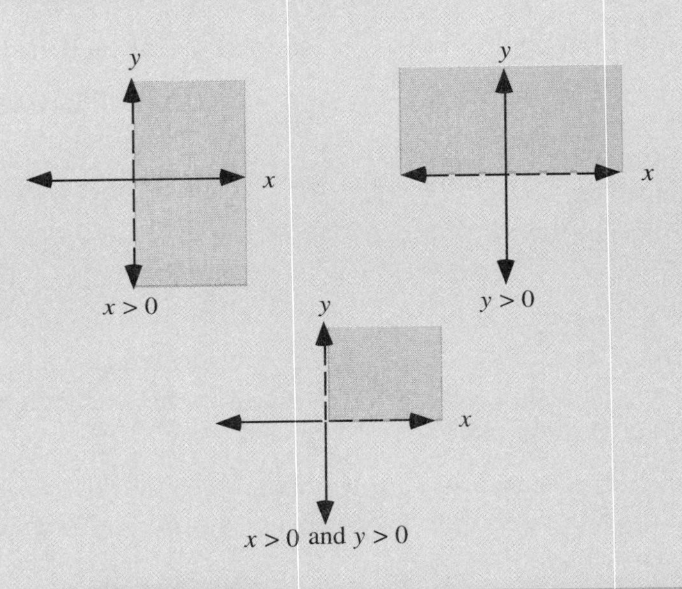

FIGURE 13-4 Intersection of two linear inequalities.

A conjunction that describes a real-number interval for one variable can be written either as a compound statement or as a single expression.

For example, the conjunction "n is greater than -3 and less than 10" can be written as $n > -3$ and $n < 10$. It also can be written as the single expression $-3 < n < 10$. This expression can be read "-3 is less than n and n is less than 10," or "n is greater than -3 and less than 10."

c. For all points in the first quadrant, the x- and y-coordinates are greater than 0. Does the conjunction shown in Figure **13-4** represent these points? Explain your response.

d. Imagine that Pablo asked Lisa "Is $x > 0$ and $y < 0$?"

  1. If Lisa answers "Yes," in what quadrant(s) could her point be located? Explain your response.

  2. If Lisa answers "No," in what quadrant(s) could her point be located? Explain your response.

e. What conjunction describes the intersection of the two inequalities shown in Figure **13-5?**

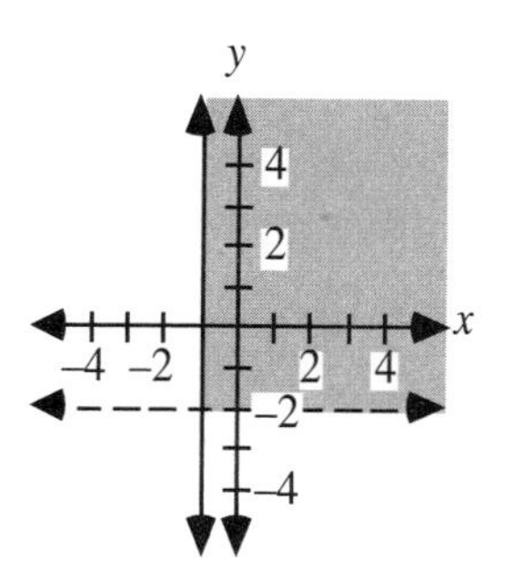

FIGURE 13-5 **Two inequalities and their intersection.**

Exploration 2

Imagine that Pablo and Lisa replay the original game of Guess My Location shown in Figure **13-1.** Pablo has chosen the point (–3,1) and Lisa has chosen (4,0). This time they ask questions that use conjunctions.

"Is $x > 0$ and $y < 0$?" asks Pablo.

"No," Lisa responds.

Pablo knows that the point is not in quadrant IV.

Now it's Lisa's turn. She asks, "Is $x \leq 0$ and $y \geq 0$?"

Pablo answers, "Yes."

Lisa knows that the point is in quadrant II.

Now Pablo asks, "Is $x \geq 0$ and $y \geq 0$?"

"Yes," answers Lisa.

Following Pablo and Lisa's example, play another game of Guess My Location. For this game, use the two additional rules described in Parts **a** and **b.**

a. Each question must be a conjunction.

b. One mathematical statement in the conjunction must refer only to x; the other statement must refer only to y.

Discussion 3

a. What advantages or disadvantages did you notice when using conjunctions to play Guess My Location?

b. Consider Pablo's first conjunction, "Is $x > 0$ and $y < 0$?" The intersection of the two boundary lines for these inequalities, $x = 0$ and $y = 0$, is referred to as a **corner point** or **vertex.**

   Is this corner point part of the solution set for the conjunction? Explain your response.

c. How do you know that a point in the first quadrant is a solution to $x > 0$ and $y > 0$?

d. Consider the points in the solution set of $x > 0$ and $y > 0$. The x-coordinates of these points must be positive real numbers. This condition on the x-coordinates is called a **constraint.**

   Describe the constraints on the y-coordinates of the points in this solution set.

e. How could you use conjunctions to describe the region shown in Figure **13-6?**

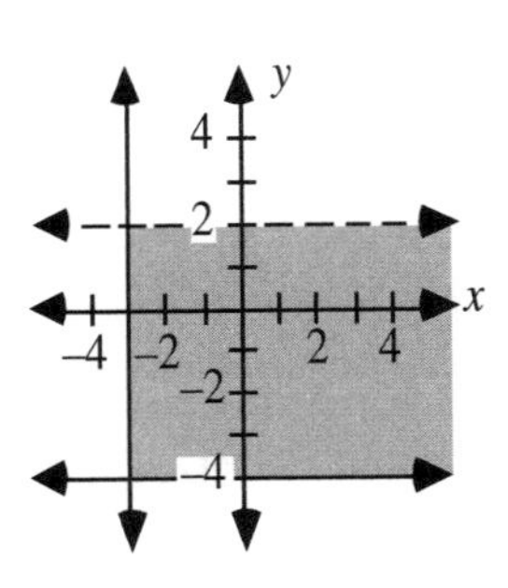

FIGURE 13-6 **A region defined by conjunctions.**

Warm-Up

1. Graph and label the following lines on the same coordinate grid.

   a. $y = 5$

   b. $x = -7$

   c. $y = -(2/3)x + 1$

2. **a.** Sketch a graph of the line $y = 4$.

   b. Write an inequality to describe all the points located on and above the line.

   c. Shade the region that corresponds to the solution set of the inequality.

   d. Write the coordinates of at least three points included in the solution set.

   e. Describe the constraints on the x-coordinates of the points in the solution set.

   f. Describe the constraints on the y-coordinates of the points in the solution set.

3. Graph each of the following on a separate coordinate grid.

   a. $x < 9$

   b. $y \geq -4$

   c. $y \leq -4$ and $x > 2$

4. The following graph shows the four quadrants of the coordinate plane. Use conjunctions of linear inequalities to describe each quadrant. **Note:** The x- and y-axes are not included in any quadrant.

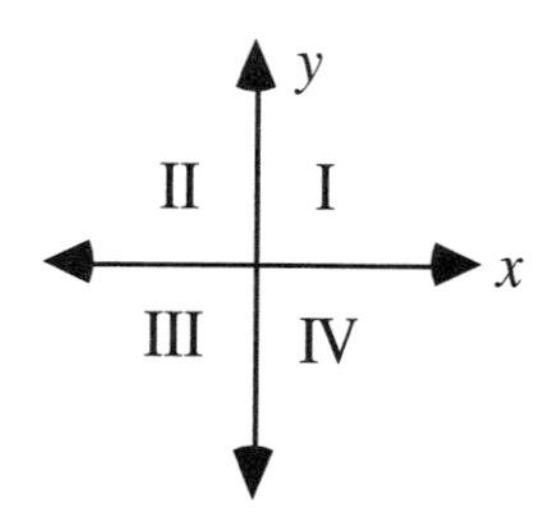

5. **a.** On a coordinate plane, graph the region defined by the intersection of the linear inequalities $x \geq -4$ and $y \leq 2$.

   b. Select a point in the intersection of the two inequalities that is not on a boundary. Verify that the point is a solution to both inequalities.

   c. Select a point outside the shaded region. Verify that the point is not a solution for at least one of the inequalities.

   d. Select a point on a boundary. Is this point a solution to both inequalities? Explain your response.

   e. Identify the corner point of the conjunction.

Assignment

1.1 **a.** Use inequalities to describe the shaded region in each of the following graphs.

1.

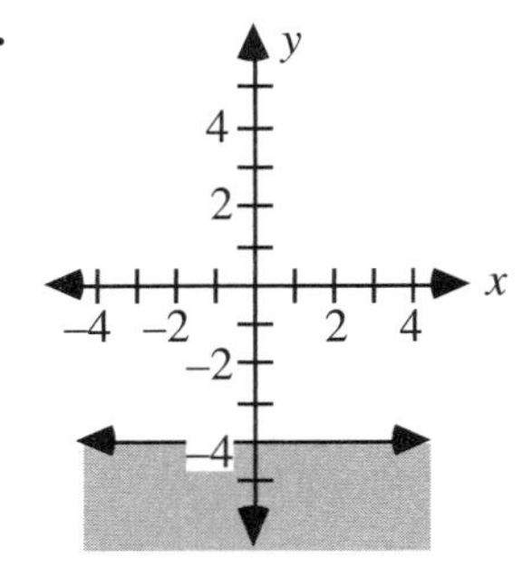

2.

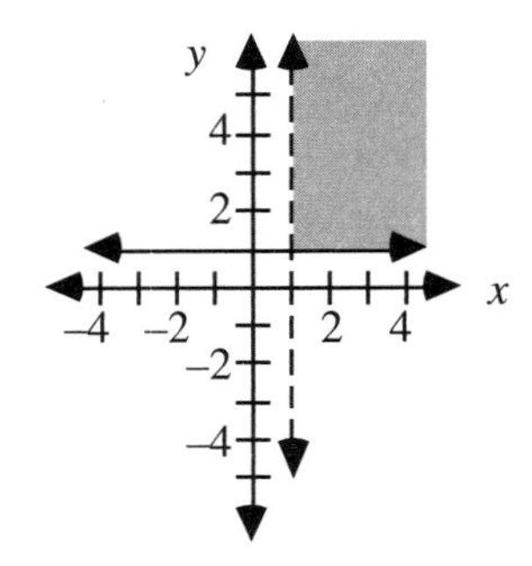

3.

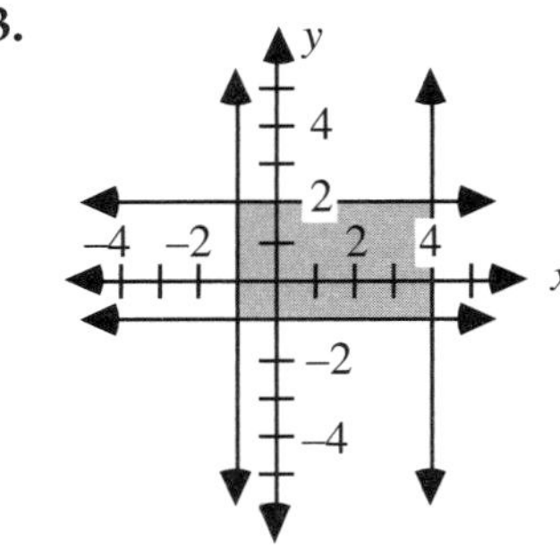

b. Identify the coordinates of any corner points for each shaded region in Part **a.**

1.2 In a game of Guess My Location, your opponent chooses the point with coordinates (0,–2). Using conjunctions, write two different questions about this point that will receive a "yes" answer.

1.3 In another game of Guess My Location, you ask the question, "Is $x = 5$ and $y > -2$?" Your opponent answers, "Yes."

a. On a coordinate plane, graph the set of all points that fit this information.

b. Describe the graph formed.

1.4 The tables in Parts **a** and **b** show some questions and answers from two different games of Guess My Location. For each game, graph the "smallest" region that contains all possible solutions and use linear inequalities to describe the region.

a.

Question	Answer
Is $x \geq 0$ and $y \geq 0$?	Yes
Is $x \leq 2$ and $y \geq 0$?	No
Is $x \geq 3$ and $y \geq 1$?	Yes
Is $x \geq 4$ and $y \leq 5$?	Yes

b.

Question	Answer
Is $x \geq 0$ and $y \leq 0$?	Yes
Is $x \geq 5$ and $y \geq -3$?	No
Is $x \leq 4$ and $y \geq -3$?	Yes

* * * * *

1.5 A cash register contains bills and coins. Using the horizontal axis to represent the value of the bills and the vertical axis to represent the value of the coins, draw a graph to describe each of the following statements:

a. The cash register contains at least $50.00 in bills and no more than $25.00 in coins.

b. The cash register contains less than $100.00 in bills and at least $10.00 in coins.

c. The cash register contains more than $75.00 in bills and no more than $50.00 in coins.

* * * * *

1.6 Use linear inequalities to describe each shaded region in Parts **a–c.**

a.

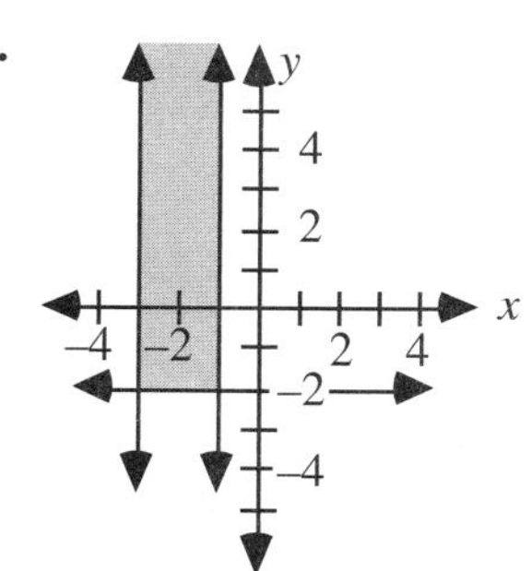

b.

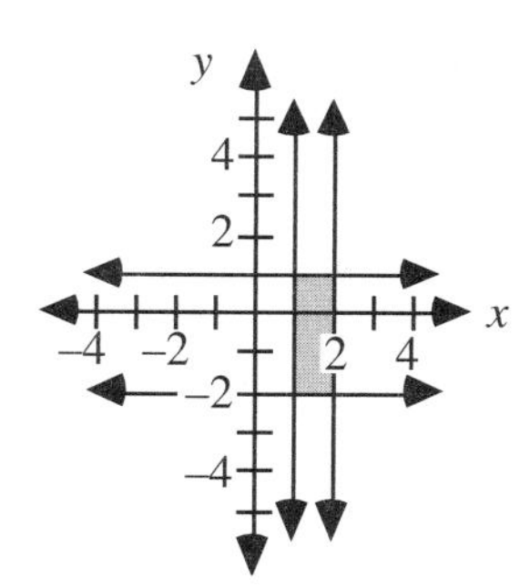

c.

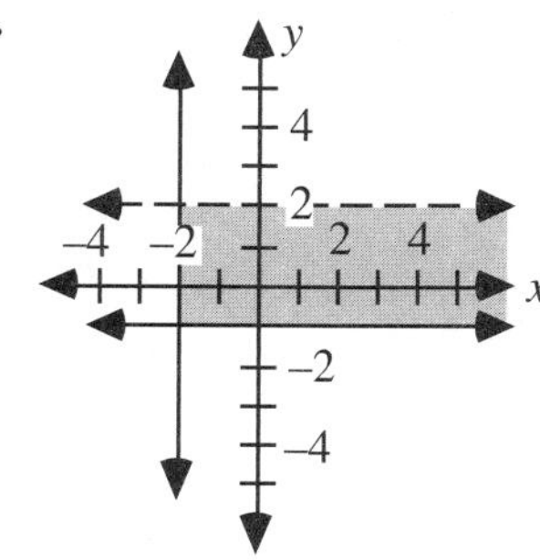

1.7 Terry, Stan, and Lindsey are designing vegetable gardens. Using the horizontal axis to represent length and the vertical axis to represent width, draw a graph to describe each of the following statements.

a. Terry decides that her garden should be no more than 8 m long and less than 6 m wide.

b. Stan decides his garden should be more than 16 m long and at least 10 m wide.

c. Lindsey decides that her garden should be at most 4 m long and no more than 3 m wide.

Anton and Sharline are the school champions at Guess My Location. In this activity, you investigate some of the tools they use to analyze the game.

Exploration 1

Anton and Sharline are playing Guess My Location. Both players have selected points with x- and y-coordinates between –10 and 10. After receiving an answer to his first question, Anton shades his game sheet as shown in Figure **13-7.**

The points A, B, C, and D in Figure **13-7** lie at the intersections of the dashed line, the solid line, and the lines that define the right-hand and lower limits of the grid. The solid line through points A and C also passes through (0,–3) and (1,–1). The horizontal dashed line has a y-intercept of 7.

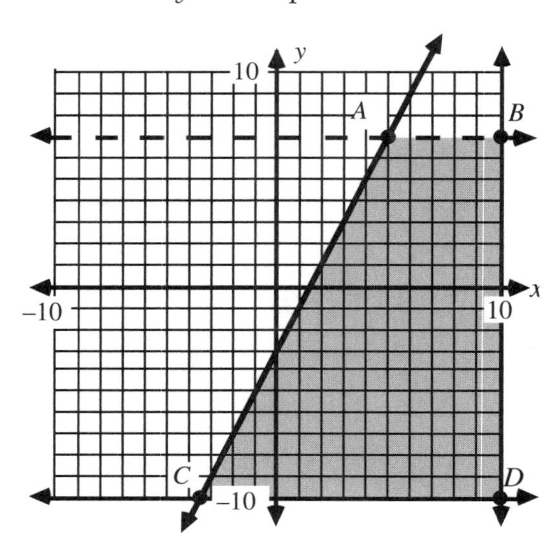

FIGURE 13-7 Anton's graph.

a. Determine the equation of each line that borders the shaded region in Anton's graph.

mathematics note

A **system of linear equations** is a set of two or more equations whose graphs are lines. A **solution** to a system of linear equations is a point where all the lines intersect. The coordinates of this point satisfy all the equations in the system.

For example, consider the following system of linear equations:

$$\begin{cases} y = 2x + 3 \\ y = x + 1 \end{cases}$$

Figure **13-8** shows that the graphs of the two lines intersect at the point with coordinates (–2,–1). Substituting –2 for x and –1 for y shows that this point is a solution to the system, because $-1 = 2(-2) + 3$ and $-1 = -2 + 1$ are both true.

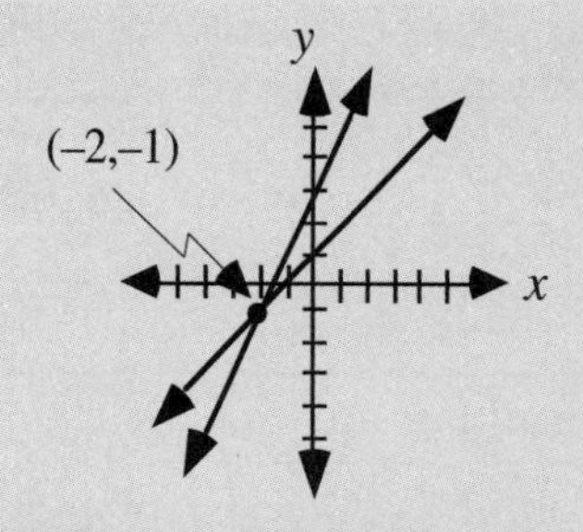

FIGURE 13-8 Solution to a system of linear equations.

b. To shade the region shown in Figure **13-7,** what question might Anton have asked? What answer must Sharline have given?

c. In Figure **13-7,** point C is one of the corner points of the shaded region.

1. Identify the system of linear equations that intersect at point C.
2. Estimate the coordinates of point C as accurately as possible.
3. Determine if the coordinates that you estimated in Step **2** are a solution to the system of linear equations.

Discussion 1

a. The shaded region in Figure **13-7** contains the location of Sharline's point. Anton used the limits of the grid, one solid line, and one dashed line to define the boundaries of the region.

1. If Anton had wanted to define the same region using two dashed boundary lines, how could he have modified his question?

2. If Anton had wanted to use two solid boundary lines, how could he have modified his question?

b. What points are eliminated from a solution set when a dashed boundary line replaces a solid boundary line?

c. The shaded region in Figure **13-7** shows the solution set for a system of linear inequalities. Which of the corner points are included in this solution set?

d. The corner point C appears to have at least one coordinate that is not an integer. Did you find the exact coordinates of this point? Explain your response.

e. The exact coordinates of a point where two lines intersect is the solution to the corresponding system of equations. To find these exact coordinates, you can use a method involving substitution.

For example, Table **13-1** lists the steps necessary to find the solution to one system of equations by substitution.

TABLE 13-1 ■ *Substitution Method for Solving a System of Equations*

Consider the given system of equations.	$\begin{cases} y = 2x - 3 \\ y = 7 \end{cases}$
Since $y = 7$ in this case, substitute 7 for y.	$7 = 2x - 3$
Solve the resulting equation for x.	$5 = x$
Write the solution to the system in the form (x,y).	(5,7)

To check the solution, you can substitute the coordinates of the point in each of the original equations in the system. If $x = 5$ and $y = 7$, then $y = 2x - 3 = 2(5) - 3 = 7$, which is true. Therefore, (5,7) is a solution to the equation $y = 2x - 3$. Because (5,7) is also a solution to the equation $y = 7$, then it is a solution to the system of equations.

1. Why are the coordinates of point C in Exploration **1** a solution to a system of linear equations?

2. How does the substitution method compare with the method you used in Part **c** of Exploration **1**?

Exploration 2

Figure **13-9** shows a graph of three linear equations. Point B is the intersection of $5x - 5y = 4$ and $3x + y = 8$.

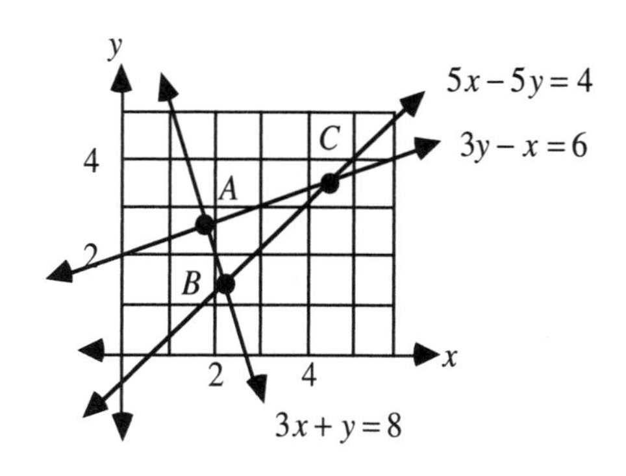

FIGURE 13-9 Three linear equations.

a. Estimate the coordinates of point B in Figure **13-9.**

b. Table **13-2** lists the steps necessary to find the solution to another system of equations by substitution.

TABLE 13-2 ■ *Substitution Method for Solving a System of Linear Equations*	
Consider the given system of equations.	$\begin{cases} 2x + 3y = 6 \\ 9y - 4x = 13 \end{cases}$
Solve one of the equations for y.	$y = 2 - \frac{2}{3}x$
Substitute for y in the other equation.	$9\left(2 - \frac{2}{3}x\right) - 4x = 13$
Solve for x.	$x = \frac{1}{2}$
Substitute for x in one of the original equations.	$2\left(\frac{1}{2}\right) + 3y = 6$
Solve the resulting equation for y.	$y = \frac{5}{3}$
Write the solution to the system in the form (x,y).	$\left(\frac{1}{2}, \frac{5}{3}\right)$

To check the solution, you can substitute the coordinates of the point in each of the original equations.

$$\begin{aligned} 2x + 3y &= 6 \\ 2\left(\frac{1}{2}\right) + 3\left(\frac{5}{3}\right) &\stackrel{?}{=} 6 \\ 1 + 5 &= 6 \end{aligned} \qquad \text{and} \qquad \begin{aligned} 9y - 4x &= 13 \\ 9\left(\frac{5}{3}\right) - 4\left(\frac{1}{2}\right) &\stackrel{?}{=} 13 \\ 15 - 2 &= 13 \end{aligned}$$

1. Use the method described in Table **13-2** to find the exact coordinates of point B in Figure **13-9.**
2. Compare your solution with the estimate you made in Part **a.**
3. Check your solution by substituting the coordinates of the point in each of the original equations.

c. Repeat Parts **a** and **b** for points A and C in Figure **13-9.**

Discussion 2

a. Did your estimated coordinates for points A, B, and C support the solutions you found by solving systems of equations?

b. Describe how to confirm the solution to a system of linear equations.

c. What system of linear inequalities could be used to describe the triangular region in Figure **13-9** with corner points A, B, and C? Assume that the region includes the lines defining its boundaries.

Warm-Up

1. Each graph below shows two intersecting lines. Use the graph to determine the equation of each line and the coordinates of their point of intersection. Substitute the coordinates of the point in each equation to verify your solution.

a.

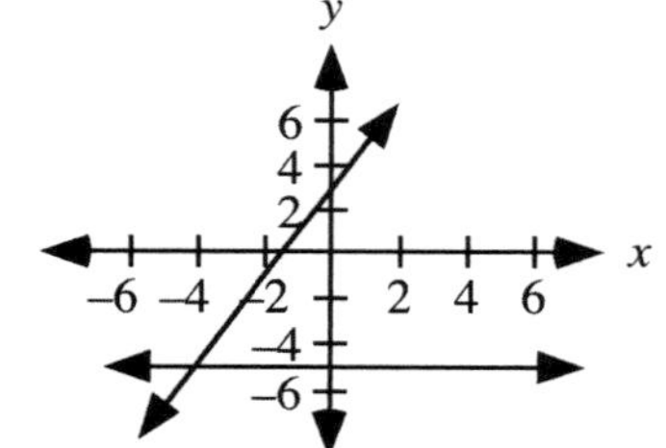

b.

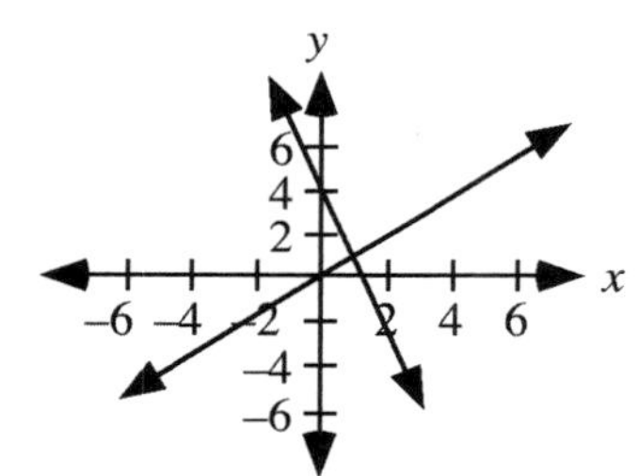

c.

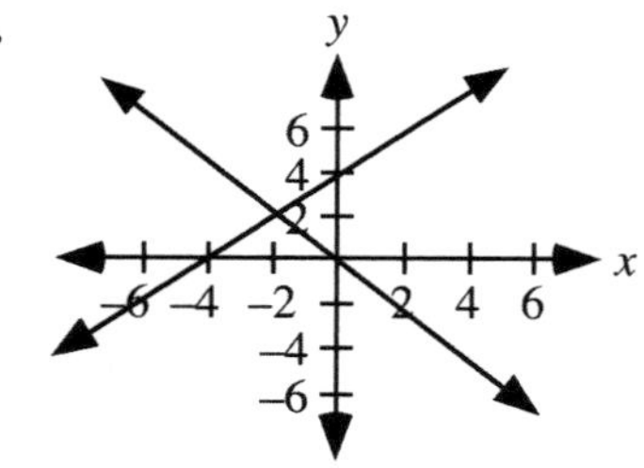

2. Solve each of the following systems of equations using the substitution method. Check your solutions by graphing the system and verifying the coordinates of the point of intersection.

   a. $y = x + 1$ and $y = 3x - 3$ **b.** $x + y = 10$ and $2x - 4y = 2$

   c. $y = x + 7$ and $y = -2x + 6$ **d.** $3x + y = 10$ and $4x + 1 = y$

3. **a.** Graph the lines $y + 3 = 2x$ and $y + 2x = 1$ on the same coordinate system.

   b. Write a linear inequality that describes the region below the line $y + 3 = 2x$ and includes the line.

   c. Write a linear inequality that describes the region above the line $y + 2x = 1$ and includes the line.

   d. List the coordinates of two points that satisfy both inequalities.

   e. Use the substitution method to identify the point of intersection of $y + 3 = 2x$ and $y + 2x = 1$.

Assignment

2.1 **a.** Draw the region defined by the following system of inequalities: $x \geq 0$, $y \geq 0$, $x \leq 8$ and $y \leq 8$.

b. Describe the shape of this region.

c. Identify the corner points, or vertices, of the region.

d. Rewrite the system of inequalities in Part **a** so that the boundaries are not included in the region.

e. Write the equations of three different lines that divide the region in Part **a** into two parts with equal area.

2.2 Graph the region defined by each of the following inequalities:

a. $y > 4x - 3$

b. $y \leq -2x + 7$

c. $-3x + 2y \geq 6$

2.3 **a.** Graph the following system of inequalities:

$$\begin{cases} x + y \leq 6 \\ y \geq -2 \\ x \geq -2 \\ x \leq 4 \end{cases}$$

b. Describe the shape of the region.

c. List the coordinates of its vertices.

2.4 Use a system of linear inequalities to describe the shaded region in the graph shown on the right.

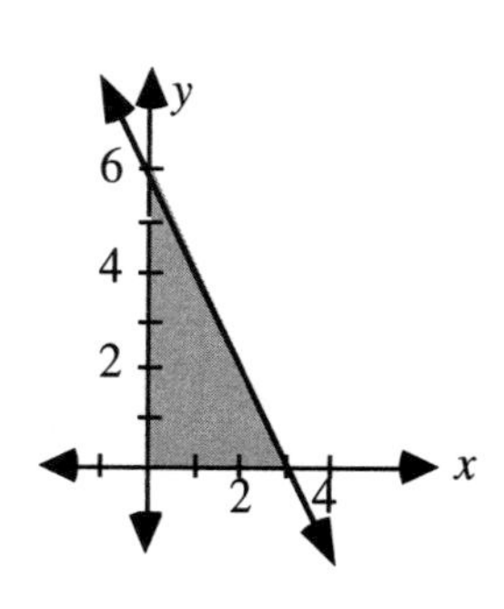

2.5 The Cronin and Nakagomi families are going camping together. At 9:00 A.M., the Cronins leave town traveling at an average speed of 90 km/hr. The Nakagomis don't leave until 9:20 A.M., but they drive at an average speed of 100 km/hr. Use a system of linear equations to determine how long it will take the Nakagomis to catch up with the Cronins. How far down the highway will the two families be before they meet?

2.6 The school library adds new books to its collection every year. According to library policy, the librarian can buy no more than 45 books each year. The number of new fiction books can be no more than half the number of nonfiction books.

a. Let x represent the number of nonfiction books and y represent the number of fiction books. Write a system of inequalities that describes the constraints on book purchases.

b. Graph the system of inequalities you created in Part **a.**

c. Identify the coordinates of the points of intersection.

d. What information do these coordinates represent?

e. Given these constraints, what is the greatest number of fiction books the librarian can buy in a year? Justify your response.

* * * * *

2.7 Graph the region defined by each of the following systems of inequalities:

a. $y > 4x - 3$ and $y \leq -2x + 7$

b. $y \leq -2x + 7$ and $-3x + 2y \geq 6$

2.8 Jasmine has $290.00 and saves $5.00 per week. Alan has $200.00 and saves $8.00 per week.

a. Write equations that describe the amount of money each person has after any week w.

b. In how many weeks will the two have the same amount of money?

2.9 In a basketball game, a player made at least five baskets (2 points each), at least four free throws (1 point each), and scored a total of no more than 20 points. (Assume no three-point baskets were made.)

a. Write a system of three inequalities to describe this situation.

b. Graph this system of inequalities. Use the horizontal axis to represent the number of baskets and the vertical axis to represent the number of free throws.

c. List the set of ordered pairs that satisfy this system of inequalities.

ACTIVITY 3

Another booth at the carnival features a game called "Roll-a-rama." This game offers many winning outcomes. In this activity, you examine the chances of winning at Roll-a-rama.

Exploration

In Roll-a-rama, players roll one white die and one red die. One roll of each die is considered a game. To win, the following must be true:

- the number on the red die must be at least 2 but no more than 5
- the sum of the two dice must be less than or equal to 7.

a. Play Roll-a-rama 10 times and record your results.

b. Determine the experimental probability of winning a game.

c. List all the possible rolls in Roll-a-rama.

d. Determine the theoretical probability of winning a game.

Discussion

a. Are you more likely to win or lose when playing Roll-a-rama?

b. Do you think it is possible to find a strategy that increases the probability of winning? Explain your response.

c. If all the possible rolls were graphed on a coordinate plane where the roll on one die is represented on the x-axis and the roll of the other die is represented on the y-axis, what would the graph look like?

mathematics note

A **feasible region** is the graph of the solution set of a system of linear inequalities.

For example, consider the following system of linear inequalities: $0 \leq x \leq 6$, $0 \leq y \leq 4$, and $x + y \leq 8$. The shaded region in Figure **13-10** is the feasible region for this system. All the points in the feasible region are solutions to all the inequalities that define it.

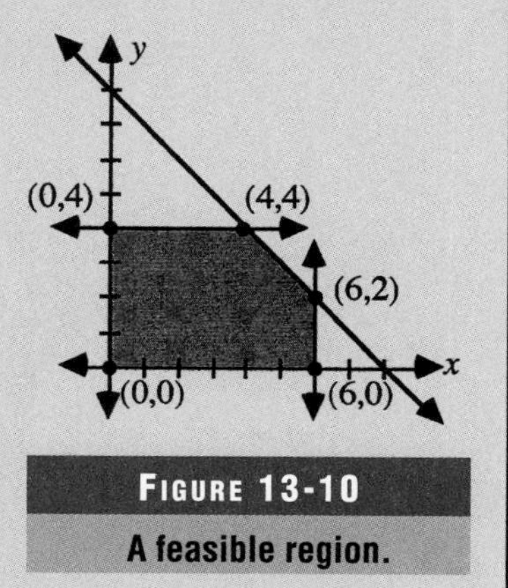

FIGURE 13-10
A feasible region.

d. The points on the boundary lines of the feasible region in Figure **13-10** are part of the feasible region.

1. How do the inequalities that define the feasible region indicate that this is true?
2. How does the graph of the feasible region indicate that points on the boundary are included?
3. How would you change the graph if boundary points were *not* included in the feasible region?

e. The winning combinations for Roll-a-rama could be graphed as a feasible region.

1. Why might it be misleading to shade the feasible region for Roll-a-rama?
2. How might you represent the feasible region for Roll-a-rama?

Warm-Up

1. For each of the following systems of inequalities, graph the feasible region and identify the coordinates of its vertices.

a. $\begin{cases} x \geq 0 \\ y \geq 0 \\ 4x + 3y \leq 12 \end{cases}$ **b.** $\begin{cases} x \geq 1 \\ y \geq -1 \\ x + y \leq 5 \end{cases}$ **c.** $\begin{cases} 2x + 3y \leq 6 \\ x - 2y \geq -4 \\ y \geq -2 \end{cases}$

d. $\begin{cases} x \geq 3 \\ x \leq 5 \\ y \geq -2 \\ y \leq 4 \end{cases}$ **e.** $\begin{cases} x \geq 0 \\ y \geq 0 \\ y \leq 8 \\ 4x + 3y \leq 32 \end{cases}$ **f.** $\begin{cases} x - 2y \geq -10 \\ 7x + 5y \leq 44 \\ 7x + 4y \geq -16 \\ 3x - 7y \leq 28 \end{cases}$

2. Describe the constraints on the feasible region in each of the following graphs. **Note:** Each axis is marked in increments of 1 unit.

a.

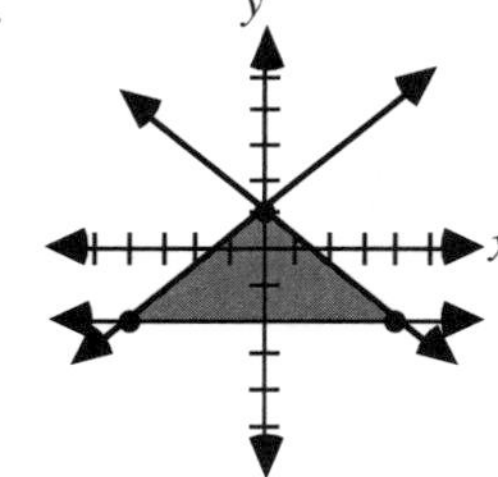

b.

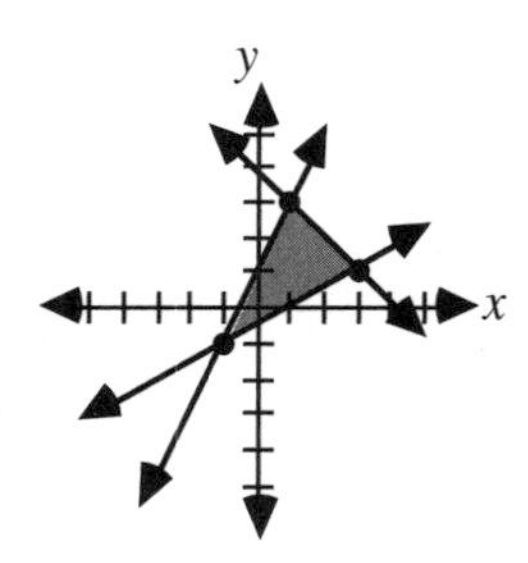

c.

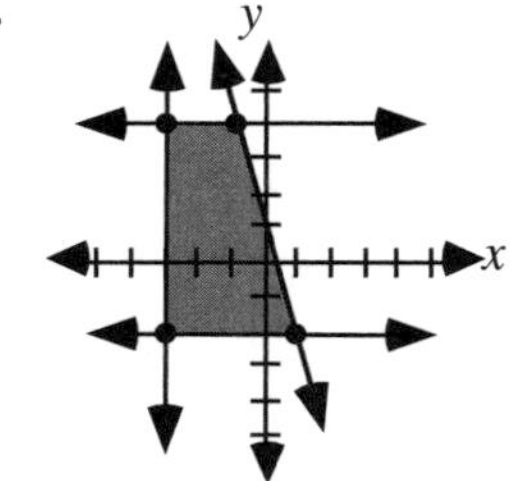

d.

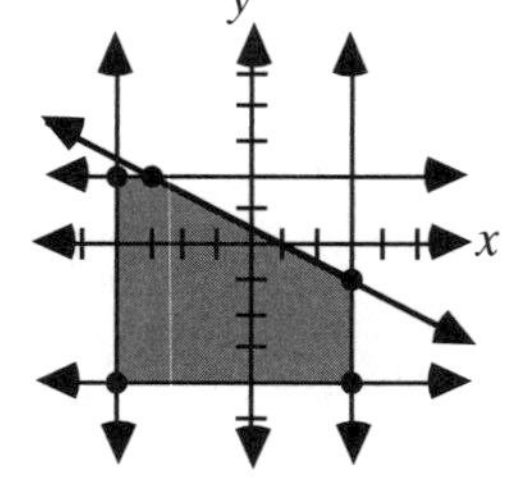

Assignment

3.1 You can identify the winning combinations in Roll-a-rama by graphing a system of linear inequalities on a coordinate plane. The inequalities that define the constraints on a winning roll can be written as follows:

$$\begin{cases} x \geq 1 \\ y \geq 2 \\ y \leq 5 \\ x + y \leq 7 \end{cases}$$

a. What do x and y represent in these inequalities?

b. Describe the rule of the game that corresponds with each constraint.

c. Graph this system of inequalities on a set of coordinate axes and determine the feasible region.

d. Identify the number of points in the feasible region that represent winning rolls.

3.2 While playing Roll-a-rama, Sharline recorded each roll as an ordered pair in the form (white die, red die). In 10 games, she obtained the following rolls: (1,4), (3,2), (6,2), (4,4), (2,1), (4,3), (5,1), (3,3), (1,6), and (5,3). How many games did she win? Justify your response using your graph from Problem **3.1c.**

3.3 **a.** How many different losing combinations are there in Roll-a-rama?

b. List at least three of these losing combinations. Use your graph from Problem **3.1c** to explain why they do not represent winning rolls.

3.4 Is the point where the line $x + y = 7$ intersects the y-axis in the feasible region for Roll-a-rama? Explain your response.

3.5 **a.** What are the constraints on the region that includes all possible rolls in Roll-a-rama?

b. Write inequalities to describe these constraints.

3.6 Rewrite the rules for "Roll-a-rama" so that the probability of winning is the same as the probability of losing. To check your rules, play the new game several times and record your results.

* * * * *

3.7 Graph the feasible region for each of the following systems of inequalities and label the vertices.

a. $\begin{cases} w \geq 0 \\ t \geq 0 \\ 2w + 3t \leq 10 \end{cases}$

b. $\begin{cases} x \geq -1 \\ y \leq 2 \\ y \geq x - 1 \end{cases}$

3.8 **a.** Describe the constraints on the feasible region shown in each of the following graphs:

1.

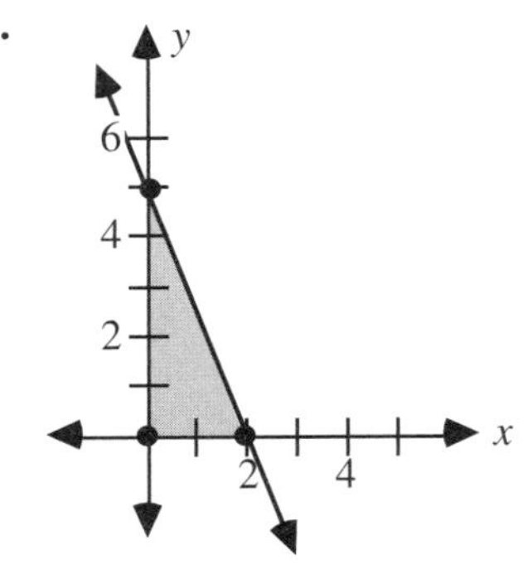

2.

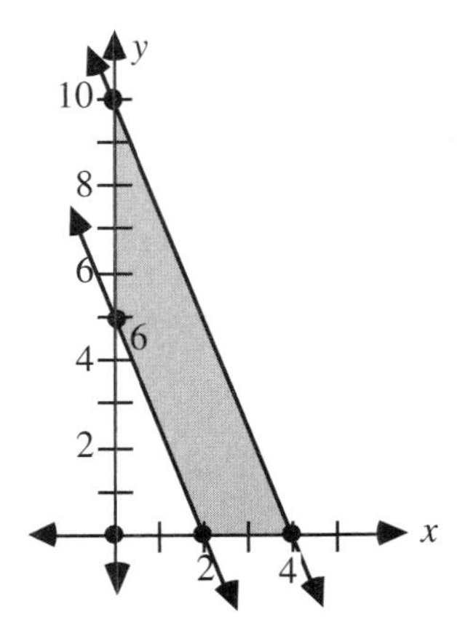

3.

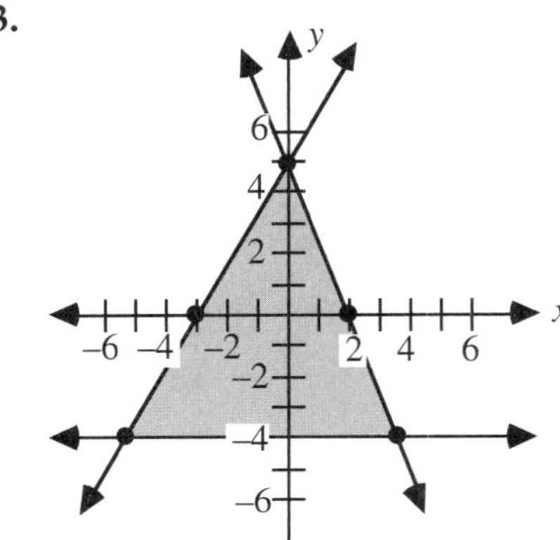

b. List the coordinates of the corner points for each feasible region in Part **a.**

3.9 A furniture manufacturer makes upholstered chairs and sofas. On average, each chair requires 4 hr to assemble and each sofa requires 8 hr to assemble. The company's carpenters can provide a total of no more than 124 hr of assembly work per day. Each chair also requires 2 hr to upholster, while each sofa requires 6 hr to upholster. According to contract, the company must guarantee at least 72 hr of work per day for the upholsterers.

a. Write a system of inequalities that describes the numbers of chairs and sofas that the company can build and upholster in one day.

b. Graph the feasible region described by the system you wrote in Part **a** and identify the coordinates of the corner points. Use the horizontal axis to represent the number of chairs and the vertical axis to represent the number of sofas. **Note:** Save your graph for use in Problem **4.3.**

3.10 A group of friends would like to order two large pizzas with extra toppings and some soft drinks. Each pizza costs $10.00. Each extra topping costs $0.50, and each soft drink costs $1.00. The group has $30.00 to spend.

a. Graph the feasible region that shows the possible numbers of toppings and soft drinks that the group can order.

b. Identify the coordinates of the corner points.

In Roll-a-rama, each winning player receives a second roll of the dice. If the player also wins on this second roll, a score is determined based on the number showing on each die. The score is calculated using the following rules:

- the number on the white die is multiplied by 2
- the number on the red die is multiplied by 3
- the two resulting numbers are added.

The object of the second roll is to obtain as high a score as possible. This score (S) can be determined by the equation $S = 2x + 3y$, where x represents the number on the white die and y represents the number on the red die. This is called an **objective function,** because finding the best value of S is the objective.

Exploration

In this exploration, you use an objective function to help determine the maximum and minimum scores in Roll-a-rama.

a. As noted in the previous activity, players roll one red die and one white die in Roll-a-rama. To win,

   - the number on the red die must be at least 2 but no more than 5
   - the sum of the two dice must be less than or equal to 7.

   The winning combinations can be described by a feasible region for a system of inequalities. On a copy of the Roll-a-rama template, graph the lines that define this feasible region.

b. Use the objective function to find the value of S for each roll in the feasible region. Record this information in a table with headings like those in Table **13-3.**

TABLE 13-1 ■ *Score for Each Winning Roll*

Winning Roll (x,y)	Score (S)
(1,2)	8

c. 1. Select two points in the feasible region with the same value for S. Draw the line that passes through these two points.

   2. Write the equation of this line in the form $y = mx + b$.

   3. Repeat Steps **1** and **2** for the remaining points in the feasible region.

d. 1. Use the information in Table **13-3** to identify the maximum value for S.

   2. Substitute this value for S in the objective function $S = 2x + 3y$. Solve the equation for y.

   3. Graph this equation on the template.

e. In Roll-a-rama, you want to find the greatest value of the objective function. In other situations, you might want to find the least value of an objective function. Repeat Part **d** for the minimum value for S.

Discussion

a. Where are the maximum and minimum values for S located on your graph from the exploration?

mathematics note

The **corner principle** helps you find the maximum or minimum values for an objective function in problems that involve a system of linear inequalities (and where the corner points are part of the feasible region). According to this principle, the maximum and minimum values of an objective function occur at corner points of the feasible region.

b. 1. What similarities did you observe among the lines graphed in Parts **c–e** of the exploration?

   2. How are the equations of the lines related to the equation for S?

c. What must a player roll to obtain the greatest possible score?

Warm-Up

1. Determine the maximum and minimum value of the objective function for each set of corner points given below.

   a. $V = 3x - 2y$; (2,3), (–1,2), (–4,–1), (0,–1)

   b. $V = -3x + 4y$; (2,3), (–1,2), (–4,–1), (0,–1)

   c. $V = -2x - y$; (2,3), (–1,2), (–4,–1), (0,–1)

2. For each of the following feasible regions, use the corner principle to find the maximum and minimum values of the objective function $V = 4x + 3y$. **Note:** Each axis is marked in increments of 1 unit.

a.

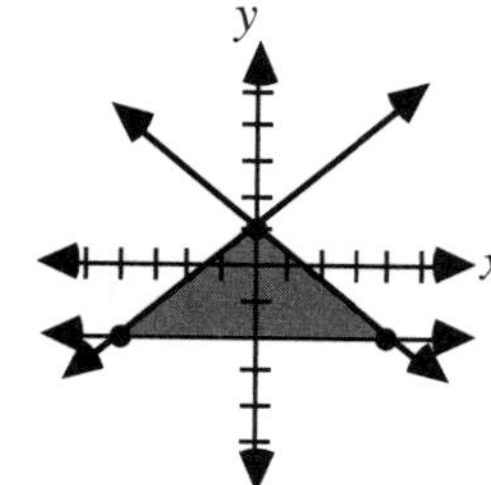

b.

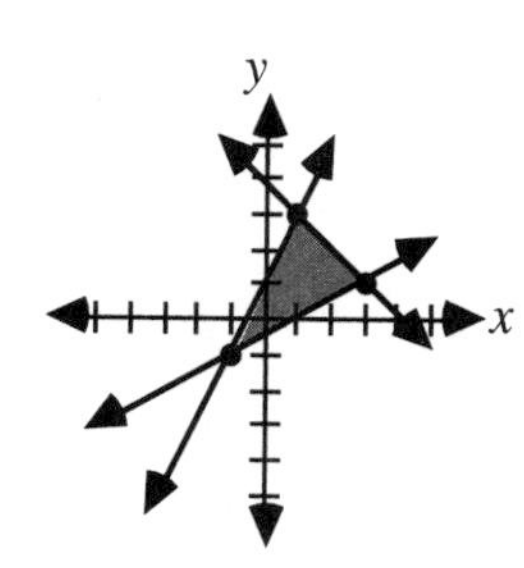

c.

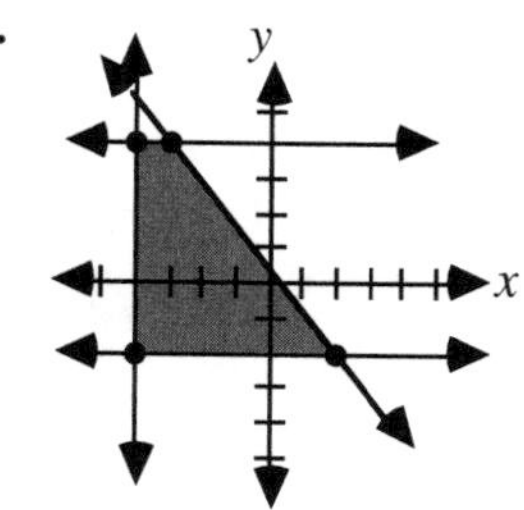

d.

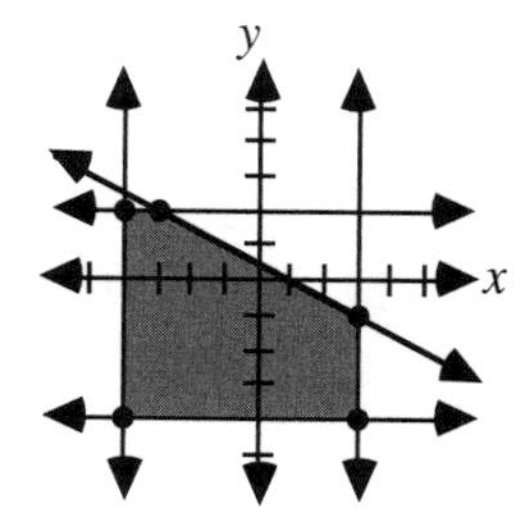

3. For each of the following systems of inequalities, use the corner principle to find the maximum and minimum values of the objective function .

a. $\begin{cases} x \geq 0 \\ y \geq 0 \\ 4x + 3y \leq 12 \end{cases}$

b. $\begin{cases} x \geq 1 \\ y \geq -1 \\ x + y \leq 5 \end{cases}$

c. $\begin{cases} 2x + 3y \leq 6 \\ x - 2y \geq -4 \\ y \geq -2 \end{cases}$

Assignment

4.1 Sharline and Anton are designing a new game for the Dantzig High carnival. They already have selected two different prizes from a catalog, and need only to decide how many of each to buy. The small prizes cost 25 cents each; the large ones cost 75 cents each.

According to carnival guidelines, the game may offer no more than 100 prizes. To make the game attractive to players, Sharline and Anton want to buy at least 10 of the large prizes and no more than 60 of the small prizes.

a. Write a linear inequality for each constraint in this situation. Let x represent the number of small prizes and y represent the number of large prizes.

b. Graph your system of linear inequalities on a coordinate plane. Identify the coordinates of the vertices.

c. List the coordinates of three points in the feasible region. What does each point mean in terms of buying prizes?

- **d.** Sharline and Anton have decided to charge $1.00 to play the game and give each player a prize. Because they have no other expenses, their **profit** is the money they take in minus the cost of the prizes.
  1. What is their profit on each small prize?
  2. What is their profit on each large prize?
- **e.** Because Sharline and Anton wish to maximize profit, write an equation that describes the amount of profit (P) for each point (x,y) in the feasible region.
- **f.** Use the corner principle to find the coordinates of the point that maximizes P. Assuming that 100 people play the game, how many of each prize should they buy?

4.2 Imagine that you are responsible for managing the concession stand at the carnival. Your budget for purchasing pizza and canned soft drinks is $160.00. A six-pack of soft drinks costs $3.00. A 12-serving pizza costs $10.00. The number of soft drinks you order should not exceed the number of slices of pizza.

- **a.** The concession stand sells pizza for $1.50 per slice. Soft drinks cost $1.00 each.

  Assuming that the concession stand sells everything you purchase, write an equation that describes the profit from pizza and soft-drink sales, where p represents the number of pizzas and s represents the number of six-packs of soft drinks.
- **b.** How many six-packs and how many pizzas should you order? Explain your response.
- **c.** If each customer buys at most one piece of pizza and one can of soda, what is the greatest number of customers you can serve while earning the maximum profit? What is the least number? Explain your responses.

* * * * *

4.3 The furniture company described in Problem **3.9** earns a profit of $50.00 on each chair and $80.00 on each sofa.

- **a.** Write an equation that describes the company's profit from sales of sofas and chairs.
- **b.** Using your graph from Problem **3.9,** determine the number of sofas and chairs the company should make each day to maximize profit.

4.4 Imagine that you are a production manager at an electronics company. Your company makes two types of calculators: a scientific calculator and a graphing calculator.

a. Each model uses the same plastic case and the same circuits. However, the graphing calculator requires 20 circuits and the scientific calculator requires only 10. The company has 240 plastic cases and 3200 circuits in stock. Graph the system of inequalities that represents these constraints.

b. The profit on a scientific calculator is $9.00, while the profit on a graphing calculator is $15.00. Write an equation that describes the company's profit from calculator sales.

c. How many of each type of calculator should the company produce to maximize profit using the stock on hand?

Summary Assessment

Instead of having a game booth, the Dantzig High Pep Club has decided to sell "Spirit Animals" at the carnival. The following illustration shows a Spirit Animal.

Spirit Animals are made from pompons and come in two sizes: small and large. Small animals require 1 pompon, and large animals require 3 pompons. The club has 270 pompons.

Seven members of the club have agreed to work for 30 min each making animals. It takes 1 min to make a small animal and 1.5 min to make a large animal.

The club plans to sell large animals for 90 cents each and small animals for 65 cents each. The club paid 5 cents for each pompon. Your job is to help the Pep Club maximize their profit.

1. Choose variables to represent the numbers of each size of Spirit Animal the club can make.

2. The project is limited by the number of pompons available. Consider how many pompons are needed for each size of animal. Write the linear inequalities for these constraints.

3. The number of minutes that members can work on the project is also limited. Consider how much time is needed to make each size of animal. Write the linear inequalities for these constraints.

4. Graph the linear inequalities from Problems **2** and **3** on a coordinate plane and shade the feasible region.

5. What is the profit on each size of animal?

6. Assuming that club members sell every animal they make, write an equation to describe the club's profit.

7. How many of each size of Spirit Animal should the Pep Club make to maximize profit?

8. Describe the steps you used to find the maximum profit.

Module Summary

* The graph of a linear inequality is a shaded region that represents the **solution set** of the inequality. The solution set contains all the points, or solutions, that make the inequality true. The graph of a linear equation forms the **boundary line** for the region. A solid boundary indicates that the points on the line are part of the solution set. A dashed boundary indicates that the points on the line are not part of the solution set.
* A **conjunction** combines two mathematical statements with the word *and*. A conjunction can be represented as the intersection of two sets.
* A **system of linear equations** is a set of two or more equations whose graphs are lines. A **solution** to a system of linear equations is a point where all the lines intersect. The coordinates of this point satisfy all the equations in the system.
* The **substitution method** can be used to solve a system of linear equations. The method begins by solving an equation for one variable. The resulting expression is then substituted for that variable in another equation in the system. This process is repeated until a solution can be identified.
* The **constraints** on a problem are the conditions that limit the number of possible solutions.
* A **feasible region** is the graph of the solution set of a system of linear inequalities.
* The intersection of two or more boundary lines forms a **corner point** (or vertex) of the feasible region.
* The **corner principle** helps you find the maximum or minimum values for an objective function in problems that involve a system of linear equalities (and where the corner points are part of the feasible region). According to this principle, the maximum and minimum values of an objective function occur at corner points of the feasible region.

Module 14

From Here to There

Introduction

Topographic maps are two-dimensional representations of regions of the earth's surface. Besides identifying roads, trails, rivers, and other landmarks, topographic maps also contain information about the elevation of the terrain.

By knowing how to read a topographic map, you can determine the height of a mountain—and make a good guess about the difficulty of the climb. For example, Figure **14-1** shows a picture of the south side of a mountain. The horizontal lines are **level curves.** Each level curve represents points of equal elevation above sea level.

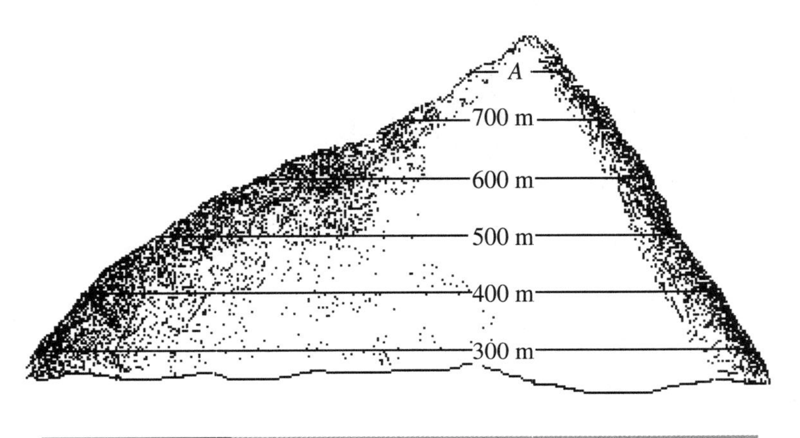

FIGURE 14-1 Level curves on the south side of a mountain.

The view in Figure **14-1** provides some information about the landscape, but a topographic representation of the mountain, as shown in Figure **14-2,** can be much more helpful. On a topographic map, the curved lines indicating points of equal elevation are **contour lines.**

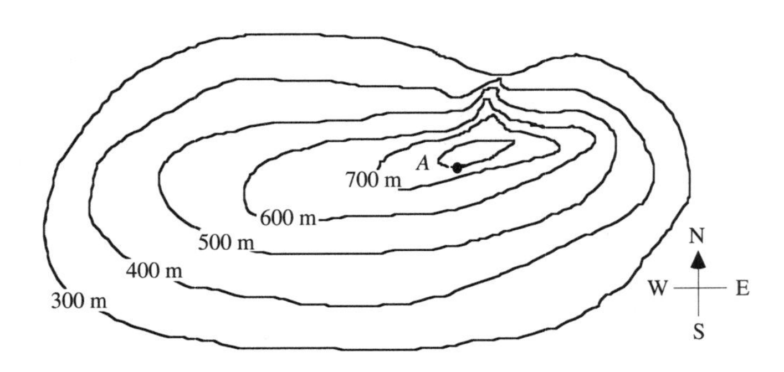

FIGURE 14-2 Topographic map of the mountain in Figure 14-1.

When these terms are used to describe features of mountainous terrain, a **summit** is the highest point of the surrounding elevations and a **saddle** is a pass between two higher elevations. Some examples of these features are shown in Figure **14-3.**

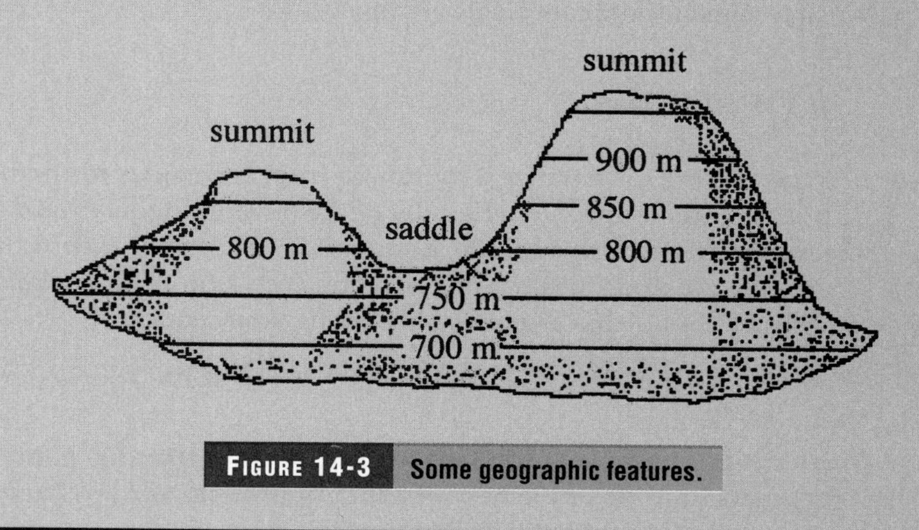

FIGURE 14-3 Some geographic features.

Discussion

a. From what perspective does a topographic map show the earth's surface?

b. In Figure **14-1,** what do the quantities expressed in meters represent?

c. In Figure **14-2,** what is the elevation at contour line *A*?

d. On a topographic map, moving from one contour line to the next consecutive line indicates a constant change in altitude. However, the contour lines themselves might not be evenly spaced.

What is indicated by the space between two consecutive contour lines? Explain your response.

e. 1. How would you estimate the elevation of a point between two contour lines?

2. What physical characteristics of the terrain could make this estimate inaccurate?

f. How does the south side of the mountain in Figure **14-1** compare with its north side?

ACTIVITY 1

In this activity, you create a topographic map for a three-dimensional surface of your own design. To investigate some of the features of your map, you use a three-dimensional coordinate system.

Exploration

When trying to visualize a mountain from a topographic map, it might help to build a three-dimensional model of the terrain. In this exploration, you build a model that contains a saddle, a summit, a cliff, and a lake. At the same time, you create a topographic map of your model on a coordinate plane. **Note:** Read the instructions in Parts **a–g** before beginning your model.

a. Draw a pair of coordinate axes on a large sheet of paper (at least 60 cm by 28 cm).

b. 1. On a sheet of cardboard slightly smaller than the paper in Part **a,** sketch the outline of the base of a mountain, such as the example shown in Figure **14-4.** Cut out this base.

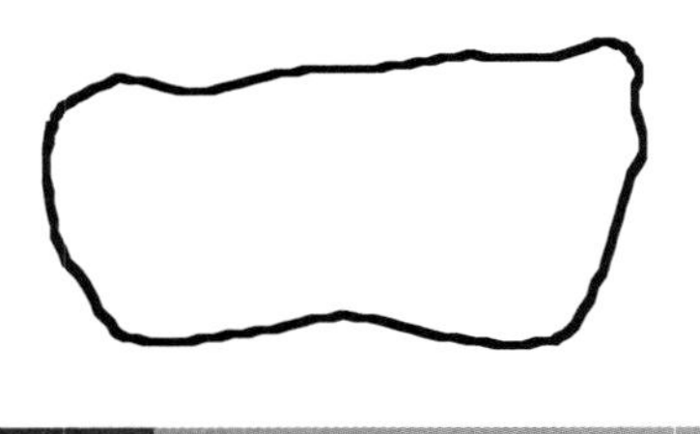

FIGURE 14-4 Outline of the base of a mountain.

2. Trace the outline of the cardboard base on the coordinate plane, as shown in Figure **14-5.** This is the first contour line of your topographic map.

FIGURE 14-5 Coordinate plane with first contour.

c. 1. Trace the outline of the base on another sheet of cardboard. Using the tracing as a guide, draw the next contour of the mountain. As shown in Figure **14-6,** make this contour slightly smaller than the base.

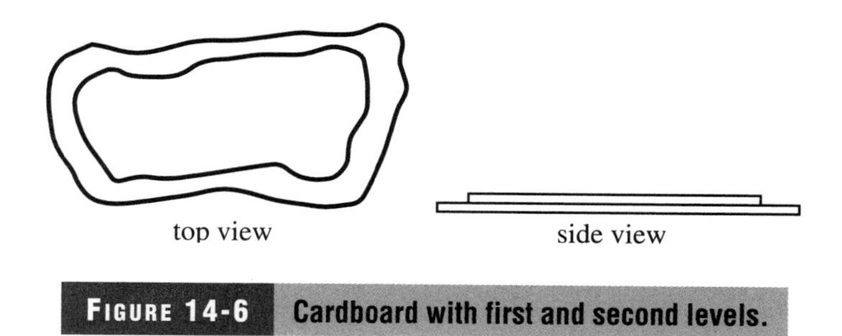

FIGURE 14-6 Cardboard with first and second levels.

2. Cut out this second level and place it on the coordinate plane inside the outline of the base. Trace the outline of the second contour on the plane, as shown in Figure **14-7.**

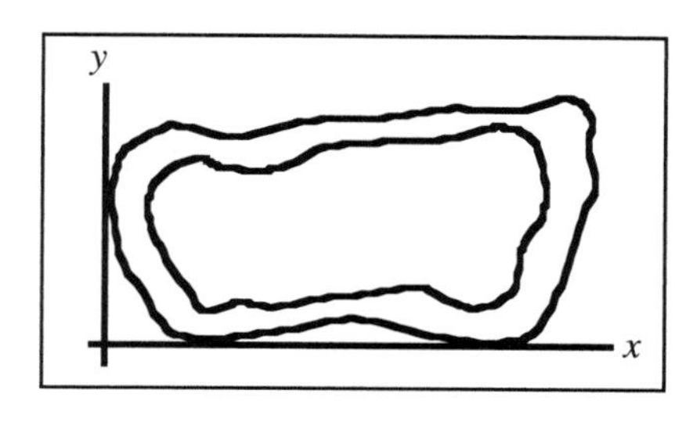

FIGURE 14-7 Topographic map of first two levels.

d. Trace the outline of the second level on another sheet of cardboard to create a guide for the third contour. Then tape or glue the second level to the base in the same relative position as the contour lines on the coordinate plane.

e. Cut out the third level and place it on the coordinate plane inside the second contour. Trace the outline of the third contour on the plane.

f. Repeat the process described in Parts **d** and **e** until you have created a complete model of a mountain along with its topographic map. Your model should consist of 10 layers of cardboard; the map should have 10 contour lines. Both should include the following geographic features:

1. a lake
2. a summit
3. a saddle
4. a cliff at least half as high as the summit.

g. Measure the thickness of one layer of cardboard. Let this distance represent 100 m in elevation and 100 m along the x- and y-axes on your topographic map.

h. Use your map to identify an ordered pair (x,y) that represents the location of the summit.

i. Identify an ordered triple (x,y,z), where z represents elevation, that designates the location of the summit.

mathematics note

Three-dimensional coordinate systems typically are represented by graphs like the ones shown in Figure **14-8.** The x- and y-axes determine the xy-plane. The z-axis is used to help depict points above, below, or on the xy-plane. The x- and z-axes determine the xz-plane, while the y- and z-axes determine the yz-plane.

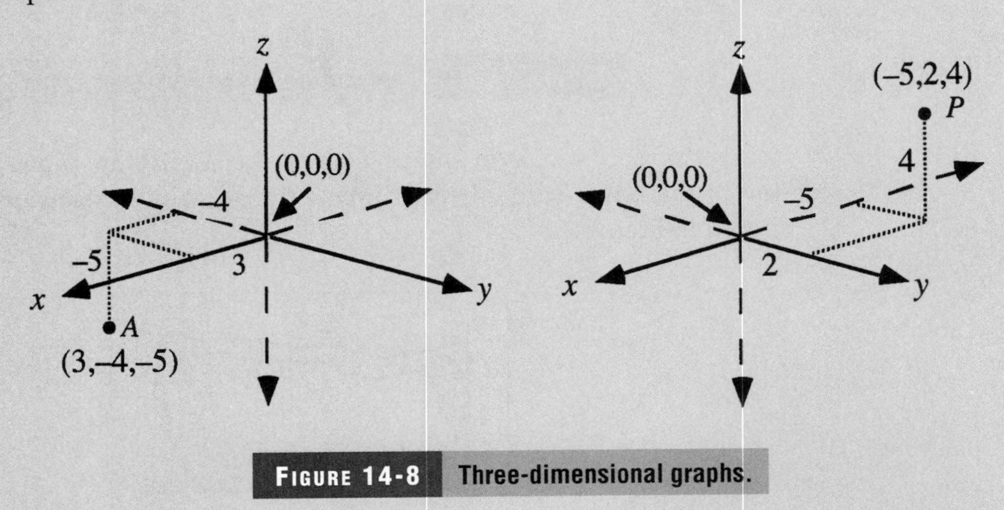

FIGURE 14-8 Three-dimensional graphs.

The coordinates of a point in this type of three-dimensional coordinate system form an **ordered triple,** (x,y,z). For example, the coordinates of point A in Figure **14-8** are $(3,-4,-5)$. In other words, the x-coordinate of point A is 3, the y-coordinate is -4, and the z-coordinate is -5, which indicates that point A is located 5 units below the xy-plane. Similarly, the coordinates of point P are $(-5,2,4)$, which means that its x-coordinate is -5, its y-coordinate is 2, and it is located 4 units above the xy-plane.

The **origin** is the point where the three axes intersect. The origin has coordinates $(0,0,0)$ because at that point $x = 0$, $y = 0$, and $z = 0$.

Discussion

a. Describe how the cliff, lake, saddle, and summit are represented on your topographic map.

b. Why does an ordered triple provide more information about the summit than an ordered pair?

c. Compare the method you used to find the thickness of one layer of cardboard with the methods used by others in your class.

d. Describe the z-coordinate of all the points that represent the surface of your lake.

e. Describe how to draw a path that provides a gradual ascent from the lake to the summit on your topographic map.

Warm-Up

To complete the following problems, assume that the orientation of each coordinate system is as shown in Figure **14-8.**

1. a. Is the z-coordinate of a point above the xy-plane positive or negative?

   b. What is the x-coordinate of a point on the yz-plane?

   c. If the y-coordinate of a point is positive, what is its relationship to the xz-plane?

2. Describe the location of a point with coordinates (–5,–4,–6) on a three-dimensional coordinate system.

3. Identify the coordinates of each labeled vertex on the following graphs.

a.

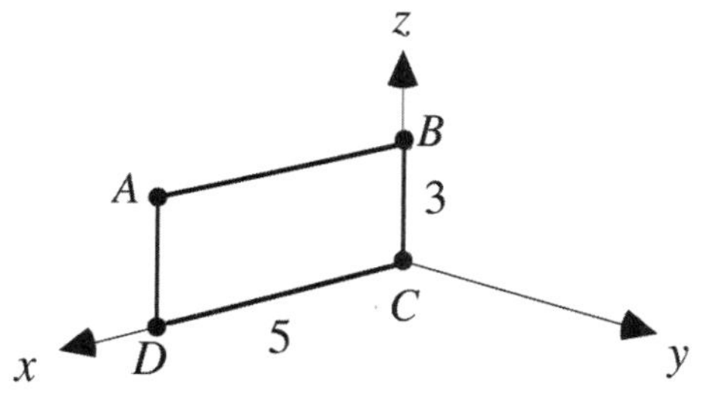

z
B
A
3
C
x D 5 y

b.

z
B 3
A C
D
2
F
x E G y
H 4

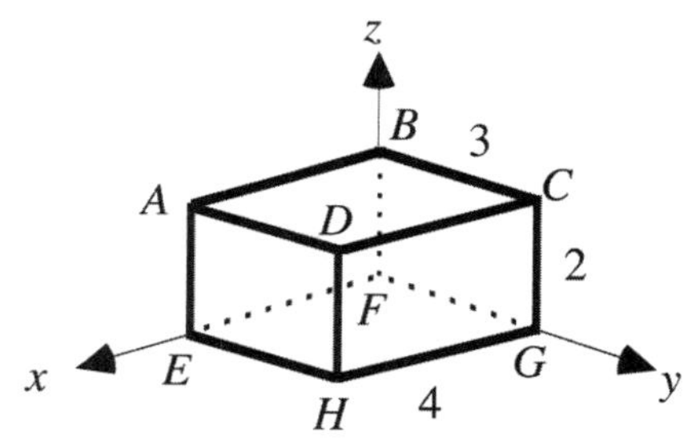

Assignment

1.1 Using your cardboard model from the exploration, locate a point on the top of the cliff. Locate another point at the bottom of the cliff, directly below the first one. Label the two points C_1 and C_2.

   a. Identify an ordered triple for each point.

   b. How do the coordinates of the ordered triples $C_1(x_1,y_1,z_1)$ and compare $C_2(x_2,y_2,z_2)$?

   c. What geometric figure is formed by the set of all points with coordinates (x,y,z) where the x- and y-coordinates are held constant? Explain your response.

   d. Where are the points that correspond to ordered triples such as C_1 and C_2 located on a topographic map?

1.2 Using your cardboard model from the exploration, label two points L_1 and L_2 on opposite shores of the lake.

a. Identify an ordered triple for each point.

b. How do the coordinates of the ordered triples $L_1(x_1,y_1,z_1)$ and $L_2(x_2,y_2,z_2)$ compare?

c. What geometric figure is formed by the set of all points with coordinates (x,y,z) where the z-coordinate is held constant? Explain your response.

1.3 The diagram below shows the north side of a mountain. Draw a topographic map that might represent this terrain.

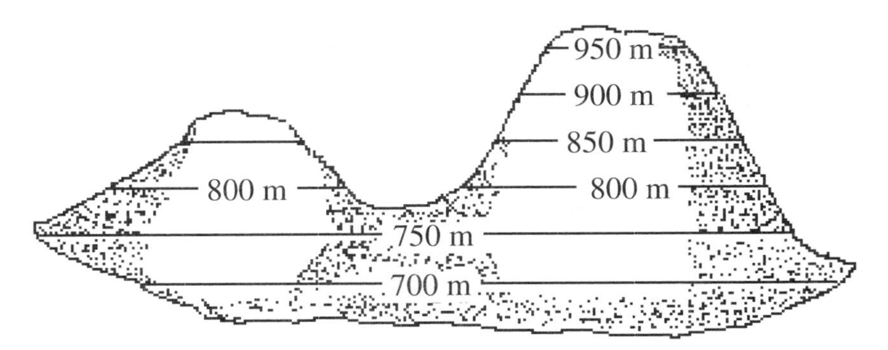

1.4 Use the topographic map below to complete Parts **a** and **b**.

a. Describe the features of the terrain at points A and B.

b. Identify the locations of points A and B using ordered triples.

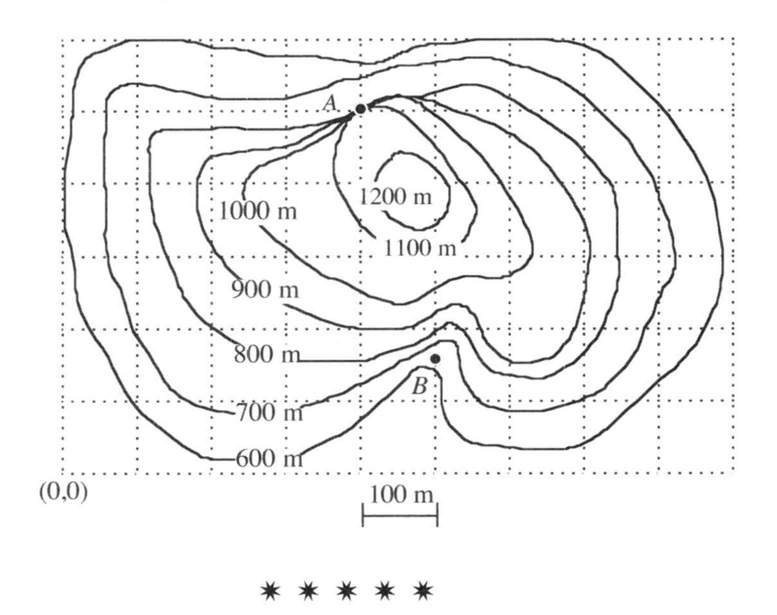

* * * * *

1.5 Create a topographic map for a right circular cone using at least five contour lines and your own grid system.

1.6 The diagram below shows the south side of a mountain range. Draw a topographic map that might represent this terrain.

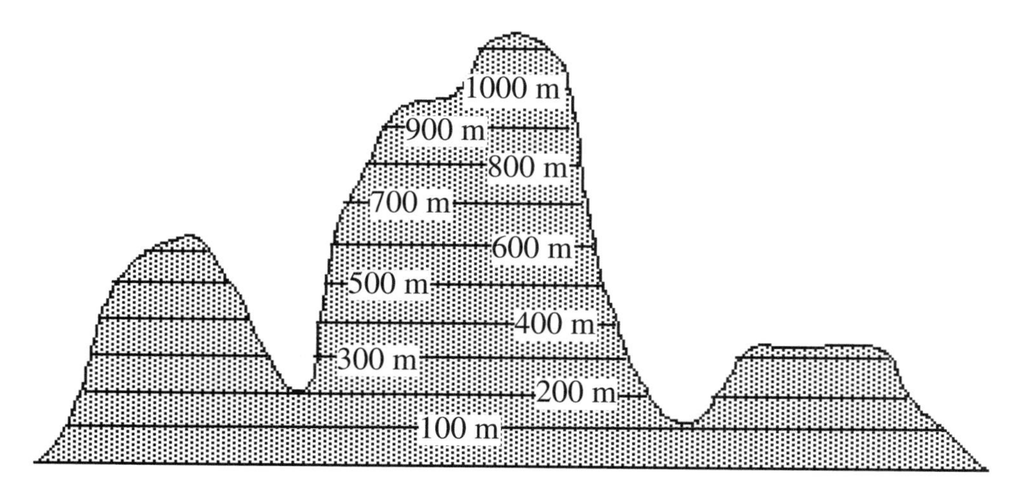

1.7 Use the topographic map below to complete Parts **a** and **b.**

a. Describe the features of the terrain around points A and B.

b. Identify the locations of points A and B using ordered triples.

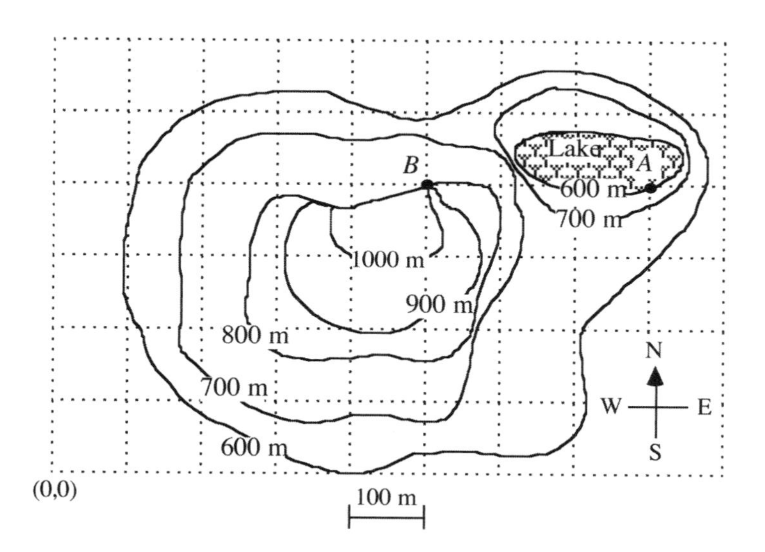

In previous modules, you calculated distances in one or two dimensions. Finding the distance from the base of a mountain to its summit, however, could require the use of three-dimensional coordinates.

mathematics note

As Figure **14-9** demonstrates, the Pythagorean theorem can be used to derive a formula for the distance between any two points, (x_1,y_1) and (x_2,y_2), on a coordinate plane.

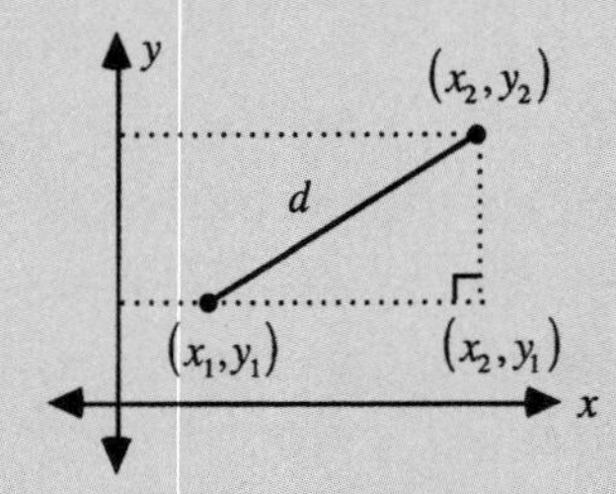

FIGURE 14-9 Distance between two points on a coordinate plane.

According to the **distance formula**, the distance d between (x_1,y_1) and (x_2,y_2) is:

$$d = \sqrt{(x_2 - x_1)^2 + (y_2 - y_1)^2}$$

For example, consider the points (–2,5) and (–4,–6). Using the distance formula, the distance between these two points can be found as follows:

$$\begin{aligned} d &= \sqrt{(-4 - (-2))^2 + (-6 - 5)^2} \\ &= \sqrt{(-2)^2 + (-11)^2} = \sqrt{125} \approx 11.18 \end{aligned}$$

Exploration

In this exploration, you develop a method for finding the distance between any two points in a three-dimensional coordinate system.

Figure **14-10** shows a three-dimensional coordinate system and three points, P_1, P_2, and P_3. Each unit on the coordinate system represents 1 m. Each edge of the rectangular prism in Figure **14-10** either coincides with or is parallel to one of the axes.

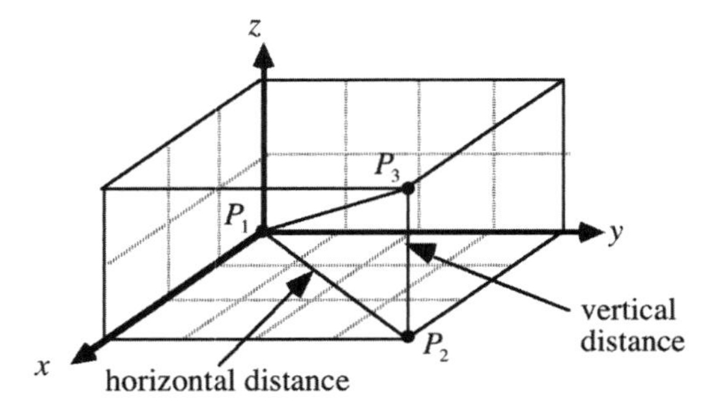

FIGURE 14-10 A three-dimensional coordinate system.

a. One way to find the length of the segment with endpoints P_1 and P_3 is through the following steps.

   1. Identify the coordinates of P_1, P_2, and P_3.

   2. Find the distance between P_1 and P_2. This is the horizontal distance between P_1 and P_3.

   3. Find the distance between P_2 and P_3. This is the vertical distance between P_1 and P_3.

   4. Use the fact that triangle $P_1P_2P_3$ is a right triangle to find the distance between P_1 and P_3.

b. The three-dimensional coordinate system in Figure **14-11** shows two right triangles $P_1P_2P_3$ and $P_1P_3P_4$, with right angles at P_2 and P_4. The coordinates of P_3 are (6,3,4), $\overline{P_2P_3}$ is parallel to the z-axis, and $\overline{P_3P_4}$ is parallel to the y-axis.

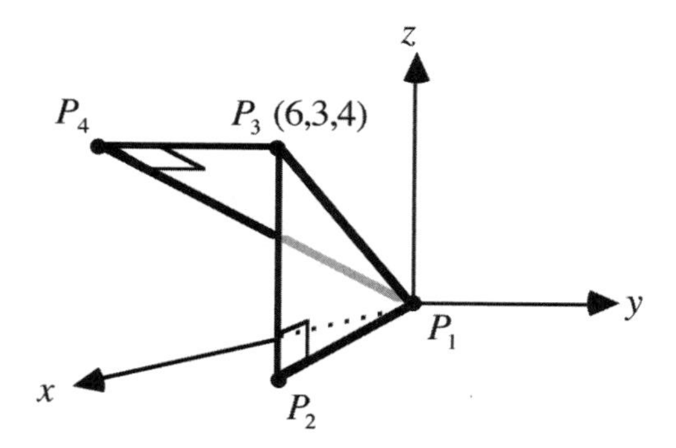

FIGURE 14-11 Two right triangles.

   1. Find the coordinates of P_2, a point in the xy-plane. Use these coordinates to find the distance from P_1 to P_3.

   2. Find the coordinates of P_4, a point in the xz-plane. Use these coordinates to find the distance from P_1 to P_3.

   3. Compare the distance found in Step **2** with the distance in Step **1**.

c. Draw and label a three-dimensional coordinate system.

   1. Plot the two points with coordinates (4,3,5) and (0,2,8).

   2. Find the distance between these two points. *Hint:* Draw right triangles.

d. The three-dimensional coordinate system in Figure **14-12** shows the locations of two points with coordinates (x_1,y_1,z_1) and (x_2,y_2,z_2). Find the distance between the two points.

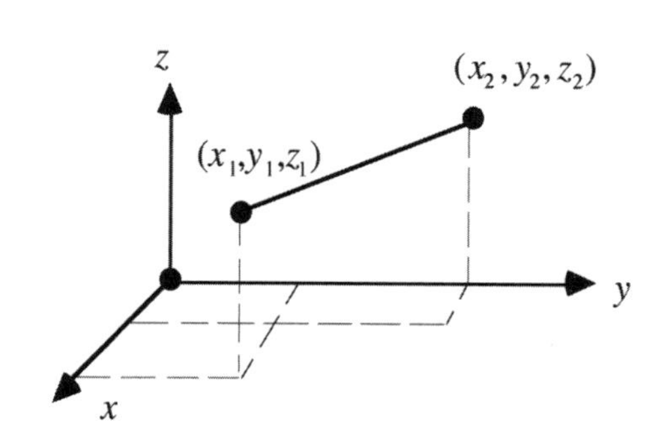

FIGURE 14-12 Two points.

Discussion

a. How many times did you use the Pythagorean theorem to find the distance between P_1 and P_3 in Figure **14-10**?

b. How would you find the distance between any two points (x_1,y_1,z_1) and (x_2,y_2,z_2)? Express your method using a mathematical formula.

c. Describe how you could find the distance between points A and B on the topographic map in Figure **14-13.**

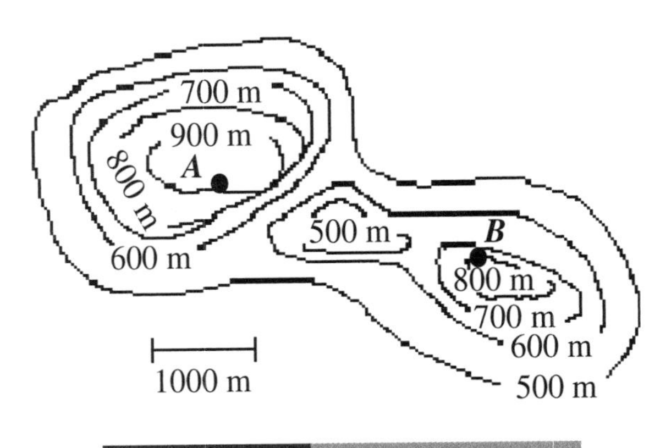

FIGURE 14-13 A topographic map.

Warm-Up

1. Find the distance between each of the following pairs of points.

   a. (9,14) and (4,1)

   b. (–12,8) and (7,–4)

   c. (–3,–6) and (–9,8)

2. Draw and label a three-dimensional coordinate system.

   a. Plot the two points with coordinates (5,0,2) and (2,2,4).

   b. Find the distance between these points.

3. Draw and label a three-dimensional coordinate system.

   a. Plot the two points with coordinates (3,4,2) and (5,4,0).

   b. Find the distance between these points.

Assignment

2.1 At the local wishing well, you throw in three coins—a dime, a nickel, and a penny. They land in the well as shown in the following diagram.

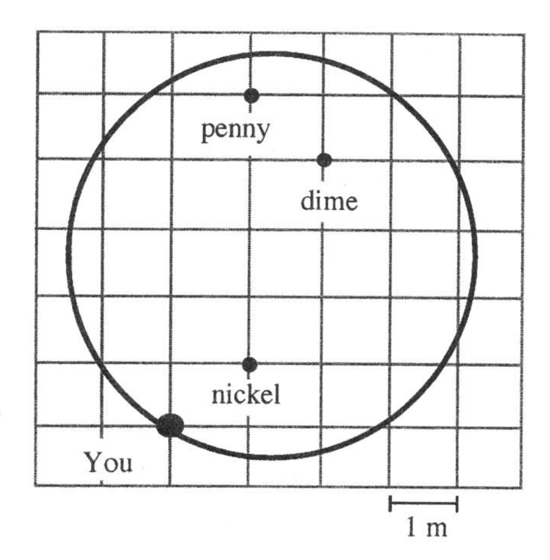

a. The depth of the water in the well is 0.5 m. If the surface of the water is the xy-plane and you are at the origin, identify the location of each coin as an ordered triple.

b. Determine the distance from yourself to each coin.

2.2 Describe the set of all points in space that are:

a. 3 cm from a point

b. 3 cm from a segment

c. equidistant from two parallel lines

d. 3 cm from a plane.

2.3 The figure below shows a topographic map of the terrain surrounding a lake, including four houses designated A, B, C, and D.

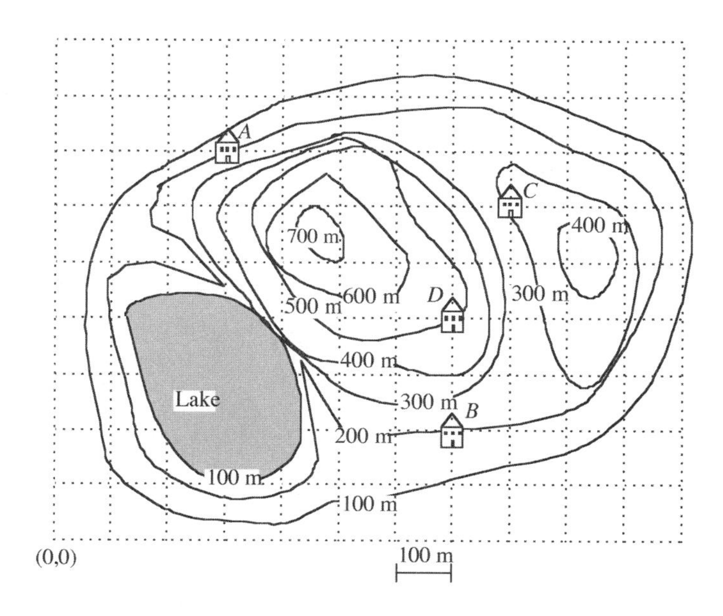

Use the map to find the distance between each of the following pairs of houses:

a. *A* and *B*

b. *B* and *C*

c. *C* and *D*

d. *A* and *D*.

2.4 The following diagram shows a topographic map of a region of the ocean floor. In this case, the contour lines represent distances below the surface of the ocean. For example, –850 indicates 850 m below sea level. The ocean floor for this region is 1000 m deep.

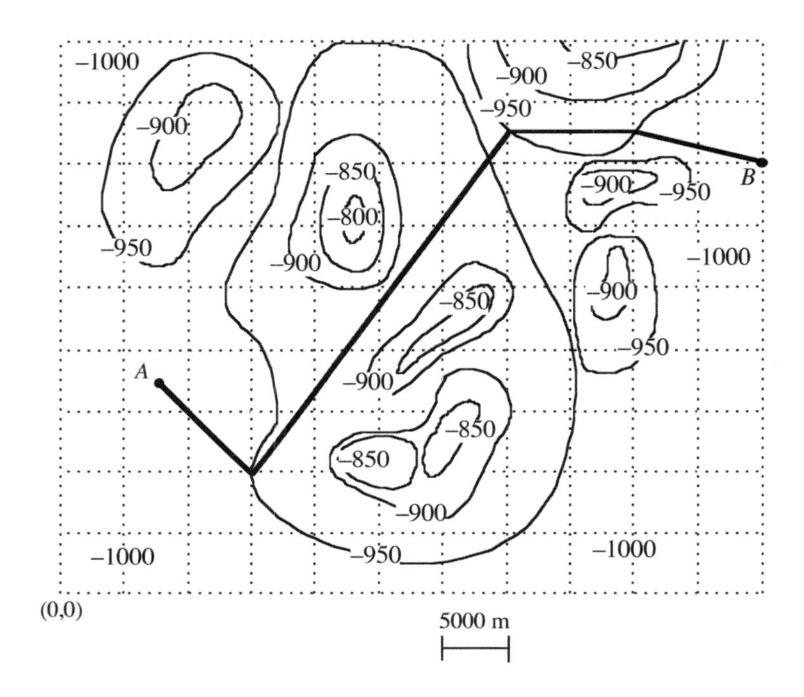

a. The captain of a submarine must navigate from point *A* to point *B* along the path shown. Assume that the submarine is 10 m above the floor at each point along the path. What are the coordinates of point *A*, point *B*, and each point where the path turns?

b. The submarine must travel no closer than 10 m but no more than 25 m above the ocean terrain. What is the total distance the sub will travel from point *A* to point *B* along the given path?

* * * * *

2.5 The topographic map below shows the routes taken by two skiers traveling down a mountain from point A to point B. Create a story for each skier's descent. In each story, include a description of the terrain and the approximate distance traveled. Assume that the terrain between contour lines is smooth, with no drops or rises other than those indicated on the map.

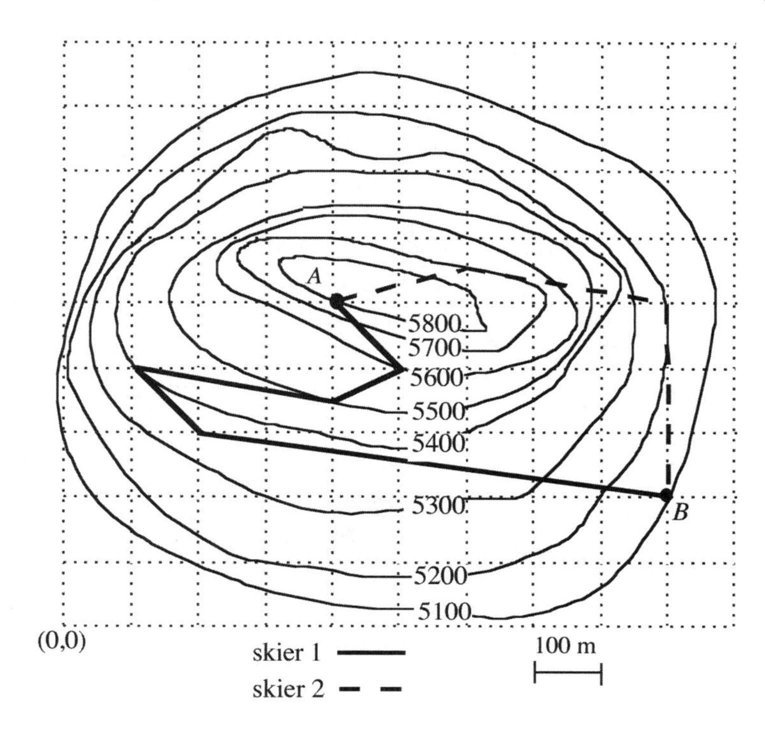

2.6 Use the map in Problem **2.5** to complete Parts **a–c** below.

a. 1. Find the vertical distance between points A and B.

2. Find the horizontal distance between points A and B.

3. Find the distance between A and B using the Pythagorean theorem.

b. 1. Determine the coordinates of points A and B.

2. Find the distance between A and B using the coordinates of the points.

c. Compare your results in Parts **a** and **b**.

ACTIVITY 3

Microwave signals are used in a variety of applications, including telephone transmissions. Because microwaves travel in a straight line and weaken considerably over distances greater than 5 km, engineers must place microwave repeaters along the transmission path to receive and relay signals.

In this activity, you use a topographic map to create a **profile** of mountainous terrain. Profiles can help provide a visual image of the landscape between two points on a topographic map.

geography note

A **profile** shows a vertical cross section or "side view" of the terrain. For example, Figure **14-14** shows a profile of a mountain valley.

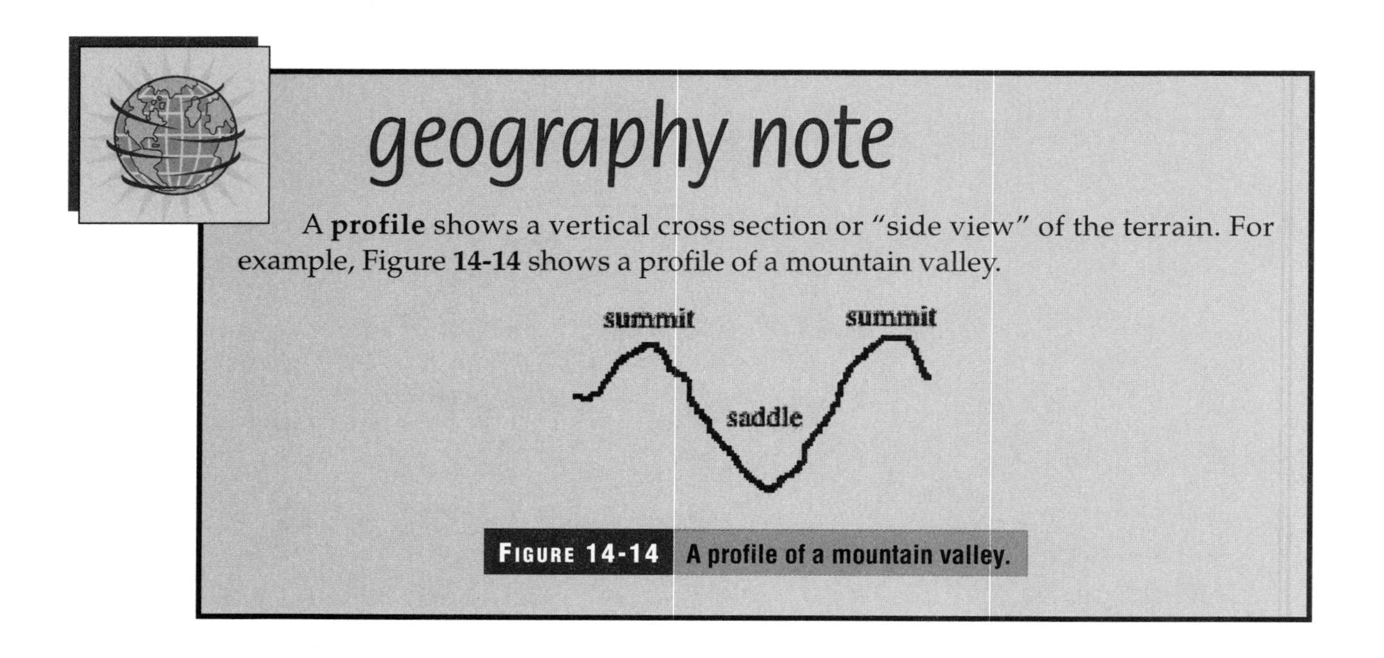

FIGURE 14-14 A profile of a mountain valley.

Exploration

a. 1. On a topographic map provided by your teacher, label two points at least 10 km apart and located on different contour lines.

2. As shown in Figure **14-15,** connect the points with a **profile segment.**

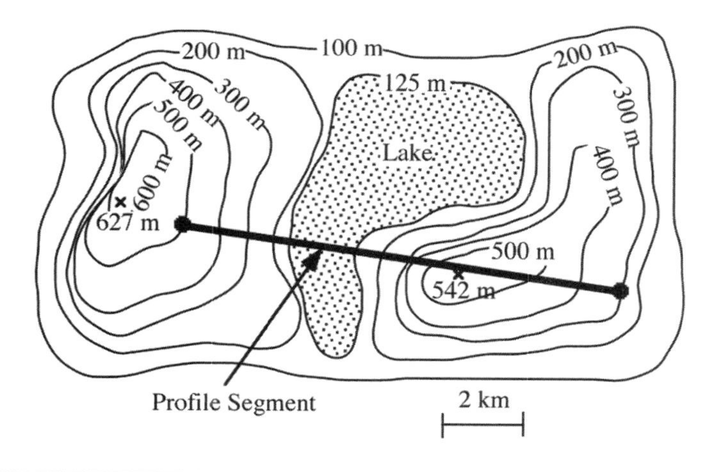

FIGURE 14-15 Profile segment drawn on a topographic map.

b. 1. Label the top line of a sheet of notebook paper with the highest elevation crossed by the profile segment.

   2. Determine the change in elevation between consecutive contour lines on the map. This change in elevation is the **contour interval** (I). In Figure **14-15,** for example, the contour interval is 100 m.

   3. Label each successive line on the notebook paper with an elevation I units less than the line above it. Continue this process until a line has been labeled with the lowest elevation crossed by the profile segment.

c. 1. Place the top edge of your notebook paper along the profile segment, as shown in Figure **14-16.**

   2. At each point where a contour line crosses the profile segment, draw a segment perpendicular to the profile segment. Extend each perpendicular segment to the line on the notebook paper that represents the same elevation as the corresponding contour line.

   3. Mark the intersections of the perpendicular segments and their corresponding lines on the notebook paper.

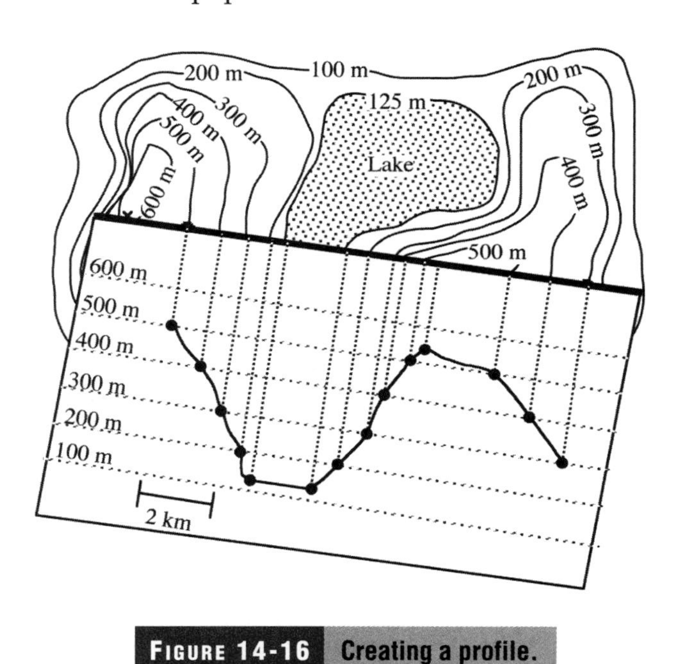

FIGURE 14-16 Creating a profile.

d. Connect the points of intersection with a smooth curve. This curve represents a profile of the terrain between the two points you located on the map.

e. Compare the vertical scale on the profile with the horizontal scale. If they are different, make a sketch of the profile using the same vertical and horizontal scales.

f. Describe any similarities or differences you observe in the two profiles in Parts **d** and **e.**

Discussion

a. What information does a profile provide about a landscape?

b. Given a profile between two points, could you recreate the topographic map from which it was derived? Why or why not?

c. Microwaves travel in a straight line and the distance between repeaters must be less than 5 km along an unobstructed path.

   Imagine that the two points you located in the exploration are the sites of a microwave transmitter and receiver, respectively. Describe how you could use the profile and topographic map to help locate appropriate sites for microwave repeaters.

d. Describe how the distance between two points on a topographic map can be approximated using a profile of the terrain.

e. Could you use a profile to determine the angle of elevation between two points (the angle formed by the segment joining the two points and a horizontal line)? Explain your response.

Warm-Up

1. Draw a right triangle, labeling all sides and vertices. Choose one acute angle and write the formulas for the three trigonometric ratios relative to that angle.

2. Determine the unknown measure in each triangle below.

a.

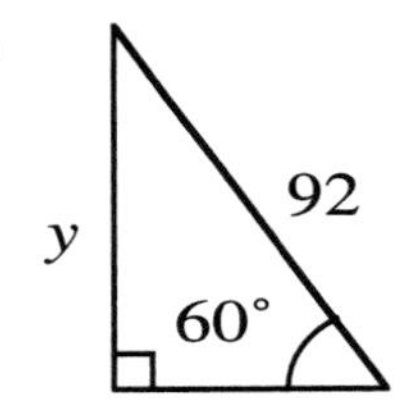

b.

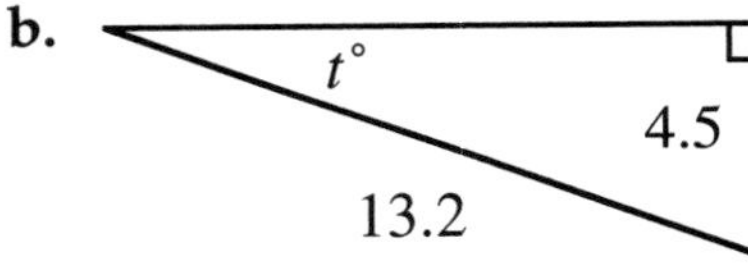

c.

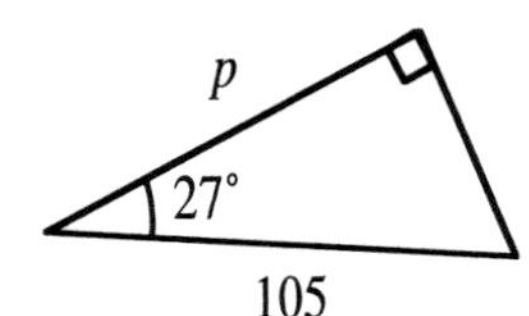

d.

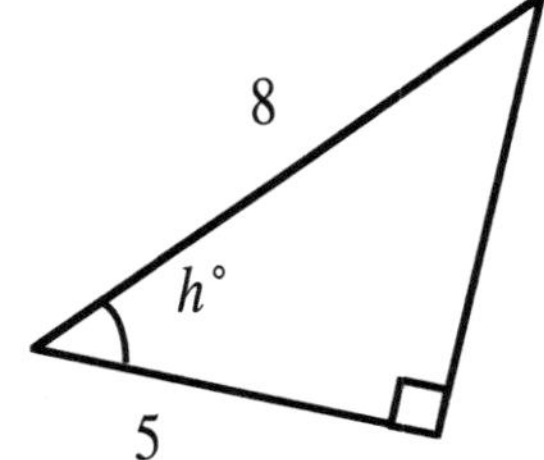

Assignment

3.1 The figure below shows a profile of a mountain landscape.

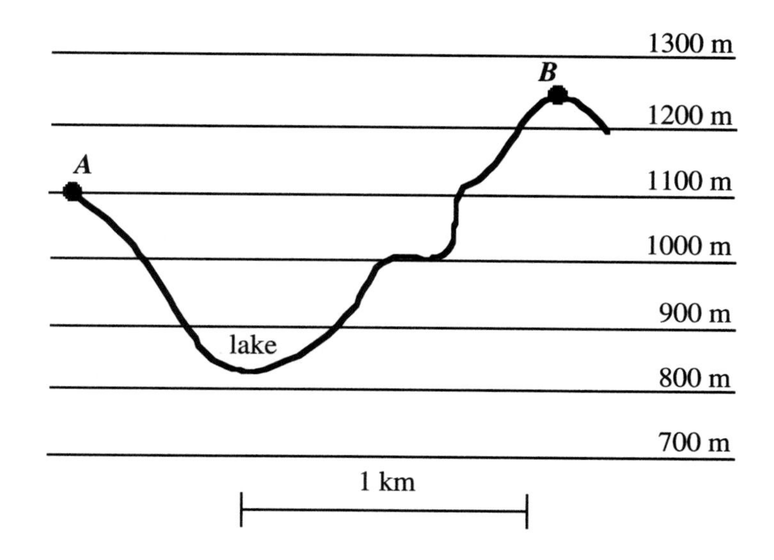

a. What is the elevation of the summit?

b. Approximately how tall is the cliff?

c. At what elevation is the lake?

d. What is the distance from point A to point B?

e. **1.** Sketch a profile of this mountain on a coordinate grid, using the same scale for both the horizontal and vertical axes.

2. Use the ordered pairs that describe the locations of points A and B to verify the distance found in Part **d.**

3.2 Imagine that a microwave transmitter is located at point A on the profile in Problem **3.1.** A receiver is located at point B.

a. Using the distances found in Problem **3.1,** sketch a right triangle like the one in the diagram below to model this situation.

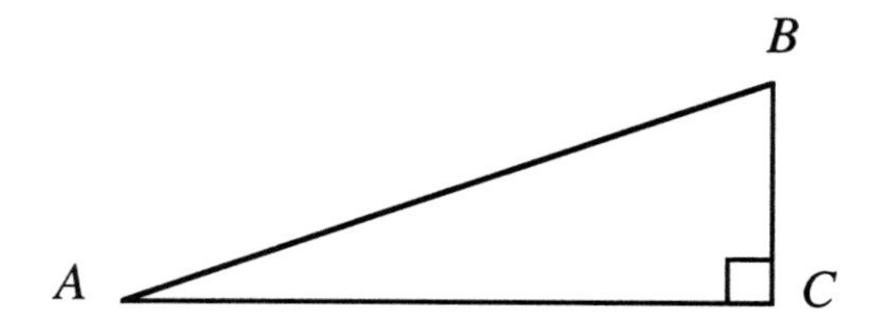

b. In the diagram, what trigonometric ratio is defined by BC/AB? Explain your response.

c. Using the trigonometric ratio you identified in Part **b,** determine the angle necessary to transmit a microwave signal directly from A to B.

3.3 The topographic map below shows the locations of a microwave transmitter and receiver. Both are built on towers 20 m above the ground.

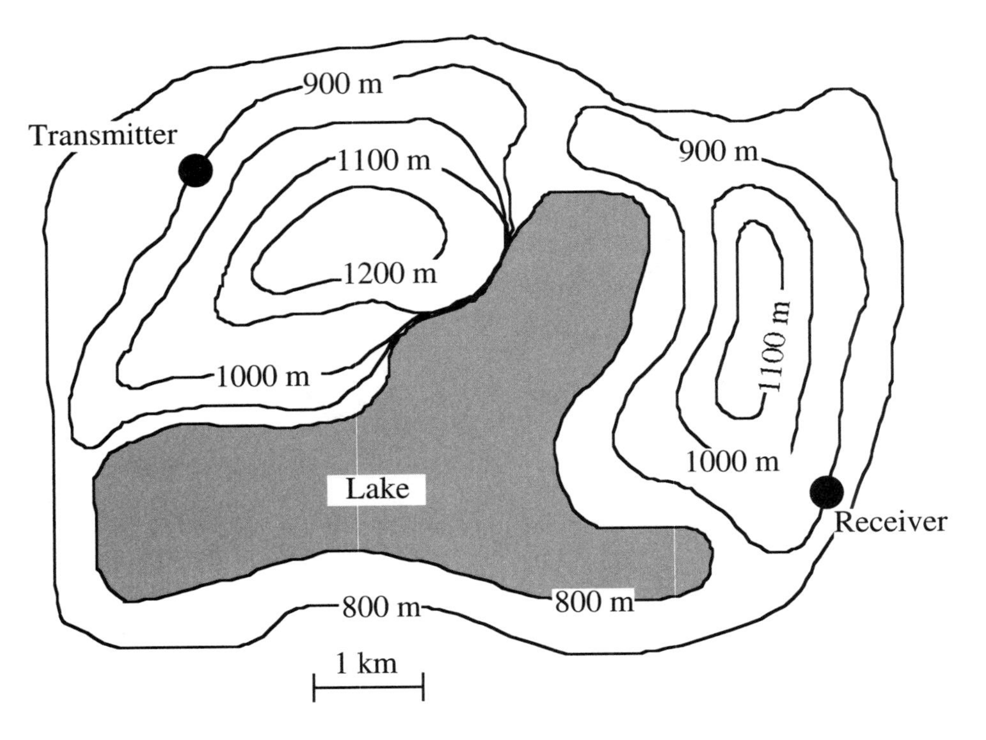

a. To relay signals from the transmitter to the receiver, two microwave repeaters must be built between them. Identify possible locations for the repeaters. (Recall that microwaves travel in straight lines and require unobstructed paths no greater than 5 km long.)

b. Demonstrate that your proposed locations are adequate by:

1. drawing profiles of the terrain
2. finding the appropriate distances using ordered triples.

3.4 Microwave signals travel at the speed of light, about $3 \bullet 10^8$ m/sec. Determine the time required for a signal to travel from the transmitter to the receiver in Problem **3.3.**

3.5 The terrain represented by the topographic map in Problem **3.3** features two summits. Write a detailed paragraph describing a journey from one summit to the other. Include an estimate of the distance traveled and describe how you determined this distance.

* * * * *

3.6 Create a topographic map that corresponds with the profile given in Problem **3.1.**

3.7 The figure below shows a profile of a valley.

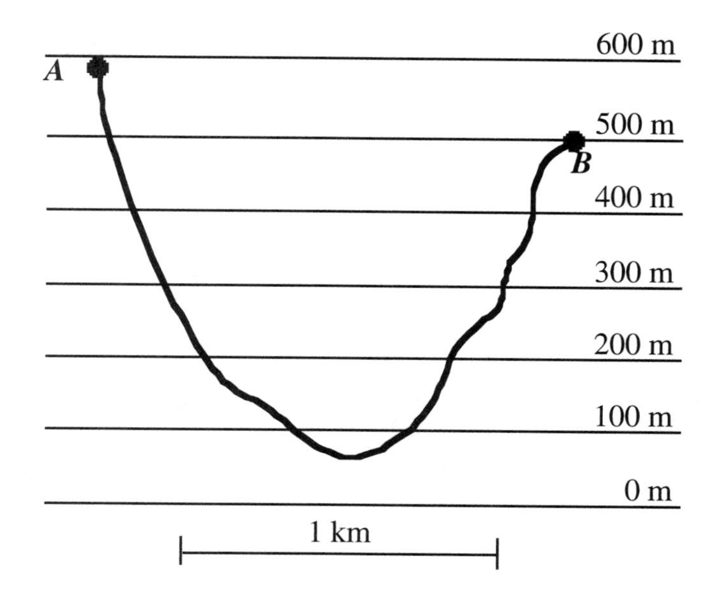

a. What is the elevation of the lowest part of the valley shown in the profile?

b. What is the distance from point A to point B?

Research Project

The U.S. Geological Survey (USGS) has published topographic maps of nearly the entire United States. Obtain a topographic map of a region near your school.

a. Identify several key features of the terrain. In a paragraph, describe how contour lines help characterize these features on the map.

b. Create a profile of the terrain.

c. Determine the straight-line distance and angle of elevation between the two highest points on the map.

Summary Assessment

The diagram below shows a map of a business district in a large city. Each polygon not otherwise labeled represents a building in the district. Each measure indicates the height above street level of the corresponding building. Use this map to complete Problems **1** and **2** below.

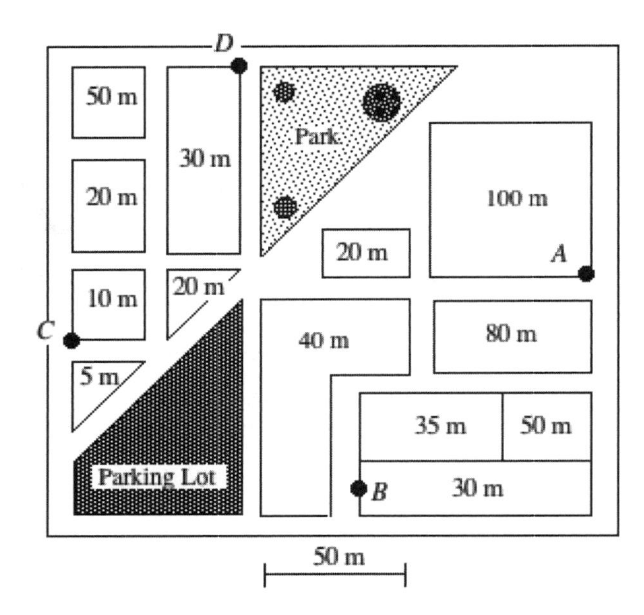

1. The local telephone company plans to build a microwave transmitter on the top of the building at point *A*. The transmitter will send signals to a receiver located on the top of a building at point *C*.

   a. Determine whether or not there is an unobstructed line of sight between points *A* and *C* by creating a profile of the terrain.

   b. Determine the distance between points *A* and *C* using the coordinates of ordered triples.

   c. Determine the angle of elevation (measured from the horizontal) necessary to transmit the signal directly from point *A* to point *B*.

2. A cable television company is trying to determine the most cost-efficient way to relay signals from its headquarters at point *B* to a substation at point *D*. The company has two choices: burying a cable underground, or installing a system on the roofs of buildings to transmit signals through the air.

   a. Burying a cable underground will cost $450 per meter. To minimize the disruption of traffic, the cable may not pass under more than three streets and must run alongside buildings.

      1. Determine a possible route between points *B* and *D*.

      2. Calculate the cost of this plan.

b. The transmitters required to send the signal through the air cost $35,000 each. The repeaters cost $15,000 each. The path between a transmitter and a repeater must be unobstructed by other buildings. If a transmitter or repeaters must be located on the roof of a building not already owned by the company, the space must be purchased for $3000.

   1. Use a profile to determine the number and location of the transmitters and repeaters necessary to relay signals between points *B* and *D*.

   2. Calculate the cost of this plan.

c. Write a letter to the president of the company describing both options. Include appropriate maps and profiles, a summary of the costs of each plan, and a report of your recommendations.

Module Summary

- The lines that indicate elevation on a topographic map are **contour lines.**
- A **summit** is the highest point of the surrounding elevations.
- A **saddle** is a pass between two higher elevations.
- The coordinates of a point in a three-dimensional rectangular coordinate system are written as an **ordered triple.**
- The **origin** of a three-dimensional rectangular coordinate system is the point where the three axes intersect. The origin has coordinates (0,0,0).
- The distance d between two points with coordinates (x_1,y_1) and (x_2,y_2) can be found using the following formula:

$$d = \sqrt{(x_2 - x_1)^2 + (y_2 - y_1)^2}$$

- The distance d between two points with coordinates (x_1,y_1,z_1) and (x_2,y_2,z_2) can be found using the following formula:

$$d = \sqrt{(x_2 - x_1)^2 + (y_2 - y_1)^2 + (z_2 - z_1)^2}$$

- A **profile** shows a vertical cross section or "side view" of terrain.

module 15

Going in Circuits

Introduction

The map in Figure **15-1** shows the floor plan of William R. Hamilton High School.

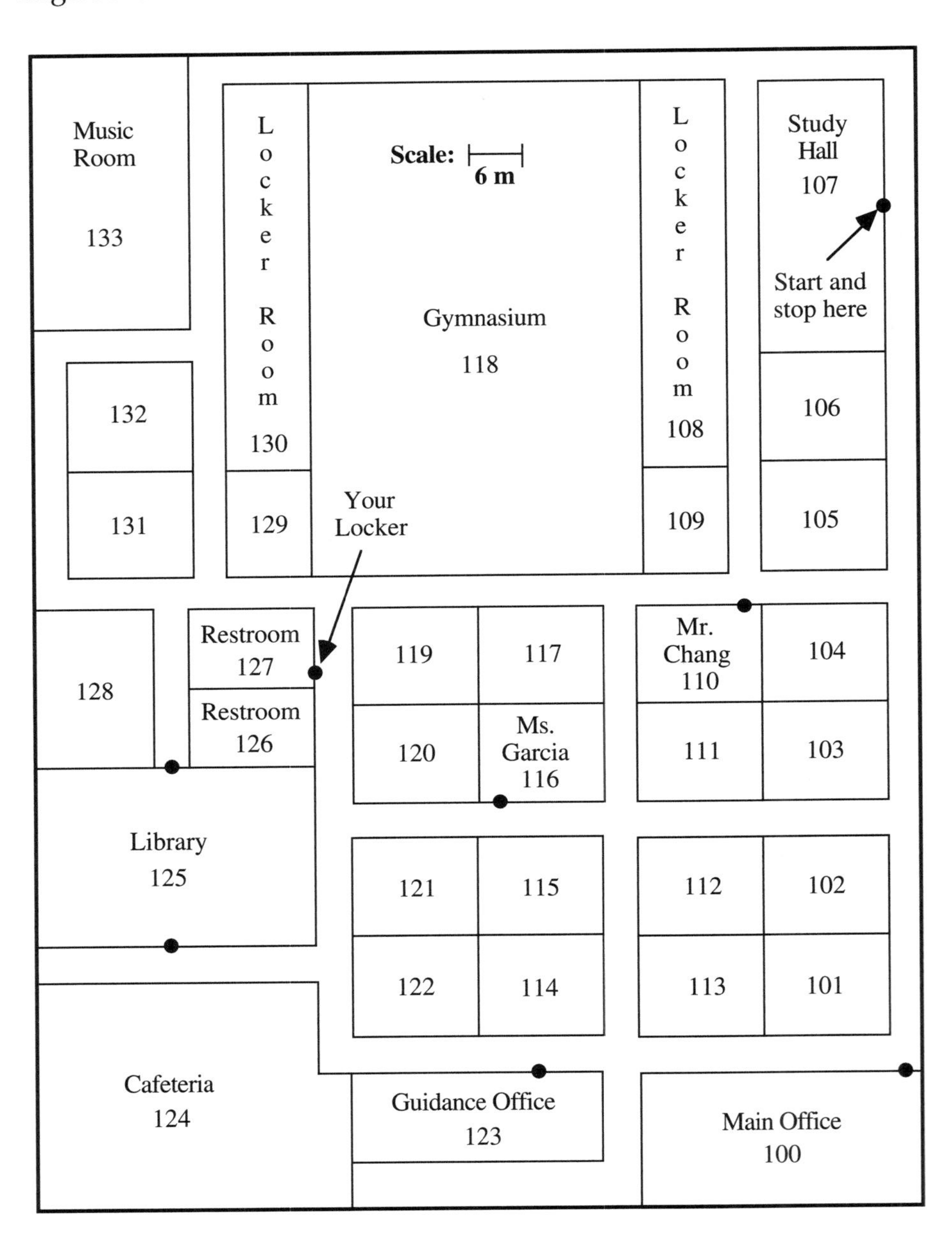

FIGURE 15-1 Floor plan of Hamilton High School.

As a new student at Hamilton High, you have a lot to do. To complete your first day on schedule, you must visit six different rooms during a 55-min study hall. The following list describes each room, the task involved, and the time required to complete the task.

- Main Office: fill out a new student information card (7 min)
- Guidance Office: make an appointment to talk to a counselor (1 min)
- Room 116: question Ms. Garcia about a science experiment (10 min)
- Room 110: talk to Mr. Chang about taking French (10 min)
- Library: find a book for an English assignment (15 min)
- Locker: pick up a notebook (1 min).

You may visit the rooms in any order. However, your route must satisfy the following requirements.

- You must start and stop in Study Hall, Room 107.
- You must visit all the rooms and accomplish all the tasks.
- You must return to Study Hall before the end of the class period (55 min).

How can you find an efficient route to all these rooms and back to Study Hall? A situation such as this one, in which an appropriate solution makes good use of time or other resources, involves **optimization.**

ACTIVITY 1

It can help to organize the available information in a table or graph before beginning to solve an optimization problem.

You can describe one possible route by representing each destination as a point, as shown in Figure **15-2.** This route leaves Study Hall, visits the locker first, then eventually returns to Study Hall. The diagram shows the sequence in which the rooms are visited, but it is not drawn to scale.

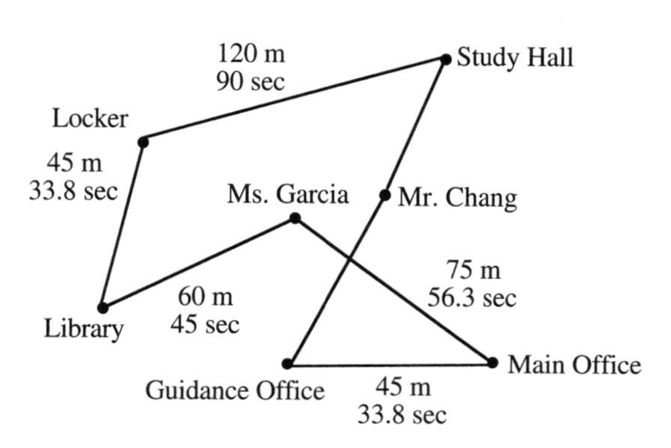

FIGURE 15-2 Possible route for completing study hall tasks.

Exploration

Figure **15-2** also shows the distances between some of the stops and the time required to walk those distances. The distances were determined by measuring the hallways on the map in Figure **15-1,** then using the map's scale to convert these distances to meters. The corresponding walking times were calculated using a rate of 4.8 km/hr.

a. 1. Use Figure **15-1** to find the distances along the hallways from the Guidance Office to Mr. Chang's room and from Mr. Chang's room to the Study Hall.

2. Using a walking speed of 4.8 km/hr, calculate the walking times for these trips.

3. Determine the walking time for the entire route.

4. Calculate the total time required to walk the route and complete all the tasks.

mathematics note

A **graph** is a set of points or **vertices** (plural of **vertex**) and the edges connecting them. For example, Figure **15-3** shows a graph with five vertices: *A, B, C, D,* and *E.* This graph has seven edges. The edge connecting vertices *A* and *D* does not intersect the edge connecting vertices *B* and *E.*

FIGURE 15-3 **A graph with five vertices and seven edges.**

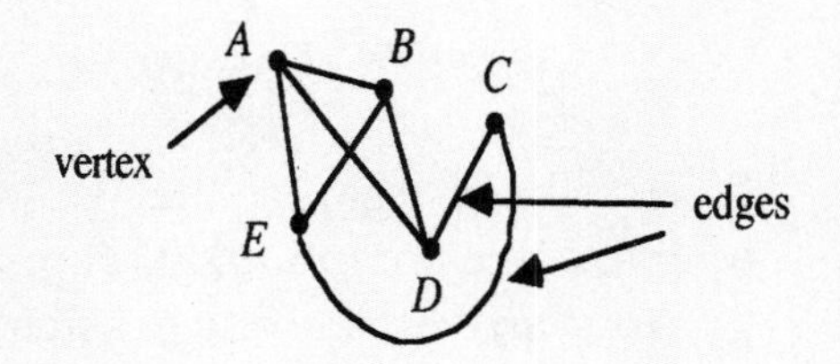

In a **weighted graph,** each edge is assigned a numerical value. For example, the numerical value on each edge in Figure **15-4a** represents the flight time between the corresponding pair of cities. In Figure **15-4b,** the numbers represent the airfares between two cities.

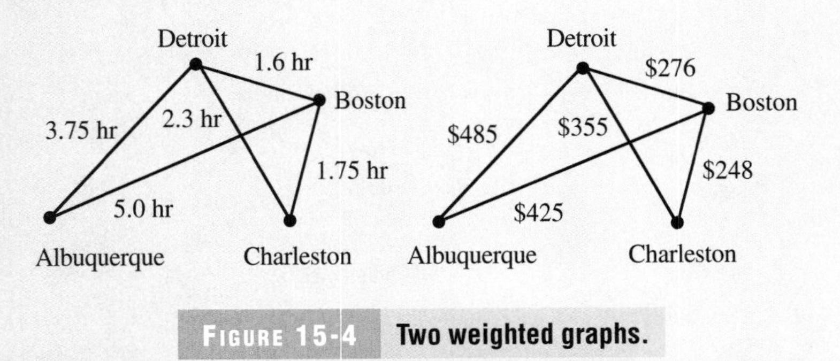

FIGURE 15-4 **Two weighted graphs.**

b. Find an acceptable route through Hamilton High School that takes less time than the one shown in Figure **15-2.**

1. Display the route as a graph.
2. Weight the edges of the graph with the corresponding walking times.
3. Find the total time required to complete the route.

Discussion

a. Which route in the exploration do you think is the better one? Explain your response.

b. What characteristics do you think describe the best possible route?

c. How could you make sure that you found the best possible route?

mathematics note

A **path** is a sequence of vertices connected by edges in which no edge is repeated. Vertices, however, can occur more than once in a path.

In Figure **15-5,** for example, *A–B–D–C–E* represents a path in which no vertex is repeated, while *B–E–A–B–D* represents a path in which one vertex (*B*) is repeated.

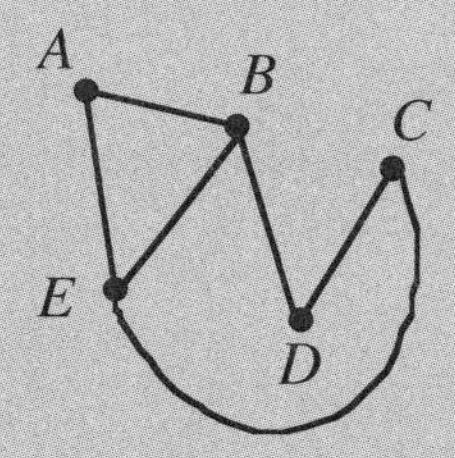

FIGURE 15-5 A graph with five vertices.

A **circuit** is a path that starts and ends with the same vertex in which no intermediate vertex is repeated. For example, *E–B–D–C–E* and *A–B–E–A* in Figure **15-5** are circuits.

A **Hamiltonian circuit** is a circuit in which every vertex in the graph is visited exactly once. For example, *A–B–D–C–E–A* in Figure **15-5** is a Hamiltonian circuit.

d. What do the vertices of the graphs in the exploration represent?

e. What do the edges of the graphs in the exploration represent?

f. Explain why your graph from Part **b** of the exploration is a Hamiltonian circuit.

g. Why is *A–B–D–C–E–B–A* in Figure **15-5** not a Hamiltonian circuit?

Warm-Up

1. The diagram below shows a graph with six vertices: *A, B, C, D, E,* and *F.*

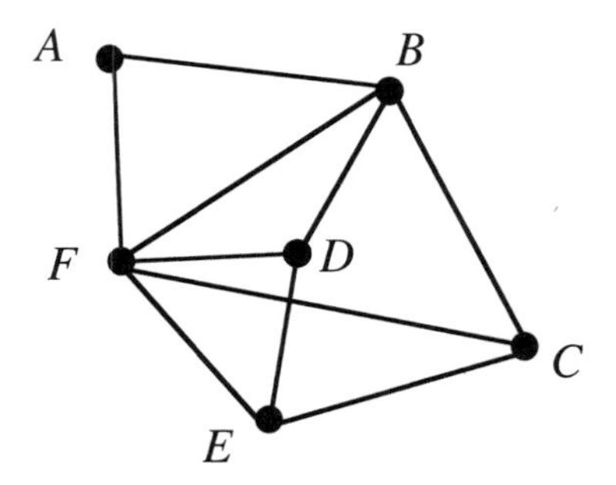

Use this graph to describe an example, if possible, of each of the following:

a. a path

b. a circuit that is not a Hamiltonian circuit

c. a path that is not a circuit

d. a circuit that is not a path

e. a Hamiltonian circuit.

Assignment

1.1 In the weighted graph below, the vertices represent cities. The numbers on the edges represent the time in minutes required to drive from one city to the next.

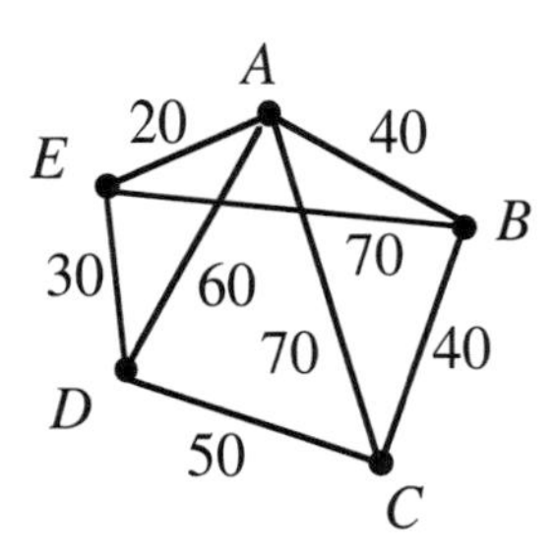

a. Find the path from *A* to *D* that uses the minimum amount of time.

b. Identify one Hamiltonian circuit in the graph. Determine the total time required for this route.

c. Identify another Hamiltonian circuit in the graph that results in a different total time.

d. Which of the circuits from Parts **b** and **c** makes more efficient use of time?

1.2 The following diagram shows a weighted graph in which the vertices represent stores in a mall and the numbers on the edges represent the time in seconds required to walk from one store to another.

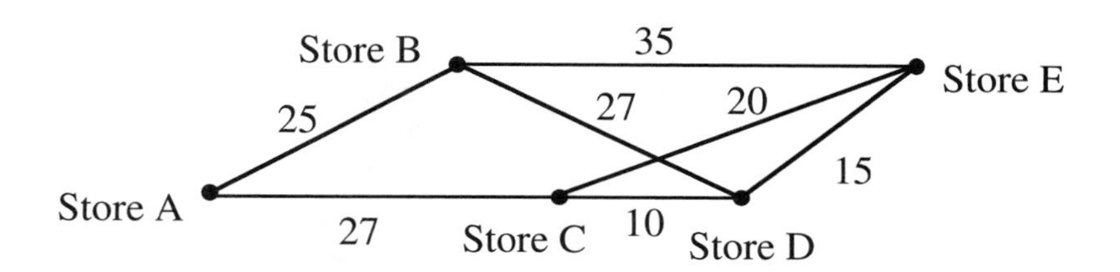

a. Find the path from Store A to Store E that takes the least amount of time.

b. Identify a Hamiltonian circuit beginning with Store A. Determine the time required to walk the circuit.

c. Identify another Hamiltonian circuit in the graph that results in a different total time.

1.3 The following chart shows the distances in kilometers between some Alaskan cities.

	Valdez	Tok	Fairbanks
Anchorage	478	520	581
Fairbanks	584	333	
Tok	409		

a. The vertices in the diagram below represent the relative locations of the cities. On a copy of this diagram, draw all the possible edges between these vertices.

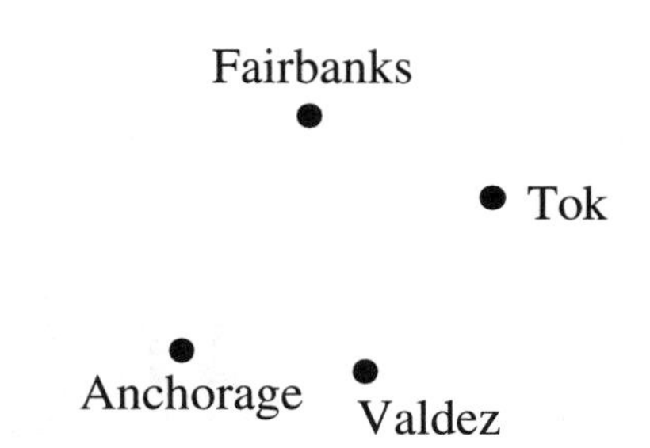

b. Weight your graph from Part **a** using the distances between cities.

c. What is the shortest path on the graph?

d. Name one circuit in the graph that is not a Hamiltonian circuit.

e. Identify two Hamiltonian circuits that result in different total distances.

* * * * *

1.4 A scoutmaster has designed an orienteering competition for six scouts. Each scout will be assigned a different course. All six courses, however, start at the same point, visit three locations, then return to the starting point. The scouts must use maps and compasses to complete the assigned course in as little time as possible.

The diagram on the left shows the relative positions of the three locations and the starting point. It also shows the presence of some obstacles on the course, including a mountain, thick brush, and a lake. The weighted graph on the right shows the distances between the locations.

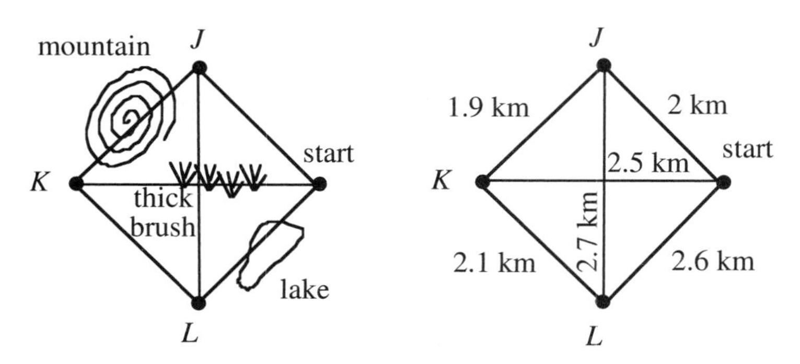

a. Each of the six possible routes is a Hamiltonian circuit. Identify the six routes.

b. Over easy terrain and around the lake, the scouts can travel at an average speed of 9.6 km/hr. Over rugged terrain, such as mountains or thick brush, the average speed is 7 km/hr.

If you were one of the six scouts participating in the competition, which route would you want to be assigned? Explain your response.

1.5 Create a weighted graph showing the distances between the following cities: Seattle, WA; Washington, DC; Orlando, FL; Los Angeles, CA; and Chicago, IL. Identify a Hamiltonian circuit that connects these cities, beginning in Seattle, and determine the total distance traveled. Compare this total with others in your class.

ACTIVITY 2

In the previous activity, you described two different routes through Hamilton High School. To determine the best route in this situation, you might be tempted to consider all the possible Hamiltonian circuits. However, this would mean taking the time to examine over 500 circuits.

In this activity, you investigate a method for quickly determining the number of possible solutions to a problem.

Exploration

Imagine that you are the manager of the most popular band in the nation. The members of the band are in Miami, Florida, and must fly to Los Angeles, California, to sign a recording contract.

There are two flights leaving Miami—one to Chicago, Illinois, and one to Kansas City, Missouri. From both Chicago and Kansas City, there are three flights going west—one to Denver, Colorado; one to Salt Lake City, Utah; and one to Las Vegas, Nevada. There are direct flights to Los Angeles from Denver, Salt Lake City, and Las Vegas.

a. A **directed graph** or **digraph** is a graph in which a direction is indicated on each edge. Draw a directed graph that shows the relative positions of the cities named above and the flights between them.

mathematics note

A **tree diagram** is a mathematical model that shows all the possible outcomes for a series of events or decisions. Each line segment in a tree diagram is a **branch.**

For example, the tree diagram in Figure **15-6** shows all the possible outcomes for rolling a six-sided die, then tossing a coin.

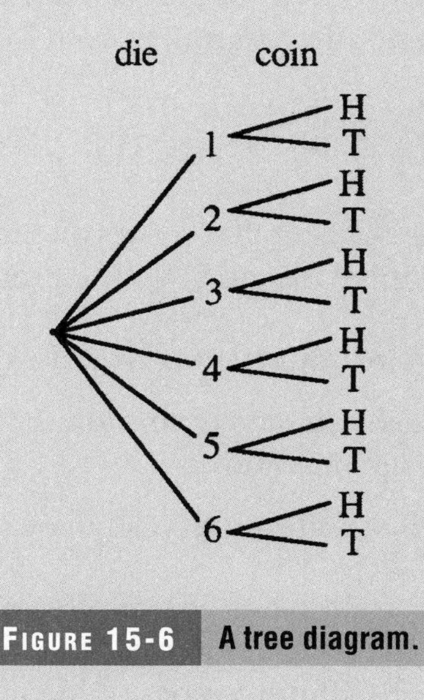

FIGURE 15-6 A tree diagram.

b. Draw a tree diagram to illustrate all possible routes from Miami to Los Angeles.

c. How many different routes are there from Miami to Los Angeles?

Discussion

a. Describe how you determined the number of different routes from Miami to Los Angeles.

b. Would your method work well if several more cities were involved?

mathematics note

The **fundamental counting principle** provides a method for determining the total number of outcomes for a series of events or decisions. If an event that can occur in m ways is followed by an event that can occur in n ways, then the total number of ways in which the two events can occur is $m \bullet n$.

For example, consider rolling a six-sided die, then flipping a coin. The die has 6 faces and the coin has 2 sides. In this situation, the number of possible outcomes is $6 \bullet 2 = 12$.

c. Describe how the fundamental counting principle can be used to determine the number of different routes from Miami to Los Angeles.

Warm-Up

1. Draw a tree diagram that shows all the three-digit numbers that can be formed using the digits 3, 5, and 9, without repetition.

2. You and two of your friends would like to pose for a group picture.

   a. Using the fundamental counting principle, in how many ways can the group be lined up in a row?

   b. Draw a tree diagram to verify your answer to Part **a.**

3. A local coffee shop has begun offering a special lunch, which includes soup, salad, and bread. Customers can choose from 3 different soups, 4 different salads, and 6 different types of bread. They also can select from 13 different beverages. How many different lunch combinations, including beverages, are possible?

Assignment

2.1 As the manager of a band, you are planning a five-city tour to promote the band's new album. The tour will begin and end in Miami, with stops in Seattle, Washington; Kansas City, Missouri; Chicago, Illinois; and New York City. The band will visit each city only once and the order of the cities is not important.

a. Determine the number of possible routes that the band can take on the tour.

b. Draw a tree diagram to verify your answer from Part **a.**

c. Describe the process you used to create the tree diagram in Part **b.**

mathematics note

An **algorithm** is a step-by-step process used to accomplish a task.

In a **brute force algorithm,** every potential solution to a problem is examined. For example, suppose that you wanted to determine the number of possible routes from your home to school. To solve this problem with a brute force algorithm, you could use a tree diagram to list every route.

2.2 On the first day of a new semester, your principal greets you with a list of the seven classes in your school day.

a. In how many different ways could these seven classes be arranged?

b. Why is a brute force algorithm not appropriate in this situation?

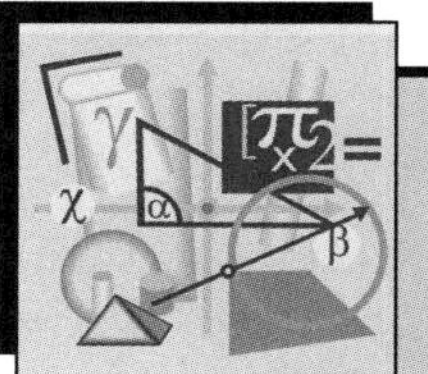

mathematics note

Factorial notation is often used to simplify the representation of the product of the positive integers from 1 to n. If n is a positive integer, then $\boldsymbol{n}$ **factorial** (denoted by $\boldsymbol{n!}$) can be expressed as

$$n! = n \bullet (n-1) \bullet (n-2) \bullet \cdots \bullet 3 \bullet 2 \bullet 1$$

Zero factorial, or **0!**, is defined as 1.

For example, the number of possible arrangements of the letters A, B, and C can be found using the fundamental counting principle as follows: $3 \bullet 2 \bullet 1 = 6$. Using factorial notation, this can be represented as 3!

2.3 As part of the publicity for their tour, the band will appear on the cover of *Singer's Circuit* magazine. Before choosing a photo, the magazine editors want to look at samples with the four band members arranged in different orders.

a. If the band members stand side by side, how many different arrangements are possible?

b. Use factorial notation to represent the number of possible arrangements.

2.4 During its concerts, the band plays 10 songs in a set before taking a break.

a. In how many different orders can 10 songs be played?

b. If the band wants to play its current hit song first, how does this affect the number of possible orders for a 10-song set?

c. How would your answer to Part **b** change if the band chose to play its hit song fourth in the set?

d. If the band wants to play its hit song first and its shortest song second, how does this affect the number of possible orders for a 10-song set?

e. In how many different orders can n songs be played?

2.5 The band is planning several tours during the summer concert season. All of these tours begin and end in the band's hometown.

a. Use the fundamental counting principle to determine the number of possible tours involving each of the following numbers of cities:

1. 2 cities (the band's hometown plus one other city)

2. 3 cities (the band's hometown plus two other cities)

3. 4 cities (the band's hometown plus three other cities)

4. 10 cities (the band's hometown plus nine other cities).

b. Use the pattern you observe in your responses to Part **a** to develop a formula for calculating the number of tours possible for n cities if all tours begin and end in the band's hometown.

2.6 **a.** Determine the number of possible routes through Hamilton High School that begin and end in Study Hall and visit all six destinations described in Activity **1.**

b. Explain why it is not feasible to list all the possible routes.

* * * * *

2.7 As captain of the softball team, Corrine must determine the order in which the team's nine players will bat. Use the fundamental counting principle to determine the number of different batting orders that Corrine could choose.

2.8 **a.** Find the value of 7!

b. Find the value of 9!/7!

c. Explain why it is possible to write 200! as 200(199!).

d. One way to find the value of 100!/95! is to calculate 100! and divide it by 95!

Describe another way to calculate the value of 100!/95!

e. Simplify the following expression:

$$\frac{n!}{(n - 1)!}$$

2.9 On his first day at Hamilton High School, Marcus forgets the combination to his locker. In an attempt to jog his memory, he tries a few different combinations.

a. The combination to the lock consists of a sequence of 3 different numbers. Each of these numbers can be chosen from 40 different numbers. How many different combinations are possible?

b. If it takes 15 seconds to try each combination, how long would it take Marcus to try them all?

In Activity **2,** you identified the number of possible routes for your band's upcoming tour. As manager, however, you must also consider the time and expense associated with the tour. Selecting the shortest route possible, for example, might save both time and money.

Exploration

The stops on your concert tour include Miami, Seattle, Chicago, New York, and Kansas City. Table **15-1** below shows the distances in kilometers between these cities.

TABLE 15-1 ■ *Distances between Cities (in kilometers)*

	Seattle	Kansas City	Chicago	New York
Miami	4400	1997	1912	1757
New York	3875	1765	1147	
Chicago	2795	667		
Kansas City	2424			

a. Without using a brute force algorithm, plan a tour that starts in Miami, ends in Miami, visits each of the other cities exactly once, and travels as few kilometers as you think possible.

mathematics note

In a **greedy algorithm,** the choice made at each step is the best of all remaining choices. One greedy algorithm is the **nearest neighbor algorithm.** The steps for the nearest neighbor algorithm are described below.

- Starting with any vertex, draw an edge to its nearest vertex. In Figure **15-7,** for example, vertex *A* is connected to its nearest vertex, *B*.

FIGURE 15-7 Connecting the first vertex to the nearest vertex.

- Continue this process from the second vertex, drawing an edge to the next nearest vertex not yet visited, and so on, until all vertices have been visited. For example, Figure **15-8** shows edges drawn from *B* to *C* and from *C* to *D*.

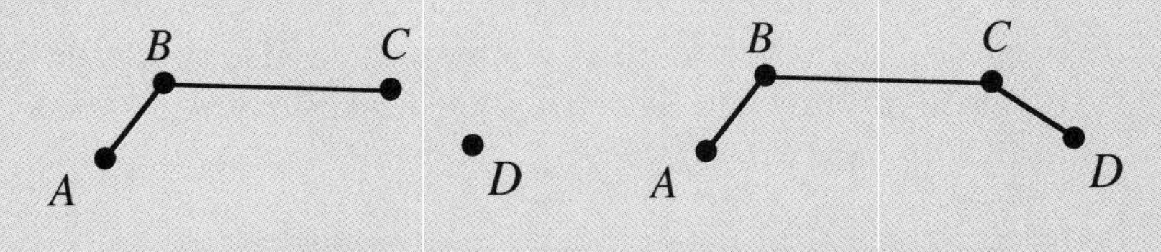

FIGURE 15-8 Continuing the nearest neighbor algorithm.

- To complete a Hamiltonian circuit, return to the original vertex. For example, Figure **15-9** shows an edge drawn from *D* back to *A*.

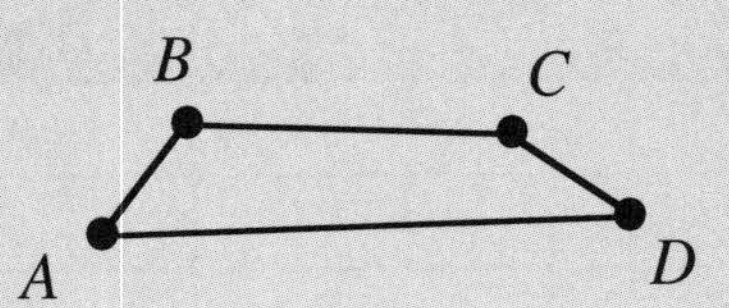

FIGURE 15-9 Completing a Hamiltonian circuit.

b. Use the nearest neighbor algorithm to draw weighted Hamiltonian circuits that start and stop in each of the five cities in Table **15-1.**

c. 1. Compare the graphs of the five circuits.

   2. Determine which weighted graph represents the tour with the shortest total distance.

d. Compare the shortest tour found using the nearest neighbor algorithm to the tour you identified in Part **a.**

Discussion

a. 1. What advantages are there to using the nearest neighbor algorithm to find a short tour?

   2. What advantages are there to using a brute force algorithm to find a short tour?

b. Describe a situation in which the nearest neighbor algorithm would provide an appropriate method for solving a problem.

c. Describe a situation in which a brute force algorithm would provide an appropriate method for solving a problem.

d. In Part **b** of the exploration, you drew Hamiltonian circuits that started and stopped in each of five cities. Which of these circuits could you use to plan a tour that starts and stops in Miami? Explain your response.

Warm-Up

1. Write each of the following expressions in factorial form.

   a. $5 \bullet 4 \bullet 3 \bullet 2 \bullet 1$

   b. $22 \bullet 21 \bullet \cdots \bullet 3 \bullet 2 \bullet 1$

   c. $n \bullet (n-1) \bullet \cdots \bullet 2 \bullet 1$

2. Simplify each of the following.

   a. $5!/3!$

   b. $\frac{42!}{3!40!}$

   c. $\frac{n!}{(n-3)!}$

3. a. Use the fundamental counting principle to determine the number of ten-digit codes that can be created using the digits 0 through 9, without repetition.

   b. Use factorial notation to represent your response to Part **a.**

   c. Determine the number of four-digit codes that can be created using the digits 0 through 9, without repetition.

   d. Represent your response to Part **c** using factorial notation.

Assignment

3.1 The band would like to add Los Angeles, California, to the tour in the exploration. The following table shows the distances in kilometers between Los Angeles and the other five cities.

	Los Angeles
Miami	3764
New York	3945
Chicago	2808
Kansas City	2182
Seattle	1543

a. Use the nearest neighbor algorithm to draw weighted Hamiltonian circuits that start and stop in each city on the tour.

b. Determine which circuit results in the shortest total distance.

c. Using the nearest neighbor algorithm, how many different routes did you have to check?

d. If you used a brute force algorithm to select the shortest tour, how many routes would you have to check?

3.2 a. About how many seconds did it take you to generate and calculate the total distance of one circuit in Problem **3.1**?

b. Using your response to Problem **3.1d,** about how long would it take you to check all the possible tours?

3.3 One of the band members suggests that this summer's tour begin with a send-off concert in your town, visit 24 other cities, then end with a homecoming concert in your town.

a. Determine the number of possible 25-city tours that begin and end in the same town.

b. Using the time you estimated in Problem **3.2,** determine the total time needed to check all the possible tour routes.

3.4 Katherine works in the admissions office at Applegate University. As part of her duties, she leads prospective students on a walking tour of the campus. The diagram below shows the relative positions of the campus buildings.

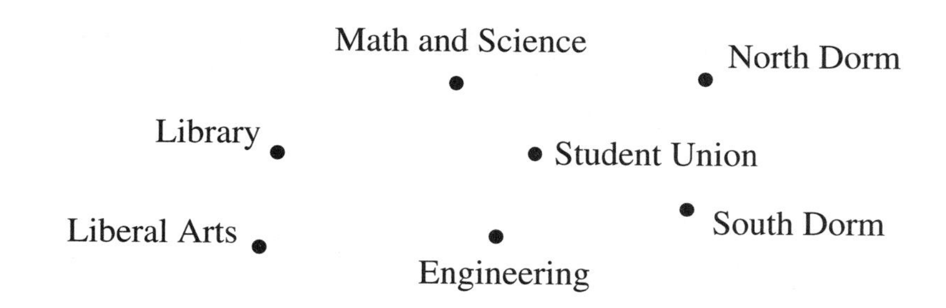

a. If she visits each of the seven buildings exactly once, in how many different ways can Katherine organize the walking tour?

b. Since new students live in South Dorm, Katherine likes to begin and end the tour there. How many ways are there to organize this tour?

c. The table below shows the distances in meters between buildings on campus. Use these distances and the nearest neighbor algorithm to graph a possible route for the walking tour you described in Part **b.**

	Student Union	**South Dorm**	**North Dorm**	**Math/ Science**	**Library**	**Liberal Arts**
Engineering	20	40	55	40	50	45
Liberal Arts	55	90	100	60	20	
Library	50	85	90	40		
Math/Science	25	50	50			
North Dorm	40	30				
South Dorm	35					

mathematics note

The nearest neighbor algorithm is just one of many greedy algorithms that can be used to solve optimization problems. In the **cheapest link algorithm,** the cheapest (or shortest) action is taken at each stage, regardless of starting and stopping points.

Individual, disconnected edges may occur at various stages. If the cheapest remaining action completes a circuit that is not Hamiltonian, then the next best action is taken. When a Hamiltonian circuit is found, the algorithm is complete.

For example, Figure **15-10** shows the steps used to draw a Hamiltonian circuit with the cheapest link algorithm.

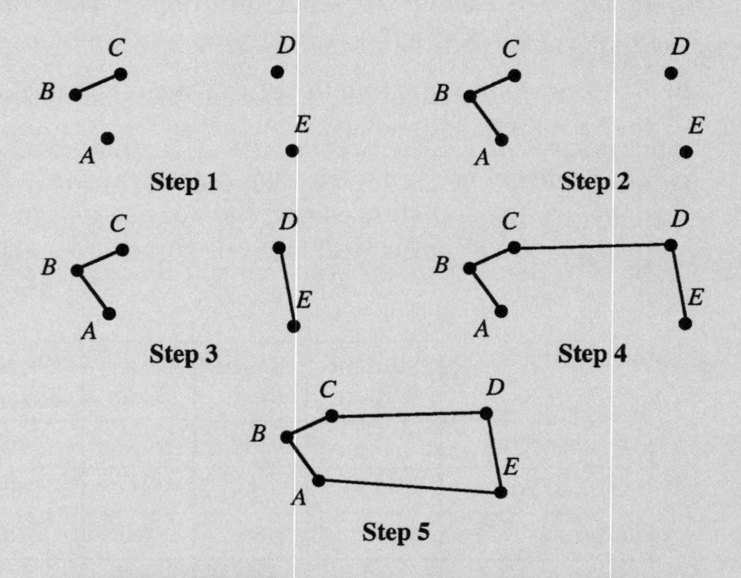

FIGURE 15-10 Steps in cheapest link algorithm.

In Step **3,** notice that *D* and *E* are connected even though these points are farther apart than C and *A*. This occurs because drawing an edge between *A* and C would complete a circuit that is not Hamiltonian.

3.5 **a.** Use the cheapest link algorithm to determine a possible route for the walking tour in Problem **3.4b.**

b. How does this tour compare with the one you identified in Problem **3.4c**?

3.6 **a.** Use the cheapest link algorithm to find a tour of the six cities in Problem **3.1** that begins and ends in Miami.

b. Calculate the distance covered by the tour.

c. Compare this distance with the distance found using the nearest neighbor algorithm.

* * * * *

3.7 As the result of a stellar performance on the state math exam, your class has been awarded a trip to four interesting places in your state. Your class may choose both the places and the route, but the trip must start and end in your town.

a. Choose four destinations and create a table that shows the distances from each one to the others, including your town.

b. Determine the number of possible routes for your trip.

c. Use the nearest neighbor algorithm to plan your route. Determine the total distance traveled.

d. Use the cheapest link algorithm to plan your route. Determine the total distance traveled.

e. Is the shorter of the two routes necessarily the shortest possible route? Explain your response.

f. Use a brute force algorithm to support your response to Part **e.**

Summary Assessment

At 4:30 P.M., Jack and Jill leave their house to run some errands for their parents. They must stop by a friend's house, the music store, the bookstore, the newsstand, and the post office. As a reward, their parents have given them enough money to play video games at the arcade. The relative positions of these destinations are shown in the diagram below.

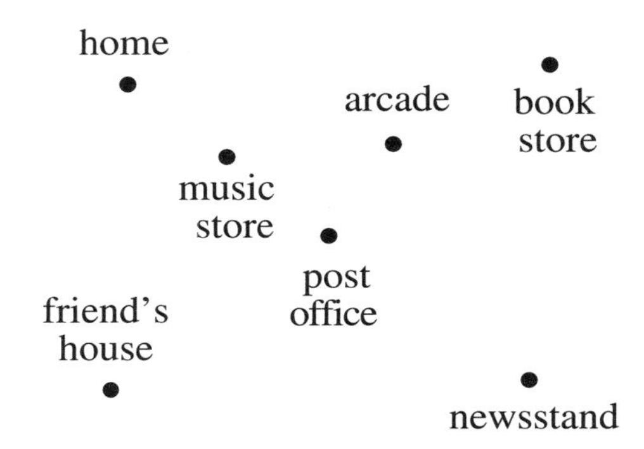

Each errand should take 5 min to complete and Jack and Jill must be home by 6:00 P.M. for dinner. The following table shows the walking time in minutes between the locations.

	Friend's House	Newsstand	Book Store	Post Office	Arcade	Music Store
Home	5.5	9.5	6.5	5.5	4.0	2.5
Music Store	3.0	6.5	6.0	2.5	2.5	
Arcade	5.0	5.5	3.5	2.0		
Post Office	3.0	4.0	5.5			
Book Store	8.5	5.5				
Newsstand	3.5					

1. Select a route that allows Jack and Jill to spend more time at the arcade. Draw a weighted graph to represent this route and indicate the order in which the edges were chosen.
2. The games at the arcade last about 5 min each. Using the route you selected in Problem **1,** how many games can Jack and Jill play?
3. Identify the algorithm you used to select a route. If you devised an algorithm of your own, describe its steps so that any student in the class could repeat your results.
4. If you had to find the quickest possible route that visited all these destinations, how many circuits would you have to check?

Module Summary

- ✷ In an **optimization** problem, the goal is to make the best use of time or other resources.
- ✷ A **graph** is a set of **vertices** (plural of **vertex**) and **edges.** Each edge connects two vertices.
- ✷ In a **weighted graph,** each edge is assigned a numerical value.
- ✷ A **path** is a sequence of vertices connected by edges in which no edge is repeated. Vertices, however, can occur more than once in a path.
- ✷ A **circuit** is a path that starts and ends with the same vertex in which no intermediate vertex is repeated.
- ✷ A **Hamiltonian circuit** is a circuit in which every vertex in the graph is visited exactly once.
- ✷ A **directed graph** or **digraph** is a graph in which a direction is indicated on each edge.
- ✷ A **tree diagram** is a mathematical model that shows all the possible outcomes for a series of events or decisions. Each line segment in a tree diagram is a **branch.**
- ✷ The **fundamental counting principle** provides a method for determining the total number of ways in which a task can be performed. If an event that can occur in m ways is followed by an event that can occur in n ways, then the total number of ways that the two events can occur is $m \bullet n$.
- ✷ An **algorithm** is a step-by-step process used to accomplish a task.
- ✷ In a **brute force algorithm,** every potential solution to a problem is examined.
- ✷ **Factorial notation** is often used to simplify the representation of the product of the positive integers from 1 to n. If n is a positive integer, then n **factorial** (denoted by $n!$) can be expressed as

$$n! = n \bullet (n - 1) \bullet (n - 2) \bullet \cdots \bullet 3 \bullet 2 \bullet 1$$

- ✷ **Zero factorial,** or **0!,** is defined as 1.
- ✷ In a **greedy algorithm,** the choice made at each step is the best of all remaining choices.
- ✷ To use the **nearest neighbor algorithm,** start with any vertex and draw an edge to its nearest vertex. Continue this process from the second vertex to the next nearest vertex not yet visited, and so on, until all vertices have been visited. To complete a Hamiltonian circuit, return to the original vertex.
- ✷ In the **cheapest link algorithm,** the cheapest (or shortest) action is taken at each stage, regardless of starting and stopping points. Individual, disconnected edges may occur at various stages. If the cheapest remaining action completes a circuit that is not Hamiltonian, then the next best action is taken. When a Hamiltonian circuit is formed, the algorithm is complete.

Glossary

absolute value of a residual—measure of the distance from a data point to the linear model; in general, the smaller the sum of the absolute values of the residuals, the more closely a line approximates the data.

acceleration—the rate of change in velocity with respect to time; has both magnitude and direction.

acceleration (due to gravity)—a constant typically denoted by g; on earth's surface, the acceleration due to gravity is about 9.8 m/sec^2 in a direction toward the earth's center.

algorithm—a step-by-step process used to accomplish a task.

angle of incidence—angle formed by the normal and the incident ray.

angle of reflection—angle formed by the normal and the reflected ray.

Angle-Angle-Angle (AAA) property—if the angles of one triangle are congruent to the corresponding angles of another triangle, then the triangles are similar.

apothem—segment whose measure is the perpendicular distance from the center of a regular polygon to one of its sides.

area (of a regular polygon)—can be calculated by $A = [(1/2)as]n$, where n is the number of sides, a is the apothem, and s is the side length.

arithmetic sequence—a sequence in which every term after the first is found by adding a constant value (the constant difference) to the preceding term.

arithmetic series—the sum of the terms of an arithmetic sequence.

average velocity—can be calculated by dividing the change in position by the change in time. See *velocity.*

back-to-back stem-and-leaf plot—stem-and-leaf plot used to compare two sets of data.

base (of a cylinder or prism)—one of the congruent and parallel faces.

boundary line—a graph of a linear equation that forms a boundary of a solution set or feasible region; a solid boundary indicates that the points on the line are part of the solution set; a dashed boundary indicates that the points on the line are not part of the solution set.

box-and-whisker plot (or box plot)—displays the median, lower quartile, upper quartile, and outliers (if any) of a data set; the whiskers are segments that connect each end of the box to the farthest values which are not outliers.

branch—a line segment in a tree diagram.

brute force algorithm—an algorithm in which every potential solution to a problem is examined.

calorie—amount of energy required to raise the temperature of 1 mL of water 1°C. **Note:** the calorie-per-gram rating on most food labels measures *dietary calories;* each dietary calorie equals one kilocalorie.

central angle (of a circle)—angle formed by two rays drawn from the center of a circle.

central angle (of a regular polygon)—angle formed by rays drawn from the center of a circumscribed circle to two consecutive vertices of the polygon, dividing the polygon into congruent isosceles triangles; the measure of a central angle of a regular polygon with n sides is: $360°/n$.

cheapest link algorithm— a greedy algorithm in which the cheapest (or shortest) action is taken at each stage, regardless of starting and stopping points; individual, disconnected edges may occur at various stages; if the cheapest remaining action completes a circuit that is not Hamiltonian, then the next best action is taken; when a Hamiltonian circuit is formed, the algorithm is complete.

circuit (in graph theory)—a path that starts and ends with the same vertex in which no intermediate vertex is repeated.

coefficient (of a variable)—a number multiplied times a product of variables or power of variables in a term; the coefficients of x in the expression $ax^2 + bx + c$ are a, b, and c.

common difference—the constant value added to each term in an arithmetic sequence to form the next term.

common ratio—the constant ratio between any two consecutive terms in a geometric sequence.

complementary angles—two angles are complementary when the sum of their measures is 90°.

congruent—exactly equal in size and shape; the symbol for congruence is $\cong$.

conjunction—combines two mathematical statements with the word *and;* can be represented as the intersection of two sets.

constant of proportionality—the constant in a direct proportion or an inverse proportion.

constraint—condition that limits the number of possible solutions to a problem.

contour line—a line that indicates elevation on a topographic map.

converse—the converse of a statement in the form "If A, then B" is the statement "If B, then A"; the converse of a true if-then statement may or may not be true.

corner point—an intersection of two or more boundary lines of a feasible region; also called a vertex.

corner principle—according to this principle, the maximum and minimum values of an objective function occur at corner points of the feasible region.

cosine (of an angle)— in a right triangle, the ratio of the length of the leg adjacent to the angle to the length of the hypotenuse.

cube root (of a number a)—a number b such that $b^3 = a$; denoted by $\sqrt[3]{a}$.

cylinder—a three-dimensional solid with bases that are congruent simple closed curves (non-polygons) in parallel planes.

density—ratio of an object's mass to its volume.

dependent variable—a variable for which values depend on the outcome of another variable.

dietary calorie—normally referred to as a Calorie with a capital *C;* equal to 1 kcal (the calorie-per-gram rating on most food labels measures dietary calories).

digraph (in graph theory)—a graph in which a direction is indicated on each edge; also called a directed graph.

dihedral angle—angle formed by two intersecting planes; the measure of a dihedral angle is the measure of the angle whose sides are the two rays formed by the intersections of the faces and a plane perpendicular to the edge.

direct proportion—a relation in which the ratio of two quantities is a constant; can be described by an equation of the form $y = mx$, where m is the constant of proportionality; the graph of a direct proportion always contains the origin because $y = 0$ whenever $x = 0$.

directed graph (in graph theory)—a graph in which a direction is indicated on each edge; also called a digraph.

displacement—the change in the position of an object; has both magnitude and direction.

distance (between two points in two dimensions)—can be found using the formula

$$d = \sqrt{(x_2 - x_1)^2 + (y_2 - y_1)^2}.$$

distance (between two points in three dimensions)—can be found using the formula

$$d = \sqrt{(x_2 - x_1)^2 + (y_2 - y_1)^2 + (z_2 - z_1)^2}.$$

distance (from a point to a line)—the distance along a path perpendicular to the line.

distance-time graph—displays the distance between two objects as a function of time.

distributive property (of multiplication over addition)—$a(b + c) = ab + ac$ or $(b + c)a = ba + ca$.

domain (of a relation)—the set of first elements in ordered pairs of the form (x,y).

equiangular polygon—a polygon for which all interior angles are congruent.

equilateral polygon— a polygon for which all sides are congruent.

event—a subset of a sample space.

expected value—the mean value of an experiment; calculated by adding the products of the value of each event and its corresponding theoretical probability.

experimental probability—(of an event) equals the number of times an event occurs divided by the total number of trials.

explicit formula—a rule for finding for calculating any specific term in a sequence.

exponential equation—an equation of the form $y = a \bullet b^x$, where $a > 0$ and either $0 < b < 1$ or $b > 1$.

exponential growth—change in a quantity or population that can be described by an equation of the form $y = a \bullet b^x$, where a represents the size of the initial population, b is the sum of two percentages—100 (representing the initial population) and r (representing the growth rate)—and x represents a time period.

exterior angle—an angle in the exterior of a polygon; the measure of an exterior angle of a *regular polygon* with n sides is $360°/n$.

factorial—a product of the positive integers from 1 to n; if n is a positive integer, then n factorial (denoted by $n!$) can be expressed as $n! = n \bullet (n-1) \bullet (n-2) \bullet \cdots \bullet 3 \bullet 2 \bullet 1$; zero factorial, or $0!$, is defined as 1.

fair game—game in which the expected value equals the cost of playing.

family (of functions)—a set of functions that have a common parent; for example, the parent of the family of quadratic functions is $p(x) = x^2$.

feasible region—a graph of the solution set of a system of linear inequalities.

first law of motion (Newton's)—an object in a state of rest or moving in a straight line at a constant speed will continue in that state unless acted on by a force.

force—a physical quantity that can affect the motion of an object (two familiar forces are gravity and friction); has both magnitude and direction.

frequency (of a data item)—number of observed occurrences of that item.

frequency table—table consisting of two columns; one displays data items, the other displays the number of observed occurrences of each item.

function—relation in which each element of the domain is paired with an element of the range and each element of the domain occurs in only one ordered pair; a function may be described by a rule or equation.

fundamental counting principle—if an event that can occur in m ways is followed by an event that can occur in n ways, then the total number of ways that the two events can occur is $m \bullet n$.

geometric sequence—a sequence in which every term after the first is found by multiplying the preceding term by a constant value (the common ratio).

geometric series—the sum of the terms of a geometric sequence.

graph (in graph theory)—a set of vertices (plural of vertex) and edges; each edge may connect a maximum of two vertices.

greedy algorithm—an algorithm in which the choice made at each step is the best of all remaining choices.

growth rate (of a population)—the percent increase or decrease in the population between two time periods.

Hamiltonian circuit (in graph theory)—a circuit in which every vertex in the graph is visited exactly once.

height (of a cylinder or prism)—perpendicular distance between the bases.

hertz (Hz)—international unit of frequency which represents one cycle per second.

histogram—graph that displays information using rectangles or bars of uniform width and scales with uniform intervals.

horizontal line—line with a slope of 0 and an equation of the form $y = c$.

hypotenuse—the longest side in a right triangle; the side opposite the right angle.

image—result of a transformation, such as a reflection; if point A is the preimage, then the image of a point A can be represented as A' (read "A prime").

incident ray—models the path that a light ray follows from an object to a reflective surface.

incoming angle—angle between the reflective surface and the incident (incoming) ray.

independent variable—a variable for which values do not depend on the outcome of another variable.

inequality—a mathematical sentence using one or more of the symbols $<$, $>$, $\leq$, or $\geq$; one way to describe a real-number interval.

infinite interval—a set of real numbers greater than or less than a given value; so called because it increases or decreases without bound.

instantaneous velocity—velocity at a particular instant in time.

interior angle—angle in the interior of a polygon.

interquartile range—difference between the upper quartile and the lower quartile.

interval (of real numbers)—set of all real numbers between two fixed endpoints; each endpoint may or may not be included in the interval.

interval notation—in interval notation, a square bracket,] or [, indicates that the endpoint is included in the interval; a parenthesis,) or (, indicates that the endpoint is not included in the interval.

inverse proportion—a relation in which the product of two quantities is constant; can be described by an equation of the form $xy = k$, where k is the constant of proportionality; the equation of an inverse proportion can also be written in the form $y = k/x$.

kilocalorie (kcal)—1000 cal; amount of energy needed to raise the temperature of 1 L of water 1°C.

lateral face (of a prism)—parallelogram formed by joining the corresponding vertices of a prism's bases.

least-squares line—the linear model that results in the least sum of the squares of the residuals; also called a linear regression.

leg (of a right triangle)—one of the two shorter sides in a right triangle; a side opposite an acute angle.

line of reflection— the perpendicular bisector of each segment connecting a preimage point to its corresponding image point under a reflection; every point on the line of reflection is its own image.

linear model—mathematical model that consists of a line or a linear equation.

linear regression—the linear model that results in the least sum of the squares of the residuals; also called the least-squares line.

lower quartile—median of the lower half of the data points.

mean absolute deviation—measure of spread that describes the average distance from the mean for the numbers in a data set.

measures of central tendency—the mean, median, and mode of a data set.

nearest neighbor algorithm—a greedy algorithm that starts with any vertex and draws an edge to its nearest vertex, then continues this process from the second vertex to the next nearest vertex not yet visited, and so on, until all vertices have been visited; to complete a Hamiltonian circuit, it returns to the original vertex.

net—a two-dimensional pattern without tabs that can be folded to make a three-dimensional solid.

newton (N)—a metric unit of force; the weight of an object in newtons is its mass in kilograms multiplied by 9.8 m/sec^2 (the acceleration due to gravity).

normal (of a reflecting surface)—the perpendicular line to the surface at the point of reflection.

***n*th root** (of a non-negative number a)—a number s such that $s^n = a$; the non-negative nth root of a is denoted as $\sqrt[n]{a}$.

objective function—a function whose value is to be maximized or minimized.

optimization—the process of making the best use of time or other resources.

ordered triple—used to represent the coordinates of a point in a three-dimensional coordinate system; can be written in the form (x,y,z).

origin (of a three-dimensional rectangular coordinate system)—the point where the three axes intersect; has coordinates (0,0,0).

outgoing angle—angle between the surface and the reflected (outgoing) ray.

outliers—extreme data values more than 1.5 times the interquartile range above the upper quartile or below the lower quartile.

parabola—the graph of a quadratic equation; has a vertex and is symmetric about a line known as the axis of symmetry.

path (in graph theory)—a sequence of vertices connected by edges in which no edge is repeated; vertices, however, can occur more than once in a path.

perpendicular bisector (of a segment)—the line perpendicular to a segment that divides the segment into two congruent parts.

pie chart (or circle graph)—graph consisting of circular regions divided into sectors that each represent a percentage of the whole.

point-slope form (of the equation of a line)—an equation of the form $y - y_1 = m(x - x_1)$, where m is the slope and the line passes through the point (x_1, y_1).

polygon—a union of coplanar segments intersecting only at endpoints; at most two segments intersect at any one endpoint and each segment intersects exactly two other segments. See *side; vertex.*

power equation—an equation of the form $y = ax^b$.

preimage—object prior to a transformation.

principal square root— the positive square root of a number, usually denoted by $\sqrt{a}$, although it also may be written as $\sqrt[2]{a}$.

prism—a three-dimensional solid determined by two congruent polygons in parallel planes whose corresponding vertices are connected by segments; the two congruent and parallel faces are the prism's bases; the parallelograms formed by joining the corresponding vertices of the bases are the prism's lateral faces; prisms are named by the polygonal shape of the bases.

profile—a vertical cross section or "side view" of terrain.

proportional—two ratios, a/b and c/d, where neither b or d equal 0, are proportional if $a/b = c/d$.

Pythagorean theorem—in a right triangle, the square of the length of the longest side (the hypotenuse) equals the sum of the squares of the lengths of the other sides (the legs).

quadratic expression (in a single variable)—an expression in which the greatest exponent on the variable is 2; also referred to as a second-degree expression; a quadratic expression in x can be written in the general form $ax^2 + bx + c$, where $a \neq 0$.

quadratic function—a function f in which $f(x)$ is equal to a quadratic expression in x; also called a second-degree function; can be written in the general form $f(x) = ax^2 + bx + c$, where $a \neq 0$.

range (of a data set)—measure of spread found by subtracting the least data value from the greatest data value.

range (of a relation)—the set of second elements in ordered pairs of the form (x,y).

rate—ratio of the change in one quantity to the change in another quantity.

recursion—the process of using a recursive formula.

recursive formula—a rule for calculating any term in a sequence by using the preceding term(s).

reflected ray—models the path of a light ray away from a reflective surface.

reflection (in a line)—a pairing of points in a plane so that the line of reflection is the perpendicular bisector of each segment connecting a preimage point to its corresponding image point; every point on the line of reflection is its own image.

regular polygon—a polygon in which all sides are congruent and all interior angles are congruent.

relation (between two variables)—a set of ordered pairs of the form (x,y).

residual—the difference between the y-coordinate of a data point and the corresponding y-value of a linear model.

saddle—a pass between two higher elevations.

sample space—the set of all possible outcomes for an experiment.

scale factor—the ratio of corresponding sides for two similar figures.

sequence—an ordered list; each item in the list is a *term* of the sequence.

side—segment of a polygon.

similar—two objects are similar if they have the same shape and the ratios of corresponding lengths are proportional; the ratio of corresponding sides is the scale factor; the symbol for similarity is $\sim$.

simple closed curve (in a plane)—a curve with no endpoints that does not intersect itself.

simulation—an experiment conducted to investigate real-world situations.

sine (of an angle)—in a right triangle, the ratio of the length of the leg opposite the angle to the length of the hypotenuse.

slope (of a line)—ratio of the change in vertical distance to the change in horizontal distance between any two points on a line; a vertical line has no slope.

slope-intercept form (of the equation of a line)—an equation of the form $y = mx + b$, where m is the slope and b is the y-intercept.

solution (to a system of linear equations)—a point where the graphs of all the lines intersect; the coordinates of this point satisfy all the equations in the system.

solution set (of an inequality)—all the points, or solutions, that make the inequality true.

square of a residual—the square of the distance from a data point to the model; in general, the smaller the sum of the squares of the residuals, the more closely a model approximates the data.

square root (of a non-negative number a)—a number s such that $s^2 = a$.

standard deviation—a measure of spread often represented by the Greek letter σ (sigma) and determined by the following formula, where μ represents the mean and n is the number of items in the set:

$$\sigma = \sqrt{\frac{(x_1 - \mu)^2 + (x_2 - \mu)^2 + \cdots + (x_n - \mu)^2}{n}}.$$

stem-and-leaf plot—displays the values in a data set in a stem-and-leaf arrangement; to simplify interpretation, data is usually ordered and a legend is included.

subscripted variable—a variable with a subscript, such as x_1 (read "x sub one").

substitution method—can be used to solve a system of linear equations; begins by solving an equation for one variable; the resulting expression is then substituted for that variable in another equation in the system; this process is repeated until a solution can be identified.

summit—the highest point of the surrounding elevations.

supplementary angles—two angles are supplementary when the sum of their measures is 180°.

surface area (of a prism)—the sum of the areas of the bases and lateral faces.

system of linear equations—a set of two or more equations whose graphs are lines; a solution to a system of linear equations is a point where all the lines intersect.

tangent (of an angle)—in a right triangle, the ratio of the length of the leg opposite the angle to the length of the leg adjacent to the angle.

template—a two-dimensional pattern with tabs that can be folded to make a three-dimensional solid.

term (of a sequence)—an item in an ordered list; may be represented by a subscripted variable of the form p_1 (read "p sub one"); the general or nth term may be represented by p_n.

tessellation—a pattern of repeated shapes that covers an entire plane without gaps or overlaps; also called a tiling.

theorem—a conjecture proven to be true for all cases.

theoretical probability—(of an event) equals the number of outcomes in the event divided by the total number of outcomes in the sample space.

tiling—a pattern of repeated shapes that covers an entire plane without gaps or overlaps; also called a tessellation.

tree diagram—a mathematical model that shows all the possible outcomes for a series of events or decisions; each line segment in a tree diagram is a branch.

trigonometric ratios—ratios of the lengths of sides in right triangles.

upper quartile—median of the upper half of the data points.

velocity—rate of change in position with respect to time; has both magnitude and direction. See *average velocity* and *instantaneous velocity.*

vertex (of a feasible region)— an intersection of two or more boundary lines; also called a corner point.

vertex (of a parabola)—occurs at the highest (or lowest point) in the graph of a quadratic function.

vertex (of a polygon)—intersection of two sides of a polygon; plural *vertices.*

vertex form (of a quadratic function)—a function of the form $f(x) = a(x - c)^2 + d$, where a, c, and d are real numbers and $a \neq 0$; the coordinates of the vertex are (c, d).

vertical line—line with no slope and an equation of the form $x = c$.

volume (of a cylinder or prism)—can be found by multiplying the area of a base by the height.

volume—amount of space occupied by an object; measured in units such as cubic centimeters (cm^3) or liters (L).

weighted graph (in graph theory)—a graph in which each edge is assigned a numerical value.

whiskers—segments that connect each end of the box in a box-and-whisker plot to the farthest values which are not outliers.

***x*-intercept**—x-coordinate of the point where a line or curve intersects the x-axis.

***y*-intercept**—y-coordinate of the point where a line or curve intersects the y-axis.

Selected References

Badawy, A. *Architecture in Ancient Egypt and the Near East.* Cambridge, MA: M.I.T. Press, 1966.

Bittinger, M. W., and E. B. Green. *You Never Miss the Water Till . . .* (The Ogallala Story). Littleton, CO: Water Resources Publications, 1980.

Britton, J., and D. Seymour. *Introduction to Tessellations.* Palo Alto, CA: Dale Seymour Publications, 1989.

Chartrand, G. *Introductory Graph Theory.* New York: Dover Publications, 1977.

Cohen, J. E. "How Many People Can the Earth Hold?" *Discover 13* (November 1992): 114–119.

Consortium for Mathematics and Its Applications (COMAP). *For All Practical Purposes.* New York: W. H. Freeman and Co., 1991.

Cozzens, M. B., and R. Porter. "Problem Solving Using Graphs." High School Mathematics and Its Applications Project (HiMAP). Module 6. Arlington, MA: COMAP, 1987.

Davidovits, J., and M. Morris. *The Pyramids.* New York: Hippocrene Books, 1988.

Dugan, J. T., and D. E. Schild. *Water-Level Changes in the High Plains Aquifer—Predevelopment to 1990.* U.S. Geological Survey Water Resources Investigations Report 91–4165. Lincoln, NE: U.S. Geological Survey, 1992.

Dugan, J. T., D. E. Schild, and W. M. Kastner. *Water-Level Changes in the High Plains Aquifer Underlying Parts of South Dakota, Wyoming, Nebraska, Colorado, Kansas, New Mexico, Oklahoma, and Texas—Predevelopment Through Nonirrigation Season 1988–89.* U.S. Geological Survey Water Resources Investigations Report 90-4153. Lincoln, NE: U.S. Geological Survey, 1990.

Eves, H., and H. Eves. *Introduction to the History of Mathematics with Cultural Connections.* Philadelphia, PA: Saunders College Publishing, 1990.

Farlow, S. J., and G. Haggard. *Finite Mathematics and Its Applications.* New York: Random House, 1988.

Frautschi, S., R. Olenick, T. Apostol, and D. Goodstein. *The Mechanical Universe.* Cambridge: Cambridge University Press, 1986.

Galilei, G. *Dialogues Concerning Two New Sciences.* Translated by H. Crew and A. di Salvio. Amherst, NY: Prometheus Books, 1991.

Garland, T. H. *Fascinating Fibonaccis: Mystery and Magic in Numbers.* Palo Alto: Dale Seymour Publications, 1987.

Gebhardt, S., and R. Matthews. *Nutritive Value of Foods.* Washington, DC: U.S. Government Printing Office, 1981.

Grünbaum, B., and C. G. Shephard. *Tilings and Patterns.* New York: W. H. Freeman and Co., 1987.

Guinness World Records 2005. New York: Bantam Dell, 2004.

Halliday, D., and R. Resnick. *Physics.* New York: John Wiley & Sons, 1978.

Iowa Academy of Science. *Physics Resources and Instructional Strategies for Motivating Students.* Cedar Falls, IA: University of Iowa, 1985.

Little, C. E. "The Great American Aquifer." *Wilderness* 51 (Fall 1987): 43–47.

Kastner, W. M., D. E. Schild, and D. S. Spahr. *Water-Level Changes in the High Plains Aquifer Underlying Parts of South Dakota, Wyoming, Nebraska, Colorado, Kansas, New Mexico, Oklahoma, and Texas—Predevelopment Through Nonirrigation Season 1987–88.* U.S. Geological Survey Water Resources Investigations Report. Lincoln, NE: U.S. Geological Survey, 1990.

Macaulay, D. *Pyramid.* Boston, MA: Houghton Mifflin, 1975.

McArdle, W., F. Katch, and V. Katch. *Exercise Physiology: Energy, Nutrition, and Human Performance.* Philadelphia: Lea & Febiger, 1991.

McMahon, T., and J. T. Bonner. *On Size and Life.* New York: Scientific American Books, 1983.

Microflect Co. *Passive Repeater Engineering.* Salem, OR: Microflect, 1984.

Milgram, J. H., and R. G. Donnelly, R. J. Van Houten, and J. M. Camperman. *Effects of Oil Slick Properties on the Dispersion of Floating Oil into the Sea.* U. S. Department of Transportation Report No. CG-D-64-78. Springfield, VA: National Technical Information Service, 1978.

Murphy, J., and R. Smoot. *Physics: Principles and Problems.* Columbus, OH: Charles E. Merrill Publishing Co., 1977.

National Council of Teachers of Mathematics (NCTM). *Discrete Mathematics Across the Curriculum K–12.* Reston, VA: NCTM, 1991.

National Council of Teachers of Mathematics (NCTM). *A Core Curriculum: Making Mathematics Count for Everyone.* Reston, VA: NCTM, 1992.

Olson, M., G. K. Goff, and M. Blose. "Triangular Numbers: The Building Blocks of Figurate Numbers." *Mathematics Teacher* 76 (November 1983): 624–625.

Packal, E. *The Mathematics of Games and Gambling.* Washington, DC: Mathematical Association of America, 1981.

Page, L., and N. Raper. *Food and Your Weight.* Washington, DC: U.S. Government Printing Office, 1977.

Paulos, J. A. *Innumeracy: Mathematical Illiteracy and its Consequences.* New York: Vintage Books, 1988.

Paulos, J. A. *Beyond Numeracy: Ruminations of a Numbers Man.* New York: Alfred A. Knopf, 1991.

Reiss, M. *The Allometry of Growth and Reproduction.* Cambridge: Cambridge University Press, 1989.

Roman, S. *An Introduction to Discrete Mathematics.* New York: Saunders College Publishing, 1986.

Schmidt-Nielsen, K. *Scaling: Why Is Animal Size So Important?* Cambridge: Cambridge University Press, 1984.

Seymour, D., and M. Shedd. *Finite Differences: A Problem-Solving Technique.* Palo Alto: Dale Seymour Publications, 1973.

Sharkey, B. J. *Physiology of Fitness.* Champaign, IL: Human Kinetics Publishers, 1979.

Sundberg, J. *The Science of Musical Sounds.* San Diego, CA: Academic Press, 1991.

Trains, Planes and Critical Paths. Videocassette. Produced by the Consortium for Mathematics and Its Applications (COMAP). Module I.3 in the series *For All Practical Purposes: Introduction to Contemporary Mathematics.* Santa Barbara, CA: The Annenberg/CPB Project, 1989. 30 min.

United Nations, Department of Economic and Social Affairs. *World Urbanization Prospects: The 2003 Revision.* New York: United Nations, 2004. (United Nations publication, Sales No. ESA/P/WP.190.)

U.S. Bureau of the Census. *Statistical Abstract of the United States: 2005.* Washington, DC: U.S. Government Printing Office, 2005.

U.S. Congress, Office of Technology Assessment. *Coping with an Oiled Sea: An Analysis of Oil Spill Response Technologies.* OTA-BP-O-63. Washington, DC: U.S. Government Printing Office, March 1990.

U.S. Department of the Army. *Map Reading and Land Navigation.* Washington, DC: U.S. Government Printing Office, 1987.

Whitmer, J. *Spreadsheets in Mathematics and Statistics Teaching.* Bowling Green, OH: School Science and Mathematics Association, 1992.

Zwingle, E. "Wellspring of the High Plains." *National Geographic* 183 (March 1993): 81–109.

Index

A

Absolute value, 192
Absolute value of a residual, 117, 125, 250
Acceleration, 227, 236, 275
  distance-time graphing and, 262–264
  gravity effects and, 265
Addition
  distributive property and, 74, 82, 256–257
  See also Multiplication
Algebraic principles
  distributive property and, 74, 82
  function, 60, 81
  parallel lines, 68, 81
  point of intersection, 73, 82
  point-slope form, 71, 82
  relation, domain/range and, 60, 81
  slope-intercept form, 67, 81
  slope of a line, 58–59, 64, 81
  solving for *x*, 57, 81
  y-intercept, 67, 81
  See also Linear models
Algorithms, 401, 411
  brute force algorithm, 401, 411
  cheapest link algorithm, 408–409, 411
  greedy algorithm, 404, 411
  nearest neighbor algorithm, 404–405, 411
Angle-Angle-Angle (AAA) property, 281, 309
Angle of incidence, 10, 29
Angle of reflection, 10
Angles
  central angles, 5, 28
  complementary angles, 11, 28, 29
  dihedral angles, 294, 309
  light ray paths and, 10, 28
  polygons and, 4–5, 28, 99
  supplementary angles, 11, 28
  See also Pyramids; Triangles; Trigonometry
Apothem, 94
Apple Lottery example, 32–40, 45–46
Area
  circles, 155
  irregular shapes, 154, 155
  oil slick estimation, 153–154, 155
  regular polygons, 95, 96, 99
  scale factor and, 212–213, 214, 215, 222, 235, 236
  squares, 223
  surface area, 86, 99
Arithmetic sequence, 314, 317, 320, 335
Arithmetic series, 320, 335
Average rate of change, 58–59, 64, 245
Average velocity, 242–243, 274
Axis of symmetry, 255, 275

B

Back-to-back stem-and-leaf plots, 183–184, 202
Bar graph, 174
Bases
  cylinders, 154, 164, 172
  prisms, 84, 99, 103, 125
Bisector (perpendicular) of a line, 17, 29
Boundary lines, 340, 344, 365
Box-and-whisker plot, 187–188, 202
Boxes, 84
  cube net/template and, 85–86, 99
  pinhole cameras, 285
  surface area and, 86, 99
  tessellation/tiling a plane and, 89–90, 99
Brute force algorithms, 401, 411

C

calorie (cal), 54–55, 81
  consumption of, 56, 58–59
  dietary calorie, 55, 66, 81
  dietary planning and, 66
  kilocalories, 55, 56, 81
Cells in a spreadsheet, 42

Central angles, 5, 28
Central tendency. *See* Measures of central tendency
Change
- average rate of change, 58–59, 64, 245
- exponential growth, 142, 149
- rate measures and, 109, 125, 133, 242, 263

Cheapest link algorithm, 408–409, 411
Circle graphs, 176–177, 202
Circles
- area formula, 155
- pie charts, 174, 176–177, 202
- polygons inscribed in, 5, 28
- simple closed curve model, 153, 172

Circuits, 393–395, 411
- brute force algorithm and, 401, 411
- cheapest link algorithm and, 408–409, 411
- directed graphs and, 399
- fundamental counting principle and, 400, 411
- graphs and, 394, 399, 411
- Hamiltonian circuits and, 395–396, 411
- nearest neighbor algorithm and, 404–405, 411
- optimization problems, 393, 411
- paths and, 395, 411
- tree diagrams and, 399, 411

Coefficients, 254, 275
Common difference, 314, 335
Common ratio, 325, 335
Comparative data. *See* Deviation; Graphs; Proportionality
Complementary angles, 11, 28, 29
Conclusion in conditionals, 281
Conditional statements, 281, 287
Congruence, 281
Conjunctions, 342, 365
Constant of proportionality, 160, 161, 167, 172, 207
Constraints, 344, 365
Contour interval, 383
Contour lines, 368, 390
Converse of a statement, 286, 287, 309
Coplanar segments, 3, 28
Corner point, 344, 365
Corner principle, 360, 365
Cosine, 303–304, 309
Cost of playing, 45–46, 52
Cross section, 230
Cube nets, 85
Cube root, 219, 235
Cubit measurement, 284
Cylinders, 154, 172
- bases of, 154, 164
- volume of, 154, 156, 172

D

Data. *See* Graphs; Information; Population studies
Decagons, 4, 94
Density of a substance, 221, 236
Dependent variables, 135, 149
Deviation
- mean absolute deviation, 192, 193, 197, 202
- standard deviation, 197–198, 203
- *See also* Measures of central tendency

Dietary calorie (Calorie), 55, 66, 81
Digraphs, 399, 411
Dihedral angles, 294, 309
Directed graphs, 399, 411
Direct proportion, 160–161, 207
Displacement, 242, 274
Distance formula, 376–377, 390
Distance from a point to a line, 15, 29
Distance-time graphs, 238, 274
- acceleration and, 262–265, 275
- average velocity, 242–243
- displacement and, 242, 274
- force and, 249, 274
- free-fall objects, 262, 264, 265, 270, 275
- gravity effects and, 265, 274, 275
- inertia and, 270
- infinite intervals and, 241
- instantaneous velocity, 243–244, 274
- linear modeling and, 248–250
- Newton's first law of motion and, 249, 270, 274
- parabolas and, 255, 275
- quadratic functions and, 254–256, 275
- real-number interval/interval notation and, 240–241, 274

residuals and, 250, 264, 274
sonar range finders and, 238–239
velocity and, 242–244, 263, 274
vertex form of a quadratic function and, 255–256
Distributive property, 74, 82, 256–257
Domain of a relation, 60, 132

E

Edges of graphs, 394, 411
Electromagnetic radiation, 169
Empirical probability, 34
Energy. *See* calorie (cal); Distance-time graphs; Temperature
Engineering measurement. *See* Pyramids; Triangles; Trigonometry
Equations
exponential equations, 142, 149
power equations, 223, 235
proportionality, 160, 167, 172
quadratic function, 254–256
system of linear equations, 349
See also Algebraic principles; Linear models
Equiangular polygons, 5, 28
Equilateral polygons, 5, 28
Errors, 121
Event, 34, 36, 37, 52
Expected value, 46–47, 52
Experimental probability, 34–35, 46, 52
Explicit formula, 320, 329–330, 335
Exponential equations, 142, 149
Exponential growth, 142, 149
Exponents
fraction raised to *n*th power, 213, 235

F

Factorial notation, 401, 411
Fair game, 47, 48, 52
Family of functions, 275
Feasible region, 344, 355–356, 365
First law of motion, 249, 270, 274
Flow, 108–110
Force, 227, 229–231, 236, 249, 274
Free-fall objects, 262, 264, 265, 270, 275
Frequency, 169, 175, 177, 202, 332
Frequency tables, 175–176, 177, 202
Friction, 249, 274
Function, 60, 81, 132
notation for, 132–133
See also Variables
Fundamental counting principle, 400, 411

G

Galileo, 270
Games
cost of playing and, 45–46, 52
expected value and, 46–47
fair game, 47, 48, 52
See also Probability
General term of a sequence, 313, 335
Geometric principles
Angle-Angle-Angle property, 281, 309
volume measurement, 103–105
See also Prisms; Pyramids; Triangles
Geometric sequences, 325, 329–330, 335
Geometric series, 325, 335
Graphs, 128
box-and-whisker plot, 187–188, 202
dependent/independent variables and, 135, 149
directed graphs/digraphs, 399, 411
direct proportion, 160–161, 172
feasible region, 355–356
frequency tables, 175–176, 202
histograms, 174–175, 202
inverse proportion, 167
linear inequality, 340
measures of central tendency and, 181
outliers and, 187, 202
pie charts, 174, 176–177, 202
stem-and-leaf plot, 183–184, 202
survey data and, 180–181
tree diagrams, 399, 411
vertical line test and, 132
vertices and, 394, 411
weighted graphs, 394, 411
See also Circuits; Distance-time graphs; Information; Topographic maps; Variables

Gravity, 227, 236, 249, 262–263, 265, 271, 274, 275
Greedy algorithm, 404, 411

H

Half planes, 340
Hamiltonian circuits, 395–396, 411
Heat energy. *See* calorie (cal); Temperature
Height
  cylinders, 154, 156, 172
  prisms, 103, 125
Heptagons, 4, 94
Hertz (Hz), 169, 332
High Plains Aquifer example, 114–116
Histograms, 174–175, 202
Horizontal lines, 64, 81
Hypothesis in conditionals, 281

I

If-then statements, 281
Images, 14, 29
  line of reflection and, 17–18, 29
  virtual images, 14, 21–22
  See also Reflection properties
Incident light ray path, 10, 28
Incoming angle, 10, 28, 29
Independent variables, 135, 149
Inequalities
  boundary lines and, 340, 344, 365
  conjunctions and, 342, 365
  constraints in, 344, 365
  corner point/vertex in, 344, 365
  corner principle and, 360, 365
  feasible region and, 344, 355–356, 365
  half planes and, 340
  intersecting linear inequalities and, 342
  intervals and, 274, 338–340
  objective function and, 359–360
  solution sets of, 340–341, 342, 365
  substitution method, solving system of equations and, 350, 351, 365
  system of linear equations and, 349, 350, 354–356, 360, 365
Inequality of an interval, 274
Inertia, 270
Infinite interval, 241, 274
Information
  mean absolute deviation and, 192, 193, 197, 202
  measures of central tendency and, 181, 190, 192, 202
  outliers, 187, 202
  quartiles of data, 187, 202
  standard deviation and, 197–198, 203
  subscripted variables and, 192, 202
  survey data, 180–181
  See also Graphs; Population studies
Instantaneous velocity, 243–244, 274
Interquartile range, 187, 202
Intersecting lines, 73, 82
Intersection of linear inequalities, 342, 343
Interval notation, 240, 241, 274
Inverse proportion, 167, 172
Isosceles triangles, 282–283

K

Kilocalorie (kcal), 55, 56, 81

L

Lateral faces of a prism, 84, 99, 103, 125
Least-squares line, 250, 274
Level curves, 368
Light rays, 8–9
  angles of incidence/reflection and, 10
  incident ray path, 10, 28
  incoming/outgoing angles and, 10, 28
  normal of reflecting surface and, 10
  reflected ray path, 10
  refraction and, 13
  virtual images and, 14, 21–22
  See also Reflection properties
Linear models, 116, 125
  absolute value of a residual and, 117, 125
  direct proportionality and, 160–161
  distance-time graphing and, 249–250
  inequalities, 340–342, 365
  percent error and, 121
  residual and, 117, 125, 250
  system of linear equations and, 349
Linear regression, 250, 274
Lines
  contour lines, 368, 390
  distance from a point to a line, 15, 29

horizontal lines, 64, 81
line of reflection, 17–18, 29
line of symmetry, 282
normal of reflecting surface, 10
parallel lines, 68, 81
perpendicular bisector of, 17, 29
point of intersection, 73, 82
point-slope form and, 71, 82
polygons and, 3, 28
real-number intervals and, 240
slope-intercept form and, 67, 81
slope of a line, 58–59, 64
vertical lines, 64, 68, 81
vertical line test, 132
y-intercept and, 67, 81
Lotteries. *See* Apple Lottery example; Match Lottery example; Probability
Lower quartile data, 187, 202

M

Mass, 221, 227, 236
Match Lottery example, 40
Mean, 181, 190, 192, 198, 202
Mean absolute deviation, 192, 193, 197, 202
Measures of central tendency, 181, 190, 192, 197, 202
Median, 181, 190, 202
Mirror line, 17–18
Mode, 181, 190, 202
Models. *See* Linear models; Prediction; Simulation models
Motion
first law of motion, 249, 270, 274
force and, 249, 274
inertia and, 270
universal gravitation law and, 271
See also Acceleration; Distance-time graphs
Multiplication
distributive property of, 74, 82, 256–257
factorial notation and, 401, 411
fundamental counting principle and, 400, 411

N

n factorial, 401, 411
*n*th root, 235
*n*th term of a sequence, 313, 335
Nearest neighbor algorithm, 404–405, 411
Net for a cube, 85, 99
newton (N), 227, 236
Newton, Sir Isaac, 249, 262, 270, 271, 274
Nonagons, 4
Normal of reflecting surface, 10

O

Objective function, 359–360
Octagons, 4
Oil spill example, 152
oil slick area/volume, 153–154, 155, 159, 164
proportionality and, 160–161
simple closed curve model and, 153
simulation modeling and, 152, 158–159, 164–165
Optimization problems, 393, 403–404, 408–409, 411
Ordered triple, 372, 390
Origin point, 372
Outgoing angle, 10, 28, 29
Outliers, 187, 202

P

Parabolas, 255, 275
Parallel lines, 68, 81
Parallelograms, 84, 99, 125
Paths, 395, 411
See also Circuits
Pattern analysis, 312–313
arithmetic sequence and, 314, 317, 320, 335
common difference and, 314, 335
common ratio and, 325, 335
explicit formula and, 320, 329–330, 335
geometric sequences and, 325, 329–330, 335
projections, formulas for, 318–320, 324–326
recursive formula/recursion and, 314–315, 335
sequences and, 313, 335
subscripted variables and, 313, 335
See also Graphs; Population studies; Prediction
Pentagons, 4, 94
Percentages, 176–177
Percent error, 121
Perpendicular bisector of a line, 17, 29
Pie charts, 174, 176–177, 202

Plimpton 322 tablet, 289, 293, 302
Point of reflection, 10
Points
- corner point, 344, 365
- distance between, Pythagorean theorem and, 376
- instantaneous velocity, 243, 274
- linear models and, 117, 125
- origin point, 372
- percent error and, 121
- system of linear equations and, 349
- *See also* Lines

Point-slope form, 71, 82
Polygons, 3, 4, 28
- central angles of, 5, 28
- equiangular type, 5, 28
- equilateral type, 5, 28
- inscribed in a circle, 5, 28
- interior angles of, 28
- tessellations/tiling and, 89–93
- *See also* Regular polygons

Population studies, 128
- characteristics analysis, 130–131
- density data, 148
- exponential growth and, 142, 149
- future growth rates, 144–145
- growth rate and, 133, 137–138, 149
- initial group size, growth modeling and, 140–141
- non-integer values and, 137–138
- simulation modeling and, 129–130

Power equation, 223, 235
Prediction, 33, 34, 110
- distance-time graphing and, 248–250
- graphs and, 128
- projections, explicit formula and, 318–320
- residual and, 117
- simulation modeling and, 129–130
- *See also* Population studies

Preimages, 14, 29
- line of reflection and, 17–18, 29
- *See also* Images

Pressure, 227, 229–231, 236
Principal square root, 214, 235
Prisms, 26, 84, 99, 103, 125
- bases of, 84, 99, 103, 125
- height of, 103, 125
- lateral faces of, 84, 99, 103, 125
- surface area of, 86
- volume of, 103, 125, 156

Probability, 32
- Apple Lottery example, 32–40, 45–46
- cost of playing and, 45–46, 52
- events and, 34, 36, 37, 52
- expected value and, 46–47, 52
- experimental probability, 34–35, 46, 52
- Match Lottery example, 40
- predictions and, 33, 34
- sample space and, 35–37, 41–42, 52
- simulation models and, 33
- spreadsheets and, 42, 43, 45, 46
- theoretical probability, 37, 47, 52
- *See also* Games

Profile of terrain, 381–383, 390
Proportionality, 160
- constant of proportionality, 160, 161, 167, 172, 207
- density-mass-volume relationship, 221, 236
- direct proportion, 160, 172, 207
- graph of, 160–161
- inverse proportion, 167, 172
- proportional ratios, 206, 207, 212–213, 235
- scale drawings and, 208–209
- similar objects, 206–207, 212, 235
- wavelength-frequency relationship, 169
- *See also* Scale factor

Pyramids, 278
- angle measurement and, 285–286, 294
- corners, location of, 279–280
- cubit measurement of, 284
- inclined ramps and, 292
- regular square pyramids, 282
- seqt relationship, 294
- similar pyramids, 283, 285
- *See also* Trigonometry

Pythagorean theorem, 286–287, 309, 376–377

Q

Quadratic expressions, 254, 275
Quadratic function, 254–256, 275
  family of functions and, 275
  vertex form of, 255, 275
  See also Distance-time graphs
Quadrilaterals, 4
Quartiles, 187, 202

R

Radiation wavelengths, 169
Radio telescopes, 26
Range of a relation, 60, 132
  data spread, 184, 187, 202
  See also Graphs
Rates of change, 109, 125
  acceleration, 262–264
  average rate of change, 58–59, 64, 245
  exponential growth, 142, 149
  population growth rate, 133, 137–138, 140–141, 149
  rate of flow, 108–110
  velocity, 242–244, 274
Real-number interval, 240, 274, 342
Recursion, 314, 335
Recursive formula, 314–315, 335
Reflected light ray path, 10
Reflection properties, 2–3
  distance from a point to a line, 15, 29
  geometry utility technology and, 15–16
  images/preimages and, 14, 17–18
  light ray paths/angles and, 8–10
  line of reflection and, 17–18, 29
  point of reflection and, 10
  polygons and, 3, 4
  radio waves and, 26
  reflection in a line, 17–18, 29
  refraction property and, 13
  virtual images and, 14, 21–22
Refraction property, 13
Regular polygons, 5, 28
  angle measures of, 90, 99
  apothem in, 94, 99
  area of, 95, 96, 99
  triangles in, 94–95
  See also Tessellations
Relation between variables, 60, 81, 132
Relationship modeling, 116–117, 125
  proportionality and, 160–161
  See also Graphs; Simulation models
Residual, 117, 125, 250, 264, 274
Rhind Papyrus, 284
Roots
  cube root, 219, 235
  *n*th root, 235
  principal square root, 214, 235
  square root, 214, 235

S

Sample space, 35–37, 41–42, 52
Scale drawings, 208–209
Scale factor, 206–207
  area prediction, 211–213, 222, 235, 236
  human body structure and, 230–231
  length prediction, 208–209
  volume prediction, 218–220, 236
  See also Proportionality
Second-degree expressions, 254, 275
Sequences, 313, 335
  arithmetic sequences, 314, 317, 320, 335
  geometric sequences, 325
  terms of sequences, 313, 314–315, 335
  See also Pattern analysis
Side of a polygon, 3, 5, 28
Similar objects, 206–207, 212, 215, 235, 309
  pyramids, 283
  triangles, 207, 280, 281
  See also Scale factor
Simple closed curve model, 153, 172
Simulation models, 33, 129, 149
  oil-slick area/volume, 152, 158–159, 164–165
  population growth, 129–130
Sine, 303–304, 309
Slope of a line, 58–59, 81
  distributive property and, 74
  parallel lines and, 68
  points of intersection and, 73
  point-slope form and, 71, 82

Slope of a line (*continued*)
rate of flow and, 108–110
slope-intercept form, 67, 81
Solutions
inequality, solution set of, 340–341, 365
system of linear equations and, 349
Sonar range finder, 238–239
Sound. *See* Frequency; Sonar range finder
Square of a residual, 250, 274
Square root, 214, 235
Squares, 212–213, 214, 222, 223
regular square pyramids, 282
See also Prisms; Triangles
Standard deviation, 197–198, 203
Statistical data. *See* Graphs; Information; Population studies
Stem-and-leaf plot, 183–184, 202
Subscripted variables, 192, 202, 313, 335
Subscripts, 192, 202, 313, 335
Substitution method, 350, 351, 365
Supplementary angles, 11, 28
Surface area, 86, 99
oil slick area estimation, 153–155
See also Area
Survey data, 180–181
Systems
linear equations, 349, 350, 355–356, 365
three-dimensional coordinate system, 372–373, 375–377, 390

T

Tangents, 296–297, 302, 309
Technology tools
geometry utility, 15–16, 94
graphing utility, 257–258
population growth modeling, 140–141
probability trials and, 35
Temperature, 163
gas volume and, 120, 168
See also calorie (cal)
Template for a cube, 85, 99
Terms of a sequence, 313, 314–315, 335
Tessellations, 89–90, 99
Theorems, 18, 29
Theoretical probability, 37, 47, 52
Three-dimensional coordinate system, 372–373
distance between points, Pythagorean theorem and, 375–377
ordered triple in, 372, 390
origin point and, 372
Tiling a plane, 89–90, 99, 284
Time function. *See* Acceleration; Distance-time graphs
Topographic maps, 368
contour interval and, 383
contour lines on, 368, 390
distance formula, 376–377, 390
level curves on, 368
profile segment and, 382
profiling mountainous terrain, 381–383, 390
saddle pass and, 369, 390
summit point and, 369, 390
three-dimensional coordinate system and, 372–373, 376–377
three-dimensional modeling and, 370–371
Tree diagrams, 399, 411
Triangles, 4, 5
corners, construction of, 279–280
isosceles triangles, 282–283
line of symmetry and, 282
Pythagorean theorem and, 286–287
regular polygons and, 94–95
regular square pyramids and, 282
right triangles, 285–286, 295–296, 302–304
similar triangles, 207, 280, 281
tangents and, 296–297, 309
See also Trigonometry
Trigonometry, 293, 302
clinometers and, 300
dihedral angles, 294, 309
hypotenuse and, 303
pyramid construction and, 293–294
right triangle trigonometry, 295–297, 302–304
sine/cosine and, 303–304, 309
tangents and, 296–297, 302
trigonometric ratios, 303–304, 309

U

Universal gravitation law, 271
Upper quartile data, 187, 202

V

Variables
  dependent variables, 135, 149
  exponential growth modeling and, 142
  function and, 60, 81, 132
  function notation and, 132–133
  graphs and, 135, 149
  independent variables, 135, 149
  relation, domain/range and, 60, 81, 132
  subscripted variables, 192, 202, 313, 335
Velocity, 242, 274
  average velocity calculations, 242–243, 274
  instantaneous velocity, 243–244, 274
Vertex (vertices)
  feasible regions and, 344, 365
  graphs and, 394
  parabolas and, 255, 275
  polygons and, 3, 28
Vertical lines, 64, 68, 81
Vertical line test, 132
Virtual images, 14, 21–22
Volume, 102, 125
  barrels of oil, 152
  cubes, 103–104
  cylinders, 154, 156, 172
  density of a substance and, 221, 236
  oil slick estimation, 153–154
  prisms, 103, 125, 156
  rate of flow and, 109–110
  scale factor and, 218–220, 236
  temperature and, 120
  three-dimensional solids, 104–105
  units of measurement in, 103, 125
  See also Water use patterns

W

Water use patterns, 102
  High Plains Aquifer example, 114–116
  personal water use measurement, 122
  rate of flow and, 108–110
Wavelength, 169
Weight, 227, 229–230, 236
Weighted graphs, 394, 411
Whiskers, 187, 188, 202

Y

y-intercept, 67, 81

Z

Zero factorial, 401, 411